D1591069

A Home for Sarah

Romaine Stauffer

Artist: Amy Lynn Stauffer

A Home for Sarah

Library of Congress Number: 2006925754

International Standard Book Number: 1-932864-78-4

Printed by
Masthof Press
219 Mill Road
Morgantown, PA 19543-9516

Dedication

Dedicated to
my devoted husband

Leroy Wenger Stauffer

who has graciously
shared with me his life
and his dear mother,
Sarah.

Table of Contents

Preface

Sarah was one of millions of children who grew up during the Depression and married during World War II. The uncertainty and instability of the nation during those years, coupled with the tragedy and turmoil in her own family, had a direct and profound impact upon her life.

The crash of the stock market in 1929 triggered the Great Depression of the 1930s. As the economy spiraled downward, banks and businesses failed. Ordinary people who had never invested a penny in stocks were caught by the undertow and sank into poverty. Multitudes lost their jobs and, subsequently, their homes. For them, the only way to survive the lean years was to live by the policy of "use it up, wear it out, make it do, or do without."

Sarah was too young to understand how the Great Depression and adverse circumstances had combined to impoverish her family. She did not realize her family was poor. The way they lived was normal to her, for she knew no other way of life. She took for granted the happiness and security she enjoyed in her home. Then, when she was ten years old, tragedy struck. The grief and anguish of her personal Great Depression began when her world crashed on a December evening in 1933. Her home was shattered and life forever changed.

As the Depression eased and the nation staggered to its feet financially, a new wave of uncertainty swept across the land. World War II began in Europe in 1939. Those who had lived through World War I watched as events unfolded and became increasingly convinced the United States would not remain neutral. When Pearl Harbor was attacked in 1941, the nation was swept into the war in a matter of hours. An undercurrent of fear rippled across the nation as people lived with the uncertainties of war-time rationing, air raid drills, curfews, and the draft.

The events in Sarah's personal life were in sync with national events. Just as she began to regain a sense of stability and security in her home life, she was once again swept away to live with strangers. As the nation vacillated between hope and despair during the war years, she slipped back and forth between homes. The thing she desired did not develop while the unexpected became reality. She was soon to learn that getting married and establishing a home of her own was no guarantee of security.

I learned the basic outlines of Sarah's childhood after she became my mother-in-law. I heard bits and pieces of her story as the years passed by and began to realize she had a story that should be told. As I asked specific questions about details, she opened a window and let me view the scenes from her early years. My admiration for her courage and patience grew with the writing of her story. She could have spent her life in self-pity, blaming every problem on her difficult childhood. Instead, she chose to accept what she could not change and not dwell on the past. Thirty-nine years ago she became my mother-in-law, but today she is my mother-in-love.

This is a true story, written in accordance with the things Sarah personally told me. I have used the real names of everyone mentioned in the story. The production of tobacco is woven into the story because it was a normal part of life for Mennonite farmers of Lancaster County at that time. As medical science proved the harmful effects of tobacco on the body, the crop became less lucrative and fell from its position as king of cash crops in Lancaster County. Today, many Old Order Mennonites have turned to truck farming and sell their healthy crops on produce markets.

I am indebted to Sarah for giving me permission to write her story and helping me find the information I needed. She patiently answered many questions, showed me the places she lived and went to school, and loaned me her father's diary. Her sister, Esther, also provided details and proofread the manuscript. Spellings of Pennsylvania Deutsch words are taken from Richard Beam's *Revised Pennsylvania German Dictionary*. Marta Weinhold also proofread the manuscript, graciously correcting my recurring errors of punctuation and spelling. The cover art was skillfully done by Amy Stauffer, who became a part of our family this year when she married our son, Eugene. I am unable to fully repay all of these people, and others, who have had a share in making this book possible.

The world in which we live today is filled with uncertainties. Terrorism has launched a new era of national insecurity. War, and the threat of nuclear war, is always on the horizon. Earthquakes, tsunamis, hurricanes, tornadoes, and other natural disasters sweep away the labor of a lifetime with one effortless blow.

The only certain thing in life is its uncertainty. Unexpected surprises or disappointments enter into each of our lives. As you read the pages of Sarah's story, may you be inspired to face the uncertainties of your life with courage and patience. May you experience the security and stability of knowing the all-wise God who is in control of both the present and the future.

Chapter 1

Sarah's little bare feet flew under her as she ran to the spring wagon that stood beside the barn. *Daed* (Dad, pronounced *Dat*) came out of the milk house carrying an enormous can of milk and swung it up onto the back of the spring wagon beside the can he had already loaded. The two cans had been kept cool all night in a cement trough of cold water, waiting until this morning when Daed could take them to the bottling plant. The water that ran from the dripping cans made tiny brown streams in the dusty lane which lay between the house and barn, but Sarah did not notice.

"Can I go with?" Sarah eagerly asked her father in the Pennsylvania Deutsch dialect of German her family spoke.

"Well," Daed answered slowly as he considered the request, "if *Memm* (Mom) says so."

Sarah's flying feet carried her back to the kitchen where she knew she would find her mother. She was so young she did not know her mother's name had been Amanda Shaub before she married Daed in 1922 and became Mrs. Amos Wenger. Neither did she know some people called her father Barney. She thought her parents' names had always had been only Daed and Memm.

"Can I go with Daed?" Sarah breathlessly asked as the wooden frame of the screen door banged behind her.

"I guess," Memm smiled as she gave her consent. "But you better put your bonnet on."

Sarah waited impatiently while Memm tied her little blue sunbonnet under her chin. Then she ran back to the spring wagon.

"Memm said yes," Sarah reported breathlessly.

"Upsy-daisy," Daed sang as he lifted Sarah and swung her up onto the seat of the spring wagon. She was small for her four years and as light as a feather in his strong hands. He sprang up into the wagon, seated himself beside her, and slapped the reins on Bill's broad back to tell the horse to go. The drop handles of the milk cans clanked behind them as the spring wagon jerked and started rolling out the lane.

Every weekday, Daed hauled the milk from the farm he rented from Mr. Miley[1] to the bottling plant the landlord owned on the outer fringe of Ephrata. Daed usually made the long four-mile round trip alone, but today he was glad for the company of his oldest child. Sarah sat up straight on the wagon seat, excited at the unexpected privilege of being allowed to accompany her father. Charlie Wentzel, who was Daed's hired man, would begin the day's field work while they were gone.

The warm sun of a late May morning smiled pleasantly on the Pennsylvania countryside, making it neither too hot nor too cold to be riding in the open air. Bill's hooves thudded softly on the dirt road that led from the farm to the place where it joined the road that snaked between the small Lancaster County towns of Ephrata and Akron. The rubber pads Bill wore on his iron shoes helped to prevent his hooves from pulverizing the dirt road and muffled the sound of his hoofbeats.

"Things are looking good," Daed said as his eyes roved across the gently rolling green fields that were bursting with promise. "I think this is going to be the best year we had yet. The cows are milking good and we're finally going to start getting ahead. As soon as the cows pay themselves off and I get a little saved up, I'm going to start looking for a farm of my own. Then we can stay put and quit this moving all the time from one place to another."

Sarah was not used to hearing Daed talk to her about farming and money as if she was a grown-up. But then, with three younger siblings, she seldom had the opportunity to be alone

---

[1] The current address of this farm is 620 Farmersville Rd., Akron, Pa.

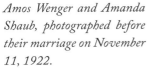

Amos Wenger and Amanda Shaub, photographed before their marriage on November 11, 1922.

with her father and enjoy his undivided attention. She turned her head to look at him through the tunnel of her sunbonnet. She could not see him unless she turned her head, because the brim of her bonnet got in the way.

"What do you mean 'all this moving?'" Sarah asked curiously. "We just moved one time."

"Once that you remember," Daed said. "That was this spring when we moved from the Horst farm to the Miley place where we live now. But before we lived at the Horst farm, we rented part of Noah Burkholder's house.[2] That's where me and

---

[2] The current address of what was the Horst farm is 800 E. Metzler Rd., Ephrata, Pa. Noah Burkholder's house stood at the back corner of what is now the parking lot of the Green Dragon Farmer's Market, 955 N. State St., Ephrata, Pa.

Sarah was born in the small addition to Noah Burkholder's farmhouse. The house was demolished in 2004.

Memm started housekeeping and where we lived in 1923 when you were born. Arthur was born there, too, the next year."

"Oh," Sarah said, trying to think who Noah Burkholder was and where he lived.

"You wouldn't remember that place because you were only two when we moved away from there," Daed explained. "I was just working at day labor then, but I wanted to farm for myself. So I rented the Horst farm and we moved there in the spring of 1925. Esther was born there, almost a year later. And of course Frank was born there, too, last fall."

Nearly three months had passed since the Wenger family had moved to the Miley farm on March 8, 1928, but it seemed much longer to Sarah. She tried to remember the inside of the house on the Horst place, but the memory had already faded. As is typical of small children in secure, loving families, she accepted life as it was at the moment without considering either the past or the future.

"Remember when the gypsies camped along the Conestoga Creek at the Horst place and the gypsy horse doctor came?" Daed asked. "You were scared of him."

"No," Sarah frowned and shook her head.

"One time the creek flooded," Daed reminded her. "Jake Burkholder's steers went with it and he was sure they would drown, but they came back out alive. Remember that?"

But Sarah could not remember the flood either. "I remember there was bee hives in the front yard," she said at last, pleased that she could at least remember one thing about living on the Horst place. "I got too close because I didn't know what they were and the bees came out and stung me."

"*Ya, wohl* (Yes, well)," Daed said apologetically, "I guess that wasn't the best place to put hives with children around. The little orchard where I have the hives now is a better spot for them than the front yard."

The spring wagon rolled down the dusty road between fields of newly planted corn and tobacco. Like the stubble on a man's shaved face, the baby leaves of the plants were obvious enough to tint the fields with color but not big enough to hide the rich brown soil in which they grew.

"Is there hives in there?" Sarah asked as they approached Morse Brossman's orchard.

"I would think so," Daed answered. "Most orchards have bee hives."

"Why?" Sarah asked.

"Because the bees like to collect the nectar in the flowers and make it into honey," Daed explained.

"There aren't any flowers on the trees," Sarah observed, looking closely at the trees in the large orchard they were passing.

"Not now," Daed said. "A couple weeks ago this orchard was all pink and white with flowers, but they all fell off now. Tiny little peaches and apples are growing where the flowers used to be."

At the corner of the crossroad where Morse Brossman's orchard bordered Milt Wanner's property, Daed pulled on the left rein to tell Bill to turn off Bethany Road and go west toward Fulton Street. Sarah could see the new Bethany School standing proudly near the T where Bethany Road intersected with Route 5 (currently Route 322). The big, two-room brick school had been built in 1923 to replace the humble one-room stone school which was still standing on Milt Wanner's property. Although the old school was now used as a shed, the bell which still hung in the cupola on the roof silently reminded passers-by of the years between 1858 and 1923 when children gathered inside its walls to learn their three-R's.

Bill clopped steadily west, pulling the spring wagon between the fields and meadows which lay on both sides of the unnamed country road. He took them safely around both sharp curves of the S-turn in the road and past the trolley tracks that hugged the bottom of the wooded hill as they went from Ephrata to Akron. At last, Bill brought them to Miley's bottling plant which stood on the corner where Fulton Street began and Lake Street ended.

Sarah did not leave the wagon but turned around and knelt on the seat as she watched Daed unload the two cans of milk. Although each can weighed at least seventy pounds, he swung them easily from the wagon to the wooden platform. The cans were taken into the plant where the milk was poured into a big tank to wait for processing.

Much of the milk that was brought to Mr. Miley's plant was pasturized, poured into clear glass bottles, and sealed tightly with paper caps. Each morning a milkman loaded his wagon with bottles of fresh milk and delivered them to the people who had ordered them. Some of the milk was made into delicious ice cream and sold in a little shop at the plant. People came from miles around to buy the cones Mr. Miley heaped high with ice cream and sold for five cents.

Sarah knew it was useless to even wish for an ice cream cone, for Daed never had five cents to spare. On the rare occasions when her family had ice cream, they made it themselves. Memm added a few simple ingredients to some of the raw milk from their cows and Daed crushed a block of ice which the ice man regularly brought to the house for the icebox. Daed could turn a whole freezer full of ice cream for much less than it cost to buy a cone for each of them in Mr. Miley's shop.

Daed brought the two empty cans out of Mr. Miley's plant and loaded them onto the back of the spring wagon. He took his place again on the wagon seat and clucked to the horse. The wagon rocked as it began rolling toward home and the empty milk cans clattered behind them. Daed slapped the reins on Bill's back to tell him to hurry along. Corn and tobacco were waiting to be planted in the spots where the first planting had not come up, a field needed to be harrowed, and hay was ready to be cut as soon as he had time to do it. Although Charlie had begun the day's work while Daed hauled the milk to town, he needed to get back to the farm as soon as possible for one man working alone can never accomplish as much as two men working together.

Bill knew he was going home and was eager to get there. His mane blew in the breeze as he briskly trotted back the way he had come to town. Daed stopped Bill between the house and barn long enough to help Sarah hop down from the wagon. She hurried to the summer kitchen where Memm could usually be found. The big kitchen they used in the wintertime was in the farmhouse, but by this time of year Daed had moved the cookstove into the smaller building behind the house. The summer kitchen had no cellar under it and was not built as solidly as the farmhouse. When freezing winter weather arrived, the summer kitchen grew too cold for everyday use and served only as the washhouse. But the farmhouse was kept cooler and more comfortable for sleeping in the hot summer months by keeping the heat of cooking and canning in the separate summer kitchen.

The spring on the wood-framed screen door automatically slapped the door shut behind Sarah as she stepped into the summer kitchen.

"There you are," Memm said. "I'm glad you're back. I must go out and butcher a chicken." She scooped up Frank from the floor where he was crawling and set him on the big rocking chair. "Watch him 'til I come back," she told Sarah.

Sarah understood what Memm did not say, for this was not the first time she had entrusted Sarah with the responsibility of keeping Frank sitting on the rocking chair where his little fingers could not reach things which were not safe for him to have. She knelt on the floor in front of him, grasped one arm of the rocker with each hand, and began rocking and talking to him in her childish voice. Arthur and Esther played around the chair and periodically ran to the window to watch their mother butchering the chicken, but Sarah had to stay where she was and watch Frank.

The old hens Memm culled from her flock had provided many meals to feed her growing family. She could pick the feathers from a chicken and clean it in a matter of minutes. The children knew she would save the heart, liver, and gizzard from the chicken's insides. All three of them wanted to eat the heart, but only one of them could have it.

When Arthur saw Memm taking the insides out of the chicken, he yelled, "The heart, the heart," and raced to the door. He wanted to claim the heart before Memm cooked it, so he would be sure to have it on his plate at mealtime.

"The heart, the heart," Esther and Sarah echoed as they followed him. Sarah completely forgot about Frank as she tried to win the race and reserve the prized chicken heart for herself.

Faster than a clock can strike the hour of three, the three children asked, "Can I have the heart?"

Before Memm could answer, they heard a bump inside the summer kitchen which was followed by a loud wail.

"Frank!" Memm exclaimed. She dropped the chicken into the pump trough, quickly rinsed her hands, and ran into the summer kitchen.

The coveted chicken heart forgotten, Sarah soberly followed her mother into the summer kitchen. She could guess what had happened.

"He fell off the chair and bumped his head," Memm told the children as they looked at her with frightened eyes. "He's getting a goose egg already. Sarah, get me a spoon from the drawer."

Memm held the spoon firmly against the lump on Frank's forehead. The coldness of the metal would help to keep the swelling down. The children's huge eyes watched as they silently listened to Frank's terrified cries. An awful feeling welled up inside Sarah. She had been told to watch Frank. In the excitement of trying to claim the coveted chicken heart, she had forgotten and left him sitting unattended on the rocking chair. Now he was badly hurt and it was all her fault.

"Hush, hush. You'll be all right," Memm tried to sooth the screaming baby. "You should have been more careful, but he's more scared than hurt," she told Sarah. Memm rocked, patted, and hummed until Frank's howls quieted. Exhausted from the exertion of crying, Frank sucked his thumb and fell asleep. When Memm laid him on an old quilt on the floor and went back to the unfinished job of cleaning the chicken, a greatly relieved Sarah went out on the porch and joined Arthur and Esther in their play.

The porch, which wrapped around the big farmhouse, was a wonderful place for children to play. It offered shade from the sun and shelter from the rain, as well as a smooth wooden floor on which they could ride their wagon and tricycle. Not all children had pedal toys, but Daed bought used things for bargain prices at public sales or the Bazaar in Ephrata. There was a high, unprotected drop-off at the end of the porch, but the children knew and respected the dangerous spot. Even when they rode their toys at breakneck speed, they never went too close to the drop-off.

When Sarah took her usual place at the breakfast table the next morning, she looked anxiously at the purple lump on Frank's forehead. He seemed to have forgotten all about it and was fine.

"We want to give thanks now," Daed said when everyone was seated.

Although Daed and Memm never prayed aloud at the table, the children knew they were going to thank God for their food before they began to eat. Every little head bowed and every eye closed for silent prayer. Only after Daed said *Aamen* would they raise their heads and be ready to eat the hot meal Memm had cooked.

If Sarah could not tell by the unpredictable weather what time of the year it was, she could always tell by the breakfast food Memm put in her bowl. In the spring and summer, the family always ate oatmeal for breakfast; in the winter they ate mush and milk or fried scrapple topped with puddin's. They could not have scrapple or puddin's in the summer because Daed could not butcher hogs in the warm months of the year. The eggs the chickens laid were rarely eaten for breakfast but used in baking or saved to trade for groceries at the store. But, since they lived on a dairy farm, milk was plentiful and they could have all the milk they wanted with their oatmeal or mush.

Because it was summer, Sarah did not expect anything other than oatmeal for breakfast. She emptied her bowl and laid her spoon on the oilcloth that covered the table. She knew she could not leave the table until they had "returned thanks" at the end of the meal, for every meal began and ended with silent prayer.

After breakfast, Daed went out to load the milk cans for the daily trip to the bottling plant. Sarah knew he would never take her with him two days in a row, so she decided to surprise Memm and hunt the eggs. The chickens roamed free around the farm buildings in the summer. Sometimes a hen got the notion to lay an egg in an odd place, but most of the time they went into the hen house and laid their eggs properly in the row of straw-filled wooden boxes that were nailed to the wall for their nests.

Memm usually took a basket to the chicken house and collected the eggs once each day. Sarah did not have a basket, but she always wore a full apron over her dress to keep it clean. The sleeveless apron, which was made of a very fine checked cotton fabric, reached from her neck to the hem of her solid-color dress. The apron fastened at the back of the plain round neck with one or two snaps but hung open below the snaps. Imitating her mother, Sarah gathered her apron in front of her and held it with one hand to form a makeshift basket. With the other hand, she carefully put the eggs she found in the nests into her apron basket. She must be careful not to break or even crack the shells of the eggs. Cracked eggs could not be traded for groceries because they would spoil more quickly than perfect eggs.

Sarah had not learned to count, so she did not know how many eggs she had found, but her apron sagged from the weight of them. As she walked to the house with her load, one corner of her apron slipped lower and lower. She knew she was losing her grip and grabbed at the apron. Instead of gaining a firmer grip she lost it entirely. The eggs crashed to the ground and broke.

Before Sarah could move, Charlie came driving by on his way to the field with the horses hitched to the harrow. "Whoa! What happened to you?" he laughed when he saw her standing in a puddle of egg yolks.

Embarrassed and ashamed, Sarah burst into tears as she ran to find Memm. It was bad enough that she had broken the eggs; there was no need for Charlie to laugh at her.

"*Ach*, Sarah," Memm sighed as she stripped off her daughter's dripping apron. "Now come out to the pump so I can wash you off before those egg yolks dry on. You must use the basket to hunt eggs. After this, don't be so *schusslich* (hurry that results in carelessness) and take more care. Remember, 'haste makes waste.'"

Chapter 2

Sarah climbed into Daed's square black carriage and sat in the middle of the back seat between Esther and Arthur. The storm front, or windshield, was the only window in the carriage. In the winter, when the sliding doors on the sides and the back curtain were closed, the children could see little other than the back of the horse that pulled the carriage. But since winter was over and the spring of 1929 had arrived, the carriage doors were open and the back curtain was rolled up. They would be able to see the lovely countryside they passed through on their way home from the Pike Mennonite Meetinghouse. The scents of apple blossoms and lilacs that perfumed the May air circulated freely through the open carriage, making it easy for Sarah to forget the long winter behind them when they had rarely been able to attend *Gemee* (church, pronounced *g'MAY*).

At the edge of the church yard, Bill responded to the pull on the bit in his mouth and turned right to begin the trip down the Pike (now Route 322) toward Hinkletown. The carriage rolled smoothly past the meetinghouse and the rail fence that bordered the little cemetery beyond the building. Sarah had always attended the Pike Mennonite Church with her parents and accepted it as a natural part of life. She was too young to know the history of their church or notice the differences between themselves and other groups of Mennonites.[3] The Old Order

---

[3] The Pike Meetinghouse was a part of the Groffdale district of the Lancaster Conference of Mennonites until 1845. Jacob Stauffer, who had been a minister in the district at that time, thought Bishop Christian Herr was too lenient. The people who agreed with Jacob Stauffer separated from the Lancaster Conference

Stauffer Mennonites continued to maintain the standards they held when they withdrew from the Lancaster Conference in 1845. Although outsiders often assumed they were Amish, the Stauffer Mennonites had never been a part of the Amish church.

The Pike Mennonite Meetinghouse, near Hinkletown, Pennsylvania.

Church services were held at the Pike Meetinghouse every two weeks. On the "Off Sunday," Memm sometimes invited company for dinner or the family might visit friends and relatives. She did not have time to cook a big dinner for a crowd on a "Church Sunday," so they would go home and eat the dinner she had prepared for on Saturday and could quickly finish after church.

As the carriage rolled through the high iron framework of the bridge that crossed the Conestoga Creek at Hinkletown,

and established a small Old Order group that was called the Stauffer Mennonites. A sister congregation in the Juniata/Snyder County area withdrew from the Lancaster Conference at the same time. The Lancaster Conference allowed the Stauffer group to have the smallest meetinghouse in the Groffdale district, which was also the one nearest Jacob Stauffer's home. It was called the Pike Meetinghouse because it was located along what was known as the Harrisburg-to-Downingtown Turnpike. The Stauffer Mennonites were often called "the Pikers" because they met in the Pike Meetinghouse.

Arthur leaned forward and asked Memm, "What's for dinner?"

"What do you think?" Memm returned the question.

"Cornstarch pudding?" Arthur guessed hopefully.

"*Ya*" (Yes)," Memm nodded and smiled. The cooked pudding was easily and cheaply made from milk, sugar, cornstarch, butter, and vanilla. They did not always have dessert with their meals, but milk was plentiful since they lived on the Miley place. No matter how often Memm made it, the children never complained about eating cornstarch pudding.

The petals of the blossoms that perfumed the air in May fell to the ground as fruits bulged and swelled in their place. Early in June, Memm went to Hahnstown and picked some scrumptious fresh strawberries from the big patch on the farm of her sister Barb and Milt Good. The plump red fruits were much better than the seedy little wild strawberries they found at the edges of the fields and woods. Memm canned as many quarts of strawberries as she could for the coming winter. But the taste of fresh strawberries cannot be preserved, so they must be freely eaten and savored while they are in season.

On the morning of June 18, Memm was too sick to get out of bed. Arthur was sent with Charlie to take the milk to the bottling plant while Daed went to a neighbor's house to call the doctor on the telephone. Sarah crept into the bedroom and sat on the chair at her mother's bedside, listening to Memm's soft moans and worrying. Daed called the doctor only when someone was seriously ill.

When Dr. Anderson came from Ephrata, Daed met him at the door and showed him to the bedroom. Sarah thought doctors always hurt people. She was terrified when she saw the doctor standing in the doorway with his big black bag in his hand. She wanted to get away from him as soon as possible, but she could not get out of the room without walking past him.

I'm stuck! Sarah thought in a wave of panic that took her breath away.

"Sarah," Daed said. "You and Esther take Frank and go over to Joe Brubakers. Stay there 'til I come fetch you."

Sarah nodded wordlessly, scurried in a wide circle around the doctor, and escaped through the door before he could say a word to her.

"Daed said to go over to Joe Brubakers and take Frank with," Sarah told Esther as she took Frank's hand. "Get our dolls and come on."

Esther grabbed the rag dolls their great-aunt, Maggie Reich, had made for them. Then the children set off across the back field to the neighbor's farm. Frank was nineteen months old and could walk, but his toddler steps across the cultivated ground of the field of waist-high corn were too slow for the girls. Sarah picked him up and sat him on her narrow hip. The two girls marched side-by-side to the row of trees which formed a natural fence and marked the boundary between the two farms.

Joe Brubaker was a minister in the Pike church. Two of Joe and Mary's daughters, Mary and Alice, were the same ages as Sarah and Esther. The four neighbor girls had made an open-air playhouse in the apple orchard between the two sets of farm buildings. They set up housekeeping with their rag dolls and the box of broken dishes their mothers had given them to use as toys. The Brubaker girls were not at the playhouse, so Sarah and Esther went on to the farmhouse.

"Memm's sick," Sarah told the mother of their little friends. "The doctor came and Daed sent us over. He said to stay 'til he fetches us."

"Come right in," Mrs. Brubaker told the girls warmly, as if she had been expecting them. She took Frank from Sarah and sat him on her own hip. "Mary and Alice aren't done with the dishes yet. As soon as they're done, they can go play."

With fresh incentive, Mary and Alice quickly finished the dishes. Then the four girls ran out to their playhouse in the apple orchard, leaving Frank under the capable supervision of Mrs. Brubaker and her three older daughters.

The four little girls picked up where they had left off in their play the previous day. Their active imaginations required few toys to play house. Sticks were laid on the ground to mark the rooms of their house and a bunch of long grass made a fine broom with which to sweep the dirt floor. They filled their cracked plates with handfuls of dandelion leaves garnished with pretend-eggs that looked suspiciously like daisies. The sun-baked mud pies they pretended to eat became any kind of food their imaginations dictated, and the plain water they drank from the chipped cups tasted like whatever they wanted to drink. When dandelions were in season, their plain little dresses turned into elegant gowns after they were adorned with golden chains of dandelion blossoms.

As the hours passed, Sarah's worries about her mother's health were forgotten. She was so absorbed in her play she was almost surprised when she looked up and saw her father standing on the other side of the fence row.

"Where's Frank?" Daed asked.

"In at the house," Sarah told him.

"I'll go fetch him. It's time to go home," Daed said as he started walking toward the Brubakers' farmhouse. When Daed came back with Frank, Sarah and Esther picked up their rag dolls and said good-by to Mary and Alice. They knew they would soon meet again to play, although they were rarely allowed to stay as long as they had this time.

The girls almost had to run to keep up with Daed as he carried Frank across the field to their home. He was smiling as if he knew a secret, but he did not say anything. The girls were surprised to find their mother's sister, Mary Shaub, in the kitchen. They had not known Aunt Mary was coming. But that was not the secret Daed knew, for he smiled at them and said, "Go in the bedroom and see what Memm has."

Sarah and Esther could not guess what their mother might have to show them. They found her propped up on feather pillows with a little bundle in her arms.

"Look what I got," Memm said with a smile when the girls came close to the bed.

"A baby!" the girls squealed in surprise when they saw the little face inside the blanket.

"*Ya,*" Mem chuckled at the shocked looks on their faces. "A baby girl. You have a little sister."

"What's her name?" Esther wanted to know.

"Mary," Memm said. "She's named for Aunt Mary because she came to be our *maad* (maid, pronounced *mawed*)."

"She's awful little," Sarah observed.

"Did you forget how little Frank was when he was born? And look what-fer big boy he is now. Babies grow up fast," Memm assured Sarah.

The next day Sarah asked Aunt Mary, "Can we go tell Mary and Alice about our new baby?"

"I guess," Aunt Mary consented. "But don't stay too long."

Sarah and Esther found Mary and Alice Brubaker already knew about the big surprise that had been waiting for them when they went home the previous day. Daed had told Mary and Alice's mother the news when he went in the house to get Frank, and she had told them.

"Did the doctor come with his black bag?" Mary asked Sarah.

"*Ya,*" Sarah nodded.

"Well, then," Mary said as if that explained everything. "Don't you know he brings babies in that?" She had older sisters who had told her all the secrets in the doctor's black bag when her brother, Elam, had been born a little over a year ago.

Aunt Mary stayed for several weeks and did the housework while Memm rested in bed and took care of the baby. Aunt Mary was eighteen and pretty. Sarah liked having her there. Somehow, helping Aunt Mary seemed to be more fun than helping Memm, although they were doing the same things they always did. But soon Aunt Mary went home and Memm was back in the kitchen doing her own work again.

Daed and Charlie were busy making hay when baby Mary was born. The cows ate a lot of hay in the winter when there was no green grass in the meadow. Eating good quality hay helped them give more milk. But Daed was worried about the cows. They were not doing as well as they had at first. Some of them gave less milk

18 *A Home for Sarah*

and were often sick. Daed tried everything he knew, but nothing seemed to help.

"The vet was here," Daed told Memm in a tight voice later in the summer. "He said the cows have Bang's Disease. We have to get rid of them all."

"All?" Memm gasped.

"The vet said when one gets it, they all get it," Daed repeated what the vet had told him. "They all have to go. Right away. The milk's no good."

"What are we going to do?" Memm asked as she groped for a chair and sat down.

"What can we do?" he asked in a discouraged voice. "Miley won't take the milk anymore. It could give people the same disease the cows have."

"But they aren't paid for yet," Memm cried. "We borrowed a thousand dollars from old Dan Stauffer to buy those cows. A thousand dollars! And there's the notes, too, for the money you loaned from Noah and Elam Burkholder. How will we ever pay all that money back if you can't ship milk?"

"I don't know," Daed admitted. "But I'm afraid we're licked. I signed an agreement with the banker when I rented this place. I have to do whatever he says."

Daed had rented Mr. Miley's farm through Clarence R. Weaver of the Farmers National Bank in New Holland. Daed was accountable to the banker because he managed Mr. Miley's farm. The children did not understand all the talk of assets and liabilities they heard after C. R. Weaver came to the farm on September 27 to assess the situation, but they did understand they would have to move by spring. Mr. Miley wanted cows on his farm to provide milk for his bottling plant in town, but their cows were gone and Daed could not borrow more money to buy another dairy herd. The banker had the authority to sell Daed's crops, cattle, and farm equipment to pay his debts. The banker made plans to hold an Assignee Sale (which was almost the same as a Sheriff Sale) in November. There was no way Mr. Miley would rent the farm to Daed for another year if he had no cows or farm equipment, so he began looking for another place to live.

On a Saturday afternoon in mid-October, Daed took a long walk alone. After supper that evening he took some short, flat sticks out of his coat pocket and asked Memm for some string. She always saved the strings that were sewed across flour and sugar sacks to close them, so she gave him the ball she had made from the strings. He sat on his chair at the kitchen table, laid the sticks and string in front of him, and took out his Barlow pocketknife.

"What are you doing?" Sarah asked curiously.

"Watch and see," Daed answered mysteriously as he opened his pocketknife.

The children crowded around Daed's elbows, watching as he bored a small hole near the end of one of the flat sticks and made more little holes and notches in other pieces. None of them could guess what he was making.

"Well, I think I found a place we might be able to live," Daed told Memm as he began carving some of the flat pieces of wood into odd-looking shapes.

"Oh? Where's that?" Memm asked. She poured the leftover mush from supper into a pan to cool. In the morning she would cut the loaf of mush into slices and fry them in lard for breakfast.

"On the other side of Ephrata," Daed said. "I walked over there this afternoon. It's the John Doster place on the road to Schoeneck. The land joins Eli Zimmerman's place where the little Springville church is. Elam Burkholder is buying the Doster place for his son, Paul. He's not married, so Elam wants a family to rent the place and board Paul while he gets started farming. I think he'd set it up so I could farm there and help Paul. It might work out if Elam will rent it to us."

"Now, *kinner* (children, pronounced *KINN-ah*), watch," Daed said as he strung the little pieces of wood on the string and tied knots to keep them in place.

"What *is* that?" Esther asked the question all of them were thinking.

"This here is a little man. He's called a Chomping Chack," Daed said. He pointed to the crudely carved, jointed figure which stood on a small platform between two flat posts. The wooden man's hands reached above his head and held onto a string fastened between the two posts. Daed set the wooden platform on the table. "Now watch," he said as he pulled a piece of string.

The children shouted with laughter as the Jumping Jack nodded his head, jerked his arms, and swung his legs while he somersaulted up over the string and came down again.

"Let me do it, let me do it," all the children begged.

"You must take turns," Daed told them. "Let Frank do it first because he's the littlest."

Sarah had just turned six. Since she was the oldest, she had to wait until last. Daed helped Frank pull the string to make the little man jump. Then Esther and Arthur had their turns. Finally, it was Sarah's turn to pull the string and make the Jumping Jack somersault over the string above his head. They played with the Jumping Jack until Memm said it was time to go to bed. Then he was set carefully on the windowsill to wait for them to get up in the morning and play with him again.

The next Thursday morning, Elam and Noah Burkholder came before dinner to see Daed.

"So I guess it's settled then," Daed told Memm at the dinner table. "We're going to move to the Doster place and board Paul."

"How soon?" Memm asked.

"Not for awhile yet," Daed told her. "Elam won't make settlement for the place until the first of April next year. We'll move in then."

Daed and Charlie had been working hard to cut and shock the corn in October. By the end of the month, the days were so short that it was too dark to work in the cornfield after supper unless there was a full moon. In November, they picked the yellow ears of corn from the shocks, loaded the ears into the wagon, and hauled them to the corn barn where they were stored in the corn crib. The sides of the corn crib were made of narrow wooden boards with spaces between them so air could circulate through the corn to keep it from getting moldy. The boards were covered with a mesh made of wire so rats and mice could not get in and eat the corn.

The last of the potatoes were dug and graded by size so they could be sold. The celery was buried in a trench where it would keep without freezing during the winter. The good apples were stored in the cold cellar, but Daed took a load of the spotty or otherwise imperfect apples to Levi Andes' press and had them made into cider.

In the midst of all this work, Daed was getting ready for the Assignee Sale and distributing sale bills to advertise the auction which C. R. Weaver had set for November 20. The farm was a busy place the last two days before the auction. Daed fetched Aunt Mary on Monday morning. She helped Memm cook for the men who came to do the last-minute work of getting ready for the sale. Some of the men helped him clean the farm equipment; Ammon and Noah Auker painted singletrees and the cultipacker; Frank Wise set the implements in a line in the field; John Williams graded potatoes.

Sale day was cloudy but not cold. Grandfather Wenger came in the morning to help finish getting ready for the auction. His son and daughter, Eli and Fannie, who were Daed's half-brother and half-sister, came with him. *Daadi* and *Mammi* Shaub[4] and the Auker brothers also came to help. Noah Auker was married to Daed's sister, Leah, and Weaver Auker was married to Memm's sister, Lizzie.

Swarms of people were walking around the farm buildings by the time the auctioneer was ready to begin the sale. While the men inspected the goods which were to be offered for sale outside, women friends and relatives came into the house to be with Memm. They brought their small children with them, making muddy tracks across the kitchen floor as they went in and out.

---

[4] Grandpa and Grandma (pronounced DAW-de and Mommy), Phares and Lizzie Shaub.

To Sarah, the sale was an exciting day. The most exciting part of all was the "huckster stand," set up on the dirt floor of the empty corn barn to sell refreshments to the crowd. Sarah dodged through the crowd to examine the wares arranged on the huckster's table, but she had eyes only for the candy and chewing gum. Three chocolate candy bars could be purchased for ten cents, but of course she could not hope for that much. If she was fortunate enough to be able to buy some candy, she knew she would have to choose from the assortment of penny candy setting in rows on the end of the table. She did not have a penny, or much hope that Memm would give her one, but it did not cost anything to smell the candy and dream what she would choose if she could buy some.

"What fer kind do you like?" a voice behind Sarah asked. She turned around and looked up to see Daed's half-sister, Fannie, smiling down at her.

"I don't have a penny," Sarah said shyly.

"Here's one," Aunt Fannie said as she pressed a copper penny into Sarah's hand. She understood the longings of a little girl's heart, because she had once been a little girl herself.

Choosing one piece of candy from all the different kinds was a big decision which could not be made hastily. Should she choose a Ju-Ju fish, a Tootsie Roll, a sucker, or a lemon drop? The lady who was tending the stand waited on some other customers while Sarah tried to decide how to spend her penny. The sing-song chant of the auctioneer came through the open door of the corn barn as she deliberated. At last, she at last exchanged the penny with the wheat motif on its back for a red sucker.

In years to come, Sarah would remember little of the sale except the excitement of spending money at the huckster's stand. She had no idea what her parents were feeling as they saw their dreams of owning their own farm fading out of the picture. Daed had borrowed several years' wages to buy the cows. He was doing well until the cows contracted Bang's Disease. If that misfortune had not struck, he would probably have been successful as a dairy farmer, but now he was bankrupt. He knew the amount the sale raised would never be enough to pay his debts. Everything was gone, but he still had a wife and five children to feed.

Three days after the sale, Daed got in Charlie's Buick and went with him to see if Elam Burkholder might give them jobs on his farm near New Holland. Elam set them to work cleaning manure out of steer stables and pulling turnips from his field. The lowly jobs were hard work, but the dollar Daed earned each day would help them keep body and soul together until spring. Then they would move to the Doster place Elam was buying and plant a new crop.

"We might be so far in the hole we have to look up to see bottom, but we'll work our way out of this yet," Memm encouraged Daed. "Those rich men that committed suicide when they lost their fortunes in the stock market crash in October were worse off than we are. We're not at the end of our rope yet."

"I guess," Daed sighed. His voice sounded as if he was twice as old as his thirty-five years.

Chapter 3

During the first month of 1930, Paul Burkholder came to meet the Wenger family. Seeing Memm was a neat housekeeper and good cook, he agreed to board with them when they moved to the farm his father was buying for him in April.

Elam Burkholder was a prosperous Lancaster County farmer who was not afraid to take risks to make money and had been successful in everything he attempted. He had bought a farm for each of his two oldest children. Since Paul was twenty-one, the time had come for him to get established in farming too. Although they kept a few cows for the milk and butter they needed, the Burkholders were not dairy farmers. They raised beef cattle and grew cash crops of potatoes and tobacco. The potatoes were sold in markets or peddled in town and the tobacco was sold through the huge tobacco warehouse Elam had built on his New Holland farm. The cattle were butchered in the butcher shop on the home farm. The meat was sold in a little store attached to the butcher shop or the market stands they tended at Downingtown and Parksburg.

In February, Daed took Memm to see Paul's farm on the north side of Ephrata.[5] The big stone farmhouse was large enough to hold two families. Daed told his friend, John Auker, that half of the house was available for rent. John was a brother of Weaver and Noah Auker, who were Daed's two brothers-in-law. John had married Anna (or Annie) Sensenig on October 7, 1929. According to the custom, they had both continued to live with their respective

---

[5] The current address of this farm is 400 Schoeneck Rd., Ephrata, Pa.

parents after they were married, but when spring arrived they were ready to set up housekeeping. John rented the other half of the farmhouse from Elam and the newlyweds established their first home there.

As soon as the Wenger family was settled on the Burkholder farm, Daed helped Paul plant twenty-six bushels of seed potatoes, many acres of tobacco, and other crops for cattle feed. The big, new tobacco shed Elam wanted to build on the farm must be finished in time to store the new crop. On the first day of May, he and his brother Noah came to the farm and put stakes in the ground to mark the corners of the building. It would be both long and high, for Elam never scrimped when he built something.

Sarah and Esther missed being able to play in the orchard with the Brubaker girls.

"Where can we make a playhouse?" Esther asked Memm.

"*Ach*, I don't know," Memm said slowly as she mentally sorted through the options. "I guess you'ns can use the top of the pig sty," she decided. "It's empty."

Memm carried some empty wooden orange crates and the heavy doll bed up the steps for them. Then she left them to set up housekeeping with the rest of their toys and dolls.

"This here is the bedroom," Sarah decided.

The sisters pushed the heavy doll bed to the spot Sarah had selected. Daed had made the little bed for them by cutting a real bed down to play size. It was strong enough for both girls to sit on it, but rolled easily on the casters on the bottom of each foot. The bed was "made up" using an old, flat feather pillow for a mattress and empty muslin feed sacks for sheets.

"Now you'ns stay here 'til we tell you," Sarah sternly told the rag dolls as she sat them with their backs propped against the headboard of the bed.

"And watch the little ones," Esther ordered the rag dolls as she set the small celluloid dolls on their laps.

"Now let's make the kitchen over here," Sarah suggested when the bedroom was finished.

The girls arranged their orange crate furniture to form a kitchen. One crate became the sideboard which held their chipped dishes and broken-handle cups. An up-ended crate served as a table. They could sit on the floor, so they did not need chairs. Beside the sideboard, Sarah set the red tin washtub Grandmother Wenger had given her. The little wooden scrub board inside the washtub was just the right size for washing doll clothes.

"You can set the table," Sarah told Esther when the house was in order. "I'm going to fetch Daisy."

Sarah ran to the house and came back with the doll Memm's brother, Uncle Christ Shaub, had given her for Christmas when she was four years old. Daisy had a beautifully painted papier-mâché face and wore a lovely pink dress with matching shoes. When the playhouse had been in the orchard, Daisy had to be brought home each day, for her face would melt and be spoiled if it got wet. But she would be safe in this playhouse, for the roof of the pig sty would keep her dry. It was not the rag dolls' fault they did not look as real as the celluloid dolls and were not as delicate as Daisy. The girls accepted all of them as they were and gave each one a place at the table. They played happily until they heard someone or something come into the pig sty below them.

"What's that?" Esther asked in alarm.

Sarah went to the top of the steps and looked down. "It's Paul's goat!" she screamed.

The goat saw her, tapped his front hooves on the second step, and bleated.

"He's gonna come up and get us!" Esther cried.

All thoughts of play were forgotten as the sisters clung to each other while they cried and yelled for help. Memm was in the house, too far away to hear the frantic screams of her terrified daughters. The men who were working on getting ready to build the new tobacco shed were making too much noise to hear the girls. Tears washed clean streaks down their dirty little faces as they cried and yelled for what seemed like hours to them.

"What's going on here?" Daed asked when he finally heard the commotion in the pig sty and came to their rescue.

"The goat's gonna get us!" the girls cried. "Get him out of here!"

Daed caught the goat, pushed him out of the pig sty, and led him away. Still crying, the girls made a bee-line for the house and the safety of Memm's protection. They were too afraid of the goat to enjoy playing in their playhouse anymore.

"You have to get rid of that goat," Daed told Paul firmly. "The children are afraid of him."

Only after the goat was gone did the girls feel safe playing in the pig sty again. But by then the building site was a more exciting place than the top of the pig sty. When the men began digging for the cellar and foundations of the tobacco shed, they found a seam of limestone running through the building site which could be removed only after blasting the rocks apart with dynamite. The little Wenger children were fascinated with the exciting project. They played at places near enough the building site to watch the action, but far enough to be safely out of the way of the workmen.

When the men yelled, "Run! We're gonna blast," the children bolted for safety in the house. They covered their ears with their hands but could not entirely shut out the boom of the dynamite. Rocks flew into the air from the open hole and sometimes small pieces of rocks struck the house. When the blasting stopped, the children were drawn like magnets to the building site to watch the rocks being removed.

Sarah and Esther had to wash and dry the breakfast dishes each morning before they could go out to watch the building project. Because she was the oldest, Sarah usually washed the dishes and Esther dried them.

Sarah stood on a little footstool, swishing the dishwater around in the dishpan, making bubbles and bursting them. Memm had gone on the other side of the house more than a half hour earlier to help Annie Auker with her new baby. Sarah set a bowl in the dishpan and gave it a little push to make it float across the water like a boat. She added a second bowl and launched the two boats on a race while Esther waited.

"Hurry up," Esther snapped. "You're just playing around." She could not go out to play until her work was done, but neither could she finish drying the dishes until Sarah had finished washing them. "If you don't hurry up, I'm going to quit," Esther threatened. "Then you can just dry the rest of the dishes yourself."

Sarah quickly rinsed the bowls and set them on the linen towel for Esther to dry. The water was getting cold and was not as much fun to play in as when it had been warm.

The girls could hear John and Annie's new baby crying weakly on the other side of the house.

"It wonders me what ails that baby," Sarah said. "He just cries and cries."

"I don't know," Esther said. "Mary didn't cry all the time like that still."

The girls did not know baby Robert had been born prematurely and his life hung in a balance. They only knew he cried a lot and was so tiny he had to be carried on a pillow. His anxious parents did everything they knew for him, but he died on May 30, eight days after his birth. A few days later he was buried in the cemetery at the Martindale Mennonite Church which John and Annie attended. The house that had been filled with the sound of the baby's incessant crying was suddenly silent and the Aukers mourned the short life of their firstborn son.

While infant death was common and bereaved parents were often advised to "get over it" by having another child as soon as possible, parents who had buried an infant understood the disappointment the Aukers were experiencing. Their friends and families came to offer support and sympathy in the days before and following the funeral.

The traffic going in and out of the long farm lane increased still more when the hole where the new tobacco shed was to be built was finally finished. The carpenters came on June 3 and began making the foundation on which the big tobacco shed would be built.

"You'ns must take your play things out of the pig sty tomorrow," Daed told the girls one evening. "It has to be moved to make room for the garage Elam wants to build. He wants to move the pig sty tomorrow when his help is here for the raising."

There was always a lot of action on the Burkholder farm, but the Wenger children thought the day of the raising was the most exciting day of all. Crowds of men came to help raise the walls of the tobacco shed, set the rafters in place, and cover them with a solid, tight roof. Elam's booming voice directed the workers at the building site while his wife, Annie, supervised the cooking of the large quantities of food needed to feed the volunteer workers throughout the day. The wives of some of the men came to help cook the food and serve it on makeshift tables set up in the yard. Of course, young mothers brought their small children with them, which added to the commotion and excitement.

"What's that?" Sarah asked as she pointed to a big, metal tub filled with glass bottles being kept cold in ice water.

"Soft drinks," Memm told her. "You may have one. What fer kind would you like?"

Sarah had never tasted a soft drink. She looked at the bottles of orange Nehi, reddish-brown Sarsaparilla, dark brown Coca Cola, Dr. Pepper, and Moxie soft drinks. How could she know which one she would like if she did not know how any of them tasted? At last Memm fished out a bottle of orange Nehi, pried off the metal cap, and handed the bottle to Sarah. She took a small swallow of the soft drink and was startled when little bubbles fizzed inside her mouth. But she liked the orange flavor, so she took another swallow.

The Burkholders sold the five-cent bottles of soft drinks in the little store behind their house. Their three youngest sons had always had free access to the drinks. Elam Jr., Lester, and Eli were not bashful now and freely helped themselves from the abundant supply in the tubs of ice whenever they wished. The three boys were about the same ages as Sarah, Arthur, and Esther. Being the youngest in the family of fourteen children, the Burkholder boys had learned to fend for themselves. Solidly built and rough in their play, they were the opposite of the skinny, timid Wenger children who watched in horror as the

"Burky boys" took the wagon to the top of the barn hill and rode down at breakneck speed.

Three-year-old Eli bounced around in the wagon, barely able to hold onto the sides, while his brothers gave him one reckless ride after another down the barn hill. When the wagon tipped and spilled him into the dirt in the driveway, Eli's laughter turned into howls of protest.

"You're all right," Elam and Lester assured their little brother as they picked him up and brushed the dirt from his clothes. "Don't *brutz* (cry)." Then they set Eli back in the wagon and were off for another rough ride.

"Do you want a ride?" Lester asked Arthur when the wagon came to a stop near the place where the Wenger children stood watching.

"*Naa-aa-aa-h* (no)!" Arthur's voice quivered with fear at the mere idea. There was no way any of the Wenger children would let those roughneck Burky boys take *them* for a ride!

When the noon dinner break was over, Elam sent some of the men to move the pig sty. They pried the little building off its foundations and nailed boards inside the shell to brace it. Then they went inside, picked up the building by the braces and carried it to its new location. The children laughed as they watched. How funny it looked to see the pig sty walking past them and going behind the barn on a row of legs!

The memory of the wonderful day lingered long after it ended and all of the workers had gone home. Although they had been afraid to join the rough play of his sons, big, tall Elam Burkholder and his booming voice had made a lasting impression on the Wenger children.

By the end of July, the potatoes Daed and Paul had planted in the spring were big enough to eat. They filled bushel baskets with potatoes and peddled them in the big city of Reading where housewives eagerly snatched up the new potatoes with their paper-thin skins. But potato digging paused when the threshers came to the farm one afternoon during the first week of August.

The threshermen set up their equipment in the barnyard but waited until the next morning to start working. Threshing day was almost as exciting as a raising. The man who owned the threshing machine, and the men he had hired to help him, must be fed large meals and snacks. Annie Auker came over from the other house to help Memm with the endless round of cooking and baking that went on the day the threshers were on the farm.

Sarah and Esther had to take care of baby Mary, but Arthur and Frank went out to watch Daed helping to pitch bundles into the threshing machine. A long belt connected the threshing machine to a Waterloo Boy tractor. It provided the power to run the machine which separated the grain heads from the stalks. The grain poured from a spout on the side of the threshing machine and into large cloth bags which one of the men hung on hooks below the spout. The bare stalks, which were now called straw, were blown out the back of the threshing machine onto a big pile. Two men forked the straw into a stationary baler which was powered by another belt connected to a second tractor.

The eight men worked like clockwork, pitching bundles into the threshing machine, bagging and hauling away the grain, forking straw into the baler, and stacking the wire-bound bales on a pile in the barnyard. Chaff flew in the air, coating the sweating men with a layer of itchy dirt. They ignored the discomfort, for if one person did not keep up the pace, the smooth rhythm would be interrupted and all of them might have to stop.

The men shut down the machinery and came into the house for dinner at noon. They washed their hands and faces in tubs of water Memm set on the porch and dried themselves on towels that had once been feed sacks. Sarah's mouth watered at the good smells coming from the kitchen, but the children must stay in the next room and wait until the men had finished eating the feast that had been prepared for them.

Memm was a good cook, able to use her imagination to make special dishes with the simple ingredients always found in her kitchen. Sarah looked longingly at the beautiful dish of dessert Memm had made from ordinary Farina. She had cooked the breakfast cereal, mixed cocoa into half of it, and poured both colors into separate pans to cool overnight. Just before dinnertime, she had skimmed the cream from the top of the milk and whipped it by hand until it formed stiff peaks. Then she cut the Farina into squares and folded them into whipped cream. The brown and cream-colored blocks nestled in the stiff white cream looked beautiful in the cut glass bowl.

After the men went back to work, the women cleared the table and set places for themselves and the children. Sarah was delighted to see the men had not eaten all of the lovely, tasty dessert. There was no time for the women to rest after dinner, for they could hear the machinery running and knew the men were hard at work again. As soon as the dishes were washed the women must begin preparing a mid-afternoon snack. After the breaktime snack was delivered to the men in the barnyard, the women must start peeling potatoes for supper.

Sarah and Esther dried the dishes as Annie Auker washed them. Before they had finished, the sound of the machinery stopped and a sudden quiet descended on the farm.

Daed came into the house to tell Memm, "The threshing machine broke down. It looks like it will take the rest of the day to fix it. The men will be here overnight, so you better figure on feeding them another day."

Memm groaned softly but nodded in agreement for there was nothing else to do. The men in the threshing crew were used to sleeping in the barns where they worked, so they made beds for themselves in the haymow. Memm got up before dawn the next morning to cook breakfast for the men. The threshing machine was fixed and ran smoothly all morning so that the threshing was finished just before noon. After dinner the threshers moved on to the next farm while Daed and Paul spent the rest of the day moving the stack of wire-bound straw bales into the top of the barn. Then the hustle and bustle of threshing day, which had stretched into two days this time, was over for another year.

Just because threshing was over did not mean life was dull, for something interesting or exciting was always happening on the Burkholder farm. Men were still coming to do the finishing work on the big tobacco shed. Paul's brother, Elmer, hauled truckloads of ground from a quarry to fill the ditches around the building. Daed helped to dig ditches and pour the foundations for the new garage that was going to be built where the pig sty had stood. Next, he started digging a big hole where a huge gas tank would be buried beside the garage.

When school began in September, Sarah had just turned seven and should have gone to first grade. Her school days had already been postponed a year, but Memm knew Sarah was too timid to get on the school bus alone and ride to school in the village of Lincoln. Also, she was used to riding in a slow-moving buggy and got carsick every time she rode in a car or trolley. She was not compelled by law to be in school until she was eight years old, so she was allowed to stay at home another year until Arthur would be old enough to go to school with her.

On a Sunday afternoon in mid-September, a crowd of visitors gathered at the farm. Daed and John Auker had been good friends before they "lived double" in the same house, so they knew many of the same people. Each family expected the other to join the group when either of them had company. The men and women formed separate groups and discussed the topics that were of interest to their gender while the little children played together in one happy group.

The men went out to inspect the damage from the previous day's storm. It had torn half of the roof from the shed and created a miniature flood that ran into and filled the hole Daed had dug for the gas tank. The men carried wooden chairs from the kitchen and sat in a circle in the yard to continue visiting. Without seeming to, they kept an eye on the children who ran back and forth, playing in the yard and driveway.

Mud squished between the toes of the children's bare feet and splashed up on their clothes, but they did not notice. Some of them ran around the puddles, but others delighted in splashing through them. Their mothers, who were in the house and out of sight, would have been upset if they had seen how muddy their children's clothes were becoming. But the fathers were too busy visiting to think about how much work the children were making for their mothers the next morning when it would be washday.

"Look at me!" Arthur cried as he puffed out his skinny little chest and hooked his thumbs under his armpits. "*Ich bin die Elam Barighalter* (I am Elam Burkholder)," he growled in the deepest voice he could muster.

"*Ich bin die Elam Barighalter,*" the other children laughed and copied his actions. They marched around the puddles in the driveway, saying *Ich bin die Elam Barighalter* as they tried to outdo each other in imitating the big man with the deep voice they had learned to know at the raising. None of them saw Frank heading straight toward the deep, water-filled gas tank hole.

Suddenly, Daed jumped up from his chair and ran toward the children. But he could not run fast enough to grab Frank before he fell into the deep water. Muddy water splashed up into the air as the two-year-old boy fell down into the hole and sank out of sight.

Without taking time to remove his shoes or any of his Sunday clothes, Daed jumped into the hole and grabbed Frank as he bobbed to the surface. He coughed and sputtered as he spit out the water he had swallowed. The children, who had stopped in their tracks when they saw Frank fall into the hole, watched somberly as the capable hands of the visiting men reached down to take Frank and help Daed climb out of the hole. Although he had come close to drowning, Frank's terrified howls assured everyone he was fine.

"Now all you *kinner* (children) stay back from that there hole!" Daed warned sternly as he took Frank in his arms again.

The other fathers echoed the warnings to their children as Daed carried the howling Frank to the house. Muddy water ran from Daed's Sunday clothes and his wet shoes squished with every step. Memm recognized Frank's cry and the tone of his voice told her something serious had occurred.

"What happened?" Memm gasped when she saw her muddy husband and son.

"He fell in the gas tank hole," Daed explained briefly and went upstairs to change his clothes while Memm stripped off Frank's muddy little clothes and dressed him in clean everyday clothes.

When the visiting mothers heard how nearly Frank had come to drowning, they rushed outside to add their alarmed warnings to those the men had already given the children. Sufficiently frightened by the near-tragedy, the children kept a safe distance from the hole the rest of the afternoon.

The next day, Daed cleaned the mud and water from the gas tank hole while the carpenters put the roof on the new garage. Two days later the tank was lowered into the hole and Daed filled it with ground so no one would ever fall into it again.

The days turned cooler as they grew increasingly shorter and the children could not go barefoot anymore. They had outgrown their shoes during the summer. Frank could wear the shoes Arthur had outgrown earlier. Esther could wear Sarah's old shoes and Mary could wear some that had been passed down from Esther. There were no shoes in the house that fit Sarah or Arthur, so Daed bought good used shoes for them at the Bazaar in Ephrata. Frank and Mary were too little to know the difference, but Esther thought it was not fair that Sarah always got the "new" things just because she was the oldest. Esther could see she would never have anything new, but was doomed to spend the rest of her life wearing Sarah's outgrown clothes.

"Don't put your Sunday dresses on today," Memm told the girls when they got up one Sunday morning in October. "We can't go to church today."

Neither Memm nor Daed told the children why they could not go to church that day. Taught to respect and obey the authority of their parents, they accepted the decision without asking for an explanation. No one came to visit, and they did not go anywhere. It was raining and too cold to go outside to play. Since no work could be done on Sunday, except caring for the animals, there was little to fill the long hours of doing nothing.

"What are you going to do?" Sarah asked curiously when Daed sat down at the table with some old, empty cigar boxes piled in front of him.

"I'm going to make you girls some little boxes to put your hankies in," Daed said as he started taking one of the wooden boxes apart.

The girls watched as Daed painstakingly carved thin strips of wood in fancy shapes and glued them onto two of the best boxes. The handcrafted boxes, sometimes known as Tramp Art, would be fine places for the girls to store the precious hankies they were beginning to collect. All girls treasured the hankies they received as gifts or tokens of friendship. The cotton hankies were not used, but carefully kept and brought out to be shown to their friends and visitors. Each hankie was duly admired while the owner showed it and told who had given it.

The boxes were not finished at the end of the day, so Daed put them away until another time. When they were finished, the girls would have nice boxes to show their friends as well as their collections of hankies.

Right after supper the next evening, Memm took sixteen-month-old Mary to Annie Auker on the other side of the house and then went to bed in the *kammer* (downstairs bedroom). Daed said the children must go to bed early too.

"Aren't you going to work on our boxes tonight?" Sarah asked Daed.

"Not tonight," Daed said. "Now up the steps. All of you."

Sarah knew it was too early to go to bed, but she also knew she could not argue with Daed. Arthur and Frank went to the room they shared while Sarah and Esther slowly got ready for bed in their room. They were not one bit sleepy, so they were in no hurry to climb into bed.

"Sh-h! Listen," Sarah said an hour or two later. "I hear a baby crying."

Esther stopped chattering and listened intently for a few seconds. "So do I," she agreed.

"It's on our side of the house," Sarah observed. "We must have company."

"Let's go see who it is," Esther suggested eagerly.

The feet of the two girls pattered rapidly down the stairs. Daed heard them coming and opened the door before they reached the bottom of the stairs. "Get back up there," he ordered firmly.

"We heard a baby crying," Esther said.

"We thought company came and wanted to see who it is," Sarah explained.

"No. We don't have company," Daed said. "Go back to bed and stay there."

The girls marched obediently back up the stairs and went to bed, but they were still sure they had heard a baby crying and knew it was not Mary. When they went downstairs the next morning they found Memm was still in bed. As soon as the girls saw the wicker baby coach setting beside the bed they rushed to look inside. Every one of them had slept in the wicker coach when they were babies. Sure enough! A brand new baby lay sleeping in the coach.

"When did you get this baby?" Sarah asked in surprise.

"Last night," Memm smiled. "This is your new baby sister. Her name is Anna. She is named for Annie Auker."

"I knew we heard a baby crying last night!" Esther exclaimed.

Sarah remembered what the Brubaker girls had told her about the doctor bringing babies. She had not seen or heard anything of the doctor and did not have the courage to ask Memm if he had come and brought Anna in his black bag.

Daadi and Mammi Shaub came later in the morning to see baby Anna and take Arthur home with them for a few weeks. Daed managed as well as he could, with the help of Grandmother Wenger and Annie Auker, until Memm was able to do her own work again.

Daed and Paul were digging all of the potatoes they had planted in the spring. The potato digger turned the soil over like a plow and brought the potatoes to the top so they could be picked up by hand and placed in bushel baskets. The potatoes were stored in the new garage until they could be sorted and bagged for sale. They were hauled away from the farm almost as fast as they were sorted. One day Paul's brother, Chester, brought his father's Stewart truck to the farm and loaded it with 132 bushel baskets of potatoes. Daed went in the truck with Chester to peddle the potatoes in the big city of Reading and smaller town of Wernersville.

While Daed and Chester were peddling potatoes, Paul began putting a new feeding trough and hay racks in the steer stable. After supper that evening, he asked Memm for an old catalog. She found an old Sears & Roebuck catalog and handed it to him. The children were horrified when they saw him tear some pages from the catalog and cut them in tiny pieces. Sarah knew she would be in deep trouble if she tore pages from a catalog, because then Memm would not be able to send mail orders for the things they needed.

"What are you *snibbling* that up for?" Sarah asked Paul as the children crowded around him to watch what he was doing.

"Naaayah," Paul drawled in a tone that implied the children were being nosy and he did not have to answer their questions. The pile of tiny pieces of paper grew as he silently continued to shred the catalog pages.

"What are you going to do with that?" Esther asked when her curiosity could not be contained.

Seeing the inquisitive little Wenger children would not leave him alone until their curiosity was satisfied, Paul said in his slow way, "I'm going to a wedding tomorrow. This is to throw at the people that are getting married."

The children looked at each other in disbelief. None of them had ever heard anything so strange. *Is he just making that up?* Sarah wondered. *Or is he gonna do that for real? Why would anybody want to throw paper at people when they get married?* But Sarah knew Paul did some other peculiar things, so she decided he probably meant what he had said even if it didn't make sense. Paul was going to a lot of weddings these days, because his friends were of marriageable age and weddings were almost always held in the fall and winter months. Sure enough! The next morning he came downstairs, dressed in his Sunday suit and carrying the little paper bag of catalog pieces in his hand.

The days grew increasingly colder during the last months of the year, but Daed had been too busy to move the kitchen back into the big house. In December, when the water froze overnight in the teakettle, the move could no longer be delayed. Daed spent a whole day moving the cookstove and furniture from the summer kitchen back into the main house. He helped Memm move all the dishes and kitchen utensils from one kitchen to the other and set up housekeeping for the winter in the house kitchen. Even if they were not leaving the property, moving day was more exciting to the children than Christmas.

Although Christmas was the climax of the year for some children, it was just another ordinary day to the Wenger children. They had never received Christmas gifts from their parents, so they did not expect anything. Earlier in the month, John Auker had gone to Bowers Beach in Delaware and loaded his automobile with oysters which he peddled in the neighborhood. The oranges Elam Burkholder had ordered from Texas arrived at the depot in New Holland and were sold directly from the train cars which had brought them to Pennsylvania. Elam's brother, Noah, did the same thing at the Ephrata depot. But Daed could not afford to buy oysters or oranges, so the Wengers did without the special Christmas treats. Christmas Day was spent quietly at home. Nothing special happened and no one came to visit. But the children were not disappointed, for they had not expected anything special to happen.

"Elam told me yesterday we have to move," Daed told Memm after dinner on Christmas Day. He had put off telling her the bad news because he knew she would dread moving again.

"I was afraid of that," Memm said in a tired, discouraged tone. She was not surprised at the news, because she knew Daed and Paul were not working well together. "Do you have any idea where can we go?"

"No," Daed admitted. "But I was thinking. Maybe we could rent Charlie Horning's small farm or buy Alvin White's house. I don't know. I'll start looking around next week and see what I can find. We don't have to move until our year is up at the end of March. I'll find something before that."

"Yes, but moving again *ferlates*[6] me," Memm sighed.

This time Daed was the one encouraging Memm. "Don't worry. We'll get back on our feet again," he assured her. "Someday we'll have a place of our own and be able to stay put."

---

[6] There is no English word equal to *ferlates*. It carries the meaning of dread or dismay.

Chapter 4

Sarah squirmed on the bare wooden church bench and slid front far enough to put her feet on the floor. Her left foot had fallen asleep. She knew the only way to relieve the sharp tingles that stabbed through her foot was to put it flat on the floor and wiggle her toes.

When her foot finally stopped tingling, Sarah slid back on the bench and unfolded her hankie. Memm had brought a few small toys for little Mary and baby Anna, but Sarah and Esther were allowed to take only their cotton hankies to church. Sarah folded her hankie in half across the corner to make a triangle and then rolled both points from the ends to the center. Carefully holding the bottom of the two rolls between her finger and thumb, she folded the rolled hankie in half. Then she separated the loose points at the top and pushed the rolls down inside as she pulled the points up. There it was! She had made a baby cradle with two babies inside. Holding one point of the hankie in each hand, she gently swung it back and forth, rocking her twin babies.

The long service seemed longer than ever today because Sarah knew that when it was over the whole family was going to Mammi Shaub's house for Aunt Mary's wedding dinner. She had married Ammon Auker, who was the brother of Aunt Lizzie's husband, Weaver Auker. Aunt Mary and Ammon had been married quietly at a preacher's house, without the presence of their families, on January 4, 1931. Their wedding dinner was considered to be the wedding, although it was held a week after the marriage ceremony. Mammi Shaub could not come to church today because she was cooking the big wedding dinner for the Shaub and Auker families.

At last, church was over and the Wenger family drove down the road that took them to the new house Daadi Shaub had built at the bottom of the of the *Katze Boucle* (Cat's Back) Hill at Fairmount. People called the hill *Katze Boucle* because they thought the way it rose so steeply and suddenly on the gently rolling landscape made it look like the arched back of a frightened cat.

Daadi Shaub's house was full of good smells from the delicious food Mammi had cooked for the wedding dinner. The kitchen was a bustle of activity as Memm and her sisters helped Mammi put the food on the beautiful table. It was stretched as long as it could be and set with the best Sunday dishes. Daadi and the other men stayed out of the way in the parlor, waiting to be called to the table. As usual, Daadi was talking about the stock market while he waited for his dinner. He did not own any stocks, of course, but he knew the stock market crash in 1929 had triggered the Great Depression that continued to deepen and wreck the nation's economy. He enjoyed watching the market and talking about what was happening as if he understood it completely.

The six Wenger children joined the dozens of cousins who filled all the little corners of Daadi Shaub's house. Sarah scanned the crowd for Edna Good, who was the Shaub girl cousin nearest Sarah's age. The girls soon found each other and ran off to play in an out-of-the-way place until they would be called to the table. They did not need dolls, for there were plenty of babies to *gnootsche* (cuddle). They knew they would not be called to eat at the first table that was served. The newlyweds would eat first, of course, with the most important guests. After they finished, the dishes would be washed and the table set again for another group. The women and children would not eat until all the men had been served. The mothers fed their babies while the men ate, but the other children were big enough to wait until all of the men had eaten. Since so many people had been invited to the wedding dinner, the children knew they would have to wait until at least the third table was set before it would be their turn to eat.

By the time the women had washed the last dishes late in the afternoon, the men were soon ready to go home to do their evening chores. But the women did not feel cheated, for their tongues flew as fast as their hands and they had visited while they worked.

The wedding dinner was a bright spot in the long, bleak winter. With the exception of the Sundays when they went to church or visiting, the days were much alike to Sarah. She was tired of being in the house and bored with life in general. Day after dreary day, everything was the same.

"Would yous like to make picture books?" Memm asked the children one day when sheer boredom had produced a morning of petty quarreling.

"How?" Sarah asked.

"You can cut pictures from these," Memm said, laying some old catalogs and *Farm Journal* magazines on the table. "I'll make some paste from flour and water, and you can paste your pictures on pieces of tobacco paper."

Arthur and Esther eagerly joined Sarah in making picture books. They spent hours choosing and cutting out pictures to make beautiful pages. Memm had promised she would sew the pages together to make books when they were finished. Frank was too little to use the scissors, so Sarah cut pictures for him and helped him paste them on the brown paper pages. The long days were shortened by the pleasant pastime as the children sat on the floor, happily cutting and pasting.

Daed spent most of his days stripping tobacco in the new tobacco shed. He did not chew or smoke tobacco himself but raised it as a cash crop. The harmful effects of tobacco use were still unproven, so the production and use of tobacco had not yet become a moral issue. Because it generated more income on less acreage, growing tobacco had become an accepted practice in eastern Lancaster County during the later half of the nineteenth century. Daed wanted to finish stripping his tobacco as soon as possible so he could ship it before moving day came. Sometimes Memm helped him, and he returned the favor by helping her with the washing.

Every Monday, Daed pumped buckets of water by hand and poured them into the iron kettle that hung in the fireplace of the summer kitchen. Then he built a fire under the kettle to heat the water. When it was boiling, he dipped the water out of the kettle with a metal bucket and poured it into the wooden tub of Memm's washing machine. He pumped more buckets of cold water and poured them into the metal rise tub he had set under the wringer of the washing machine.

While the water was heating in the iron kettle, Memm boiled the white pieces of clothing in the washboiler on the stove. Daed carried the washboiler to the summer house and emptied it into the washing machine. It had been leaking from the cracks between the upright boards, but he had fixed it by putting new hoops around the tub to hold it tightly together. He fitted the wooden lid in place and started the gasoline engine that was connected to the washing machine with a belt. The engine made the paddles inside the wooden tub go back and forth to beat the dirt from the clothing. As it ran, the steady firing of the one-and-a-half horsepower Fairbanks engine sounded like it was saying, *Putt, putt, putt, putt.*

When the clothes were clean, Memm picked each piece from the water and ran it through the wringer on the back of the tub. As she turned the handle, the twin rollers of the wringer squeezed the water from the clothing before it dropped down into the rinse water. Clothing with pockets must always be run through the wringer from the bottom up so the water could drain from the pockets before they went through the wringer. If the pockets were full of water, the wringer would squirt the water all over Memm and the floor.

After all of the white things were washed, the second go (load) of colored clothing was put into the water. The water was quite dirty by the time the last go was put into the washing machine, but it did not matter because it was just Daed's barn clothes.

When they were first married, Memm had been able to do the wash alone. Now, with six children, she had many other things to do and the weekly laundry pile was larger. Daed knew she had never regained her full strength after Anna's birth and the heavy, back-breaking work of washing was too much for her to do alone.

On the second day of February, Daed said to Memm at the dinner table, "The groundhog saw his shadow this morning. So I guess that means six more weeks of winter."

"I think we'll have six more weeks of winter whether the groundhog saw his shadow or not," Memm said mildly.

Of course, neither of them really believed the old German folk-tale that the groundhog came out of hibernation on February 2 to see if spring had arrived. If he saw his shadow, he ran back in his hole to sleep for another six weeks. But if he did not see his shadow, he stayed above ground and everyone knew there would be an early spring. Groundhog Day was more of an interesting diversion for winter-weary souls than an established truth.

Although winter weather continued for another six weeks, by the middle of March definite signs of spring were in the air. The cold was weakening as the sun shone longer each day. The ice had melted and the waters of the once-frozen creeks tumbled over each other in their rush to go downstream and become bigger creeks and rivers.

"I'm going for a walk," Daed told Memm one Sunday afternoon. It was an Off Sunday, and he had been sitting in the house so long he was beginning to feel like a chicken in a coop.

"Can I go with?" Sarah asked eagerly.

"Not this time," Daed told her. "It's not warm enough for you to go so far."

"How far are you going?" Sarah asked.

"That depends," Daed said. "I'll tell you where I was when I get back."

Sarah knew Daed had gone far, because he was gone a long time. When snow began to fall, she was glad she had not gone with him. He was cold and wet when he came home, for the snow had changed to a light drizzle.

"Where were you?" Sarah asked as Daed held his cold hands over the warm, black cookstove.

"Well," Daed said slowly as his eyes twinkled at her. "I walked along the trout stream all the way to Ephrata. By then it was snowing, so I went in the light plant and talked to Walter Dickersheid awhile. Then I started to go to Check (Jake) Stauffers, but when I was almost in town I met them on the road. Since I knew they weren't home, I walked over the mountain to see the Morrow place we're going to move to in a couple weeks. I stopped at Noah Burkholder's place on my way home, but they weren't home either, so after that I just came home again."

"What is the Morrow place like?" Memm asked Daed.

"Not near as big or nice as this place," Daed answered honestly. "The house isn't fancy, but it's big enough for us. There's a peach orchard on the place and we can keep some laying hens. Henry Hess lives up on the hill. He goes around the neighborhood there picking up eggs to peddle in town. We can sell peaches and eggs, and I can pick up some day labor to earn a little more. We'll make it."

The next day Daed finished stripping his tobacco and sold the crop to the Mead Tobacco Company. The bales were trucked to the big tobacco warehouse on Elam Burkholder's farm where they were kept until they could be delivered to the buyer. After Daed collected his tobacco money, he bought a few used farm implements and started getting ready to move to the small farm he had rented from Leslie Morrow.[7]

By the time the family was settled on the small farm, spring work had begun. Daed planted some potatoes and broomcorn for cash crops, the corn and other things he needed to feed and care for his animals, and tended the peach orchard. The trees had been pruned in March before new growth started. The blossoms that covered the trees like a pink blanket in April changed into little green ovals.

"Why are you picking them off?" Sarah asked in a shocked voice when she saw Daed thinning the peaches in June.

---

[7] The current address of this farm is 121 Valley View Drive, Ephrata, Pa.

"So it gives bigger peaches," Daed told her. "There's not enough room on the tree for all these here peaches to grow big."

"But you're picking off more than you're letting on," Sarah observed.

"I know," Daed admitted. "It seems wasteful, but that's what I have to do. If I let all them peaches on the tree they'll be so little nobody will want to buy them. If nothing happens, by August we should have lots of nice big peaches to sell. I'm hoping for a good peach crop, because I don't have any tobacco this year."

The peaches grew round as the weeks passed and turned from olive green to a beautiful ripe golden-pink. Naturally, some of the peaches dropped to the ground and began to spoil. Memm saved the ones that could not be sold by cutting out the rotten spots and canning the good parts. Canned peaches had been a rare delicacy when they lived on farms where there were no peach trees, but now rows of filled green glass jars stood on Memm's canning shelves. Sarah felt rich when she looked at the golden hoard that would be eaten in the winter. Never in all her life had she seen so many jars of peaches on Memm's can shelves.

Another benefit of living on the Morrow place was being closer to Daadi Shaub's farm. The children occasionally took turns spending a few days with Mammi Shaub, but the most fun times were when the Shaub family gathered there for a Sunday dinner. In the summertime, the farm was one huge playground for the cousins who needed no suggestions of ways to entertain themselves.

"Let's go play with the Aunt Ricky clothes," cousin Vera suggested.

"Yeah, let's," her girl cousins chimed, knowing what she meant without further explanation.

Sarah, Esther, Miriam, Irene, Vera, and Edna ran to the top of the barn where Mammi Shaub had piled the boxes of old clothes Aunt Ricky had sent to her. Aunt Ricky was not really their aunt. She was Mammi Shaub's cousin who lived in Brooklyn, New York. Her real name was Friederika Barschow, but everyone called her Aunt Ricky. Once each year, Aunt Ricky came to Lancaster on the train and spent several days visiting her Mink, Seibel, Zimmerman, and Shaub relatives in Lancaster County.

"Look at this," Sarah laughed as she pulled a dress from one of the boxes. The beautifully tucked and shirred black silk dress had immense balloon sleeves and a bustle. She slipped the dress over her head, pushed up the sleeves, lifted the skirts, and swept grandly across the dirty barn floor with the long skirt trailing behind her.

"Here," Edna cried, "you need a hat yet." She pulled a huge Victorian hat from one of the boxes and set it on top of Sarah's head.

The hat slid down over Sarah's eyes, so she pushed it to the back of her head. The big feathers on the hat proudly waved back and forth as she pranced across the floor and curtsied to the other girls. Her little bare feet and apron-covered plain dress were completely concealed by the elegant dress. The fancy hat hid the braids that were pinned in a circle on the back of her head.

The girls flung clothes right and left as they dug through the boxes to see what treasures they could find and modeled one outfit after another. Each outfit was duly admired before it was tossed aside and replaced with a new one. There were high button shoes, hats, fancy dresses, coats, old corsets, and all sorts of clothes the girls had never seen before.

The boxes of clothing had been left in an old warehouse Aunt Ricky's husband, Edward, had purchased in Brooklyn to house the equipment he used in his scrap metal business. Aunt Ricky had been born in Germany and come to America with her parents, Johannes and Katherina Münk (Mink), when she was nine years old. Her frugal German nature did not allow her to discard the old, out-of-style clothes, so she shipped the boxes to her cousin, Lizzie Shaub, in Lancaster County.

Aunt Ricky knew the Old Order Mennonites would not wear the once-stylish clothes, but she also knew her relatives were good seamstresses. As Aunt Ricky expected, Mammi Shaub and her daughters cut the clothes apart to make wearable, plain clothing for themselves and their children. As the

Depression deepened, they had resorted to making much of their clothing from feed sacks, because they could not afford to buy fabric from the stores or mail order catalogs. The coats in the boxes were especially useful, for winter coats could never be made from feed sacks.

"Look at me," Esther giggled. She held up the long skirt of the dress she was wearing and clopped unsteadily across the wooden floor in a pair of shoes that were much too big for her little feet. "*Ich bin en reich Englischer fraa* (I'm a rich English lady)."

"*Ach*, you are not," Sarah contradicted. "You can't even talk English."

"Neither can you," Esther retorted.

"I can so," Sarah argued. "Well, anyways, more than you, because I have to go to school soon."

"Oh! Look at these!" Miriam cried as she held up a pair of silk gloves and a folded fan. "This is just what I need," she snickered as she opened the fan and fanned her hot, dirt-streaked face.

The girls took turns fanning themselves with the delicate fan and went on playing with the clothes until they heard their parents calling for them. Then they tossed the clothes back in the boxes, ran out of the barn to climb into their respective buggies, and went home. The wonderful boxes of clothes would be there to play with again the next time they visited Mammi Shaub.

The hot summer sun beat down on the black buggy as it rolled slowly toward the Wenger home. Not a breath of air stirred anywhere. Crammed into the back of the buggy with her siblings, Sarah felt the sweat trickle down her back as Dewy plodded on, pulling the buggy through the little village of Hahnstown. The road dipped down and then rose steeply upward to cross the Ephrata Mountain.

"Whoa!" Daed called to the horse. When Dewy stopped, Daed jumped out of the buggy to make the load lighter for the horse.

"Can we walk with you?" Esther called to Daed.

"I don't care," Daed gave permission.

Sarah, Arthur, and Esther scrambled out of the stifling hot buggy, leaving only Memm and the little ones for the horse to carry up the hill.

"Git-up," Daed said as he gently slapped the reins on Dewy's broad back.

Sarah was glad to be walking in the open air beside Daed as Dewy pulled the buggy up the long, steep hill. She could not express her feelings in words, but the special privilege of walking with Daed somehow made her feel loved and secure.

When they reached the top of the mountain, Daed stopped the horse under the trees that offered some shade from the punishing sun. "Jump in," he told the children as he climbed into the buggy and took his place again on the seat beside Memm.

The children scrambled aboard for the more rapid and slightly cooler descent down the north side of the shady hill. Almost at the bottom of the hill, Daed turned Dewy to the left onto the road that would take them to their home on the edge of the woods.

The children tumbled out of the buggy and ran to the house while Daed unhitched Dewy and parked the buggy in the barn. Memm set out a light supper of bread and butter and a bowl of the last peaches. They had eaten a big dinner at Daadi Shaub's house, so they did not need much to eat for supper.

The next Tuesday was the first day of September and also Sarah's eighth birthday. The 1931-32 school term began a week later, the day after Labor Day. She knew her school days could not be postponed any longer. She would have to find the courage to face all the strange children and enter first grade with Arthur at Mohler's School.

"Now don't play around on the way," Memm warned the two children as she handed Sarah the lunch bucket. "Yous must not be late on the first day of school."

Sarah and Arthur knew the way, because Daed had taken them to Ephrata with him one day the previous week and showed them how they would have to walk to get to the one-room school. After walking nearly a mile and passing several farms, the road would end at a hump where it joined the Reading Road. At this T, they would turn left and walk toward Ephrata for another half-mile on the Reading Road, which lay between the Cocalico Creek and Noah Burkholder's farm. Mohler's School stood across the road from the lane that went into Noah Burkholder's buildings. Neither Sarah or Arthur remembered living there, but Daed had told them they had both been born in that house.

Sarah and Arthur set out, trying to be brave as they walked down the long dirt road to school. As they approached the first farm before the T-road, two big dogs saw them coming and rushed out to meet them, barking as they came.

"*Schpringe* (Run!)," Sarah yelled. The lunch pail in her hand banged against her skinny legs as her feet flew over the ground.

Arthur ran beside his sister, as fast as his legs could carry him, while the two barking dogs chased the terrified children. They could hear the jaws of the dogs snapping as they barked and their claws scrabbling as they bounded over the ground in big leaps. At last, when the children had run beyond the boundaries of the farm, the dogs slowed and turned to go back to the farm they guarded. They had done their job of chasing off strangers and keeping their farm safe.

"Whew!" Arthur puffed as he brushed his long bowl-cut hair out of his eyes and replaced the suspender that had fallen down from his shoulder.

"They almost had us!" Sarah cried as she and her brother slowed to a brisk walk. Now that the dogs had stopped barking, she could hear her heart pounding in her ears. "I hope there aren't dogs any more places."

Sarah's wish was granted, and the remainder of the long walk passed uneventfully. She and Arthur reached Mohler's School before the bell rang and timidly joined the other children who were milling around on the school grounds. They did not know anyone or have any idea what they should do next. Miss Royer spotted the two little new scholars and took them inside. She showed Sarah where to set the lunch pail and wrote the children's names and ages in her record book.

"Since you are both beginners, you will sit in these front seats," Miss Royer told Sarah and Arthur. She showed them two desks at the front of one of the short rows of desks that filled the room. The varnished desks were supported by black wrought iron legs and had seats which could be folded back. The desktop had a groove in the center to hold pencils and a glass inkwell that fitted snugly into a hole in the right corner. Books and tablets could be stored in the space under the desktop.

Miss Royer went to the door and swung the handbell to call the children into the school room. Sarah looked around the room while the children trooped noisily into the building and found seats. A big, black piece of slate was framed with wood and fastened to the wall behind the teacher's desk. Alphabet cards were mounted in a long row above the blackboard with a picture of George Washington and Abraham Lincoln on each side. She did not know who these men were or why their pictures were in the school room. Nor did she know what the letters were on the alphabet cards or that the first thing she would have to do was memorize and say them in English.

There was much to see and learn on the first day of school. The teacher was a lady from the Brethren Church. She understood Pennsylvania Deutsch, but spoke English in school. Sarah and Arthur were forced to hear English words all day and try to reply with their limited vocabulary. Noah Burkholder's daughters, Emma and Lena, were about the same age as Sarah. She was glad when they spoke to her in her own familiar language at recess, but they had not known each other before. By the time school was dismissed for the day, she was glad to go home and back to familiar things.

Steve Sweigart's children joined Sarah and Arthur on the long walk home. Grace Sweigart was almost the same age as Sarah. The Sweigarts lived beyond the Wengers and had even further to walk, so their father took them to school in his car in the mornings. But his car was full with his own children. There had been no room for Sarah and Arthur to ride to school in the car with their neighbors.

The barking dogs that had chased Sarah and Arthur in the morning came out again in the afternoon, but they felt a little less vulnerable in the larger group of children. The next morning, when they were walking to school again by themselves, the dogs came out and chased them until they were beyond the perimeters of what the dogs claimed as their property. Every day, the dogs chased the children each time they passed the farm. The dogs never got used to seeing the same two harmless children pass by each day, and the children never overcame their terror of the barking dogs.

"Let's cut through the meadow instead of going by the road," Sarah suggested one morning. "That way, we won't have to go past that place with the dogs."

"Okay," Arthur agreed. He was as much afraid of the dogs as his sister.

The two children slipped under the rail fence and headed diagonally across Noah Burkholder's meadow. They planned to come out on the road somewhere beyond the farm with the big, barking dogs. Before they were halfway across the meadow, the children were spotted by a pair of geese who were not willing to share their territory with trespassers. The geese stretched their necks and honked as they ran toward the children.

"*Schpringe!*" Sarah yelled. The lunch pail bounced with her as she ran over the clumps of meadow grass with Arthur at her heels. His broad-brimmed black hat flew off and tumbled away across the meadow. He darted after and managed to grab it but did not take the time to put it back on his head.

The geese flopped their wings, honked, and hissed as they chased the children out of their territory. The goats heard the commotion and came running to join in the excitement. At last, the children reached the other side of the meadow, climbed over the rail fence, and were safe.

"That was just as bad!" Arthur puffed as he stepped out into the middle of the road and tried to catch his breath.

"I would think!" Sarah agreed. She pulled up her long cotton stockings and readjusted the rubber garters, made from strips of old inner tubes, that held them in place. Her pounding heart

Mobler's School, 1931–32. Students included in the picture have identified their schoolmates as: Row 1: Romaine Hertzog, Lena Burkholder, Wilmer Long, Mae Martin, Aaron Sweigart. Row 2: Christian Zuck, Emma Burkholder, Clarence Martin, Anna Weaver, unknown boy, Richard Shimp, **Arthur Wenger, Sarah Wenger**. *Row 3: Ivan Weaver, John Weaver, Richard Royer, Vera Simmons, Esther Weinbold, Suie Sweigart, David Burkholder, Alvin Sweigart, Edna Weaver. Row 4: Erla Staver, Arlene Martin, Violet Simmons, Irene Hertzog, Norman Sweigart (mostly hidden), Jane Zuck, Anna Mae Weinbold , Levi Burkholder, Arlene Zuck, Sadie Rickenbach, Naomi Martin, Teacher: Miss Ruth Royer. Courtesy: Lena Burkholder Nolt.*

gradually slowed to a steady, quiet rhythm as she and Arthur walked on toward Mohler's School.

As the days turned cooler, the walk to school seemed to become longer and longer. On frosty, gray November mornings the children felt half-frozen by the time they got to school. Once in awhile, if the weather was too inclement or Daed happened to be going that way at the right time, he took them to school in the spring wagon or buggy. But he was busy cutting wood in John Schaeffer's woods up on the mountain, which was the opposite direction from the school. So the children usually walked the mile and a half between their home and the school twice a day. Still, they dreaded the animals that chased them more than the long, cold walk. There was simply no way to go to school and back again without the danger of being chased by either dogs or the animals in the meadow.

November was also corn husking time. Daed had cut and shocked his small crop of corn. He picked the ears from the shocks and hauled them in the wagon to the corn barn. The ears were dumped on a pile on the floor where they waited until he had time to husk them. Then they were stored in the corn crib until they were fed to the cattle. He always brought some of the ears to the house for Memm to roast slowly in the oven overnight before they were taken to the mill and ground into cornmeal.

"I'm going to fire up the old bake oven to roast the corn," Daed said one morning.

"You wouldn't have to," Memm said. "I have the cookstove going anyway."

"I know," Daed said cheerfully. "I just thought it would be nice to do it the old-fashioned way while I have the chance. It isn't every place that has a good bake oven like this one. And besides, the old bake oven is big enough to do the whole batch at once."

The bake oven was a separate little brick building behind the house. Daed built a fire inside the oven and closed the small iron door. The stones inside the oven heated as the fire burned. When he thought the oven had reached the right temperature,

Daed raked all the coals and ashes outside. He put the ears of hard yellow corn in the oven and closed the door. The heat of the hot stones inside the oven would roast the corn slowly without it burning or needing any attention.

After supper the next evening, Daed set a big tub beside the stove and sat on the lid of the old wood box with a pile of roasted ears beside him. The golden kernels of roasted corn fell with a clatter into the metal tub as he shelled the ear and tossed the empty cob into the coal bucket to be used for kindling.

"Can I help?" Sarah asked.

"*Ich denke* (I guess)," Daed gave permission. He knew her small hands would soon tire with the effort shelling corn required, but he welcomed her willingness to help.

"Me too," Esther, Arthur, and Frank chimed. They did not want to be left out of anything.

Daed showed the children how to turn the ear with one hand while twisting off the kernels with the other hand. The corn the chickens ate was easily and quickly shelled with the corn sheller, but this corn must be shelled by hand because it was not animal food. It was going to be the cornmeal Memm would use to make the mush they would eat for breakfast all winter.

"It's not as easy as it looks," Sarah observed after a few twists had produced small results.

"Most things aren't," Daed chuckled. "But you don't learn much chust watching."

The shelled corn slowly spread to cover the bottom of the tub and began forming a small heap in the middle. What had seemed like an interesting diversion became hard work and soon lost its appeal.

"My hands are all red," Esther said, holding her open hands in front of her.

"So are mine," Sarah said.

Mary reached into the tub and grabbed a handful of corn. She flung it on the floor and reached for another handful.

"No, no, Mary," Daed said. "Take her away, girls."

Not disappointed to be dismissed from the tedious job, Sarah and Esther ignored Mary's loud objections as they dragged her away from the tub of corn and tried to interest her in something else.

"I got a card from Montgomery Ward today," Memm told Daed. She bit off the thread she had been using to sew a button on the shirt she was mending. "Our mail order is in."

"I'll go after it on Saturday," Daed promised. "I want to clean the broomcorn tomorrow."

The broomcorn Daed raised was a type of sorghum. The stalks resembled corn, but instead of growing ears they produced a bushy head similar to sorghum. Daed had cut these heads and piled them in the top of the barn. After the seeds were separated from the stiff fibers, he would tie the bunches of clean broom straws into bundles and sell them to the man who made brooms. Cleaning broomcorn was a dirty job, but Daed was willing to do anything he could to make a little extra money to feed and clothe his family.

"I'm going to see if I can borrow a chicken coop from Henry Hess," Daed told Memm as he pushed his chair back from the breakfast table on Saturday morning. "I think I'll take some of those extra roosters to sell at the Bazaar while I'm in town."

"Can I go with?" Sarah asked eagerly. The Bazaar was always an interesting place. One never knew who would be there or what might be sold.

"What do you think?" Daed asked Memm. He knew she had not been feeling very well that morning and thought she might want to keep Sarah at home to help her with the little ones.

"I don't care," Memm gave permission. "Take Frank along too. We won't get many such warm days this year anymore."

The unexpected Indian Summer weather that had blessed the county the past few days was pleasant, but everyone knew it was also unnatural and sure to disappear as quickly as it had come, for Thanksgiving was only five days away. Memm said Sarah's light jacket and bonnet would provide all the warmth she needed to drive into Ephrata on the spring wagon with Daed. The six roosters in the wooden chicken coop nervously voiced their reservations about the trip they were taking as the wagon rolled through the golden brown countryside.

The Reading Road climbed a little hill beyond Mohler's School and then dipped down before climbing another little hill that sloped gradually as it reached the outskirts of town, became North State Street, and went straight to the square of Ephrata. When they were within one block of the square, they crossed Locust Street, bumped across the railroad tracks, and took the shortcut to the Ephrata Railroad Station by going down the alley that angled from North State Street to the back of the little station.

Daed tied Dewy at one of the hitching posts outside the station and lifted Frank out of the wagon while Sarah jumped down by herself. They could hear the whistle of the train announcing its approach as it came into town on the tracks that ran between the Mt. Vernon Hotel and J. C. Penney's store.

"Let's go see the train come in," Daed urged as he grabbed Sarah's hand.

"No. I don't want to," Sarah protested, pulling in the opposite direction. She was afraid of the enormous, puffing black steam engine that pulled the train.

"Aw, come on. It can't hurt you," Daed encouraged. He pulled her after him as he walked briskly toward the railroad tracks, carrying Frank in his arms.

The steam engine came straight at them, down the shining rails toward the station. They could see the pointed cowcatcher on the front and then big, black wheels rolling and the connecting rods between them pumping back and forth. The rods pumped slower and slower as the train came closer and closer. The ground shook as the train lumbered across Main Street with its brakes screeching and whistle blowing. Sarah wanted to hold her ears shut, but she was afraid to let go of Daed's hand. She darted behind him and hid until the train stopped.

Automobiles waited on both sides of the railroad tracks while the Main Street of Ephrata was blocked by the train. No passengers got on or off the train, because this was only a freight train. The freight that was being delivered and shipped was soon exchanged.

"Let's go get our order now," Daed said as the train slowly moved away from the station, following the rails toward Reading.

Sarah trailed Daed into the station and stood quietly beside him while he waited his turn and received their order. She looked at the wooden crate with eager anticipation, not knowing how hard it was for Daed to earn the money he needed to pay for mail orders. To her, mail orders were exciting because one never knew what surprises might be hiding inside the crate. She and her siblings spent hours poring over the catalogs from Montgomery Ward and Sears & Roebuck Company, making wish lists that changed each time they went "window shopping" in the catalog. Mail orders usually contained only basic necessities, but one could always hope for a surprise. The surprises had been almost nonexistent since money was "as scarce as hen's teeth" during these Depression years, but wishing and hoping were still free.

Daed stowed the Montgomery Ward order in the spring wagon and lifted out the wooden chicken coop. Sarah held Frank's hand as they followed Daed, who needed both hands to carry the chicken coop. They crossed the street to the Bazaar which was held every Saturday in the parking lot behind the Ephrata National Bank, across from C. P. Wenger's mill. The worst fire in Ephrata's history had destroyed the mill in 1924, but Mr. Wenger had promptly rebuilt and expanded the feed mill. The parking lot was filled with bargain hunters who were being forced by the Depression to stretch every penny. Jakey Beamesderfer auctioned the goods people brought to be sold at the Bazaar. Mammi Shaub went to the auction every Saturday, because she liked to watch for bargains on things she or her married children could use. Daed did not go to the auction every week, but sometimes he took potatoes or other things he could spare to be sold and used the money to buy the things they needed.

Memm did not need six roosters to keep her flock of hens laying eggs and hatching peeps to replace themselves, so Daed had brought the roosters to the Bazaar. Some housewife who needed a rooster for her flock, or meat for her soup pot, would buy them. While they waited for the roosters to be sold, Daed watched the auction for things they could use that sold cheaply. The money he had earned from cutting wood in John Schaeffer's woods could be stretched through buying used things at bargain prices. Daed kept one eye on the auctioneer and a firm grip on Frank's hand while he visited with the people standing around him. Standing on the opposite side of Daed, Sarah was surrounded by people taller than herself. She could not see the auctioneer, but she could hear his sing-song voice as he sold one item after another.

"Five, five, five, five," the auctioneer chanted as he tried in vain to entice someone to bid five cents for the carpet beater and flatiron he was holding up for sale. Even at the bargain price of five cents, no one wanted the household items.

"Lizzie Shaub, you buy this," Jakey called out.

"How does he know my name?" Mammi Shaub snorted in embarrassment as she turned and wormed her way out of the laughing crowd.

Of course, the auctioneer had known her name! She was at the auction every week and the clerk wrote down her name with the item and price every time she bought something.

"Can I go over to Mammi?" Sarah asked Daed when she saw her grandmother on the edge of the crowd.

"*Ya*," Daed gave permission. "But don't go too far. I don't want to have to hunt you when I'm ready to go."

Sarah wriggled through the crowd and darted after her grandmother. "What did you get?" she asked when she caught up with Mammi.

"Not much," Mammi said as she showed Sarah a few small items in her shopping basket. "I'm going to the 5 & 10. *Gehscht mit* (Going along)?"

Sarah nodded. She would much rather be with Mammi

than standing beside Daed listening to him talk to the men in the crowd. Sarah crossed the street with her grandmother and went into J. J. Newberry's store. The 5 & 10-cent store had recently moved into the building, located between the train station and Sprecher's Hardware Store, which had previously been Pott's Department Store. The 5 & 10-cent store had the lowest prices in town. Sarah never tired of looking at all the things in the glass-topped wooden display cases in the store.

By the time Mammi took Sarah back across the street to the Bazaar, Daadi Shaub was helping Daed load the things he had bought at the auction. The money he got for the six roosters had been exchanged for two geese; and his wood-cutting money had bought a big parlor stove. They would need more than the kitchen cookstove to heat the downstairs of the house in the winter weather which was not far away. The geese would be fattened and then dressed to make some fine holiday meals. Sarah and Frank rode home with Daed through the warm countryside with their precious purchases, eagerly anticipating Memm's reaction when she would see the wonderful surprises they were bringing for her.

Daed was glad to see Memm felt better when they got home, but they soon learned the sickness had not gone away. It came back and got worse every morning until she was so sick she could not get out of bed on the first of December. Daed walked to the neighbors and asked them to call Dr. Anderson. He came to the house, examined Memm, and ordered total bed rest for her. The next day Daed fetched his stepmother, Grandmother Wenger. She did nursing jobs like this to earn a living and, fortunately, was free at the time. She stayed for a week, doing the housework and caring for the children until Memm felt well enough to be out of bed again.

As the month of December slipped away, Sarah and Arthur learned things at school about Christmas which their parents had never told them. They occasionally went to a relative's house for dinner or had visitors at home on Christmas Day, but most of the time Christmas was no different than any other day.

Miss Royer brought a spruce tree to school in the trunk of her car. She stood the tree in the corner of the school room, decorated it with shiny balls and other things, and called it a Christmas tree. The smell of the beautiful tree filled the room and hinted of wonderful things to come, creating an undercurrent of excitement that made it difficult for the children to properly study their lessons.

Every day, Miss Royer led the children in singing Christmas songs and read a story about Christmas to them. Of course, she read the story of Baby Jesus in the manger, the shepherds, and the wise men. But she also read stories about things Sarah and Arthur had never heard. Now, they learned, everyone was supposed to get presents at Christmas. There was a jolly man named Santa Claus, it was said, who came on Christmas Eve in a sleigh pulled by eight reindeer. Children hung their stockings on the fireplace before they went to bed. Santa Claus supposedly came during the night, slid down the chimney with a pack of presents on his back, filled the children's stockings without making a sound, and left again. In the morning when the children got up, they found their stockings stuffed with little toys, candy, and maybe even an orange.

One day Miss Royer read a sad story about some poor children who woke up on Christmas morning and found their stockings were still empty. While other children found toys, candy, and oranges in their stockings on Christmas morning, the poor little children had nothing. Sarah felt a great pity well up in her heart for the poor little children. She could see their thin, dirty bodies shivering in their ragged clothes as they cried with hunger when they found their stockings empty on Christmas morning. She could not imagine how it must feel to be poor.

Sarah had never looked forward so eagerly to Christmas Day. The wonder and excitement of the Christmas celebration at school had planted new ideas in her head and possibilities she never dreamed existed.

"I'm going to get candy and an orange for Christmas," Sarah said to Arthur as they walked home from school a few days before Christmas.

"How?" Arthur asked.

"I'll hang up my stocking and Santa Claus will fill it," Sarah told him.

"You think so?" Arthur asked skeptically. "You think there really is such a Sandy Claws?"

"We can hang up our stockings and find out," Sarah pointed out. "Maybe he never stopped at our house because we weren't ready for him."

The kitchen was warm from the heat of the coal fire in the cookstove on Christmas Eve. Memm was feeling a little better now, but she tired easily and needed to rest often. She rocked gently back and forth beside the stove with Anna on her lap while Daed sat on the lid of the wood box fixing Mary's shoes. Sarah and Esther had both worn and outgrown the little shoes that Mary now wore. Holes had worn through their soles. Daed carefully fitted little pieces of leather on the bottoms of the shoes to close the holes so Mary's feet would stay dry and warm.

In the far corner of the room, Sarah and Arthur whispered their big Christmas Eve secret to Esther. The three little ones were too young to understand, but Esther was easily convinced to join her older sister and brother in hanging up their stockings before they went to bed. They did not have a fireplace, so they agreed to hang their stockings over the back of a wooden kitchen chair near the stove.

Furtively, the children crept up the stairs to their cold bedrooms and each brought a long black stocking down to the kitchen. Without saying a word about their intentions, they hung the stockings over the back of a chair. Visions of sugar plums danced through their heads while they slept and waited for the morning.

As soon as they awoke on Christmas morning, the children eagerly ran downstairs to see what was in their stockings. No one was in the kitchen when the children stepped into the warm room. Daed was finishing morning chores in the barn. Memm was in the summer kitchen running the milk from the morning milking through the hand-operated separator.

Sarah stared at the stockings hanging over the back of the kitchen chair. She could not believe her eyes! The three black stockings hung there, flat and empty, exactly as they had been left the night before. She grabbed her stocking and reached down inside. There had to be at least one piece of candy or a penny in the toe. But there was not.

Arthur and Esther reached into their stockings, just to be sure, but with the same results. All three stockings were completely empty. None of them had gotten one little thing.

Sarah and Arthur looked at each other soberly as the terrible truth dawned on them. *Our stockings are empty. There is no Santa Claus. We are just like the children in the story Miss Royer read at school!* **We are poor children!**

The whole day was spent quietly at home. They did not go anywhere and no one came to visit them. Memm cooked the goose Daed had dressed for Christmas dinner, but she was not hungry and did not eat any of it herself. All day, Sarah pondered in her heart the revelations that had come with the dawn. Learning there was no Santa Claus was not a huge disappointment. But were they really and truly poor children? She did not feel poor. They had a good father and mother, so they were not orphans nor did they have a wicked stepmother. Memm's cupboard had never been bare like Old Mother Hubbard's cupboard. They always had enough mush to eat and had never gone to bed hungry. Memm kept their clothes clean and patched, so they were not ragged. They got a bath every Saturday night, so they were not dirty. Their downstairs was warm and their beds had plenty of covers to keep them warm at night. *We're* **not** *poor*, she decided, *even if we didn't get anything in our stockings.*

Chapter 5

As the earth turned and lifted its face to receive the warm kiss of the spring sun, the snows that had fallen during the first months of 1932 melted and soaked into the dark brown earth. The warmth and moisture encouraged the dead brown grass to turn green. Birds returned from their winter homes in the south and set up housekeeping in the trees and bushes of Lancaster County. The voices of the peepers were heard every night, singing the praises of their Creator and the spring season.

Early in April, Daed turned over the soil in the garden with a hand shovel and helped Memm plant seeds in straight rows. They planted lettuce, radishes, spinach, carrots, peas, sugar peas, onion sets, and the cabbage plants Memm had started growing in a wooden box in the house. In May, when the baby peas had grown big enough to form narrow green stripes across the garden, it would be time to plant green beans, lima beans, red beets, pickles, sweet corn, and pumpkins. The whole world was bursting with new life and the promise of rich rewards to come.

The nausea and dizziness which sent Memm to bed in December had disappeared during the winter months, but she had never fully regained her former strength. Only by sheer determination was she able to do the housework and care for her family. She practically fell into bed at the end of each weary day and slept the sleep of the righteous until the next rays of light called her to drag herself out again to face another day.

When she first noticed the swelling at her ankles, Memm was not overly alarmed for she knew this was common when women were "in the family way." But the swelling increased rapidly until within a few days she was too miserable to leave her bed. Daed went to neighbor Harry Cooper's house and called Dr. Anderson.

"Her kidneys are not working properly," Dr. Anderson told Daed after he had examined Memm. "She needs to go to the hospital right away. I'll call the ambulance."

The children watched with frightened eyes as their mother was carried out of the house on a stretcher and placed in the back of the ambulance. They knew only deathly ill people went to the hospital. The driver moved the ambulance carefully out the short, rutted dirt lane and then picked up speed when he reached the road. The ambulance quickly disappeared, taking Memm to the St. Joseph's Hospital in Lancaster.

Once again, Daed fetched Grandmother Wenger to keep house and take care of the children. Daed's half-brother, Eli, came in his Buick to take Daed to Lancaster to be with Memm.

"I don't know when I'll be back," Daed told Grandmother Wenger. "It depends how things go."

"Stay as long as you need to," Grandmother told him. "We'll manage all right."

Grandmother was used to stepping into a house on short notice and taking over the housekeeping. She knew what needed to be done and saw everything was taken care of properly and on time. Of course, she did not do all the work herself but assigned various chores to the children according to their ages.

"Yous girls can wash the front porch," Grandmother told Sarah and Esther.

The porch needed frequent washing because it was dirtied by the chickens that roamed free around the property until they went in the rain shelters at night. The girls found the corn broom and two metal buckets which they filled with rainwater pumped by hand from the cistern behind the house. Instead of walking around the outside of the house with her bucket of water, Sarah took a shortcut through the kitchen with Esther following close behind. Water slopped over the tops of their buckets, splashed on their skirts, bare feet, and the kitchen floor. The screen door slammed behind them as they went out on the porch.

"Let's start over here," Sarah told Esther as she threw the water from her bucket across the far end of the porch.

The girls swept the wet spot and went back through the kitchen to the cistern to pump more buckets of water. Back and forth they went, slopping their way through the kitchen. With every trip, the floor got wetter and wetter, but the girls did not notice.

"Must yous slop so?" Grandmother groaned when she saw the mess the girls were making. She got a rag and wiped up the puddles on the kitchen floor. "Either be more careful or don't make your buckets so full," she told them.

Washing the porch was a valid excuse to slop with water on a warm May day, and the girls took full advantage of the opportunity. By the time they finished, their dresses and the aprons that covered them were soaking wet. But it was only water which soon dried in the warm sun, so no harm was done.

When Daed came home from the hospital, he told Grandmother, "It was a girl. We named her Margaret."

"Did she live at all?" Grandmother asked. The look on his face and the way he spoke in the past tense told her the baby was dead.

"No," Daed shook his head. "But maybe now Amanda can get well."

Daed and the preachers went to the cemetery at the Pike Mennonite Meetinghouse and buried the infant with only a short, private graveside service. Memm was still in the hospital fighting for her life. No one thought it was necessary for the children to attend the burial, so they never saw their baby sister who had been stillborn on May 20. They were told only that Memm "got a baby in the hospital that didn't live." Except for the fresh little mound in the cemetery, there was no evidence Margaret had ever existed.

Daed went to Lancaster often to visit Memm while she was in the hospital. Sometimes he was taken to Lancaster or brought home by friends who had an automobile, but other times he went on the trolley. Children under twelve years of age were not allowed to go beyond the lobby of the hospital, so he seldom took any of his children with him.

"Yous have to go with me to Lancaster today," Daed told Sarah and Esther one morning. "Get yourselves ready."

The girls put on their good dresses and bonnets. When they knew it was almost time for the trolley to come, they walked with Daed to the tracks that cut through Noah Burkholder's field and meadow. Daed waved his arm up and down to signal that he wanted the trolley to stop.

Each seat on the yellow Conestoga Traction Company trolley car held two people. The seats were set in pairs, so four people could sit facing each other as they traveled. After Daed paid their fare, the girls followed him down the center aisle of the trolley as he looked for an empty pair of seats.

"Here," Daed said when he found seats near the end of the car. "Yous take that one," he said as he motioned toward the seat that faced forward. He could ride facing backward, but he knew the girls would get carsick if they did not sit facing forward.

By the time the girls slid into the seat Daed had found for them, the trolley was rocking on its way toward Ephrata. As it swayed across the short bridge above Noah Burkholder's field, Sarah thought about the terrible trolley and freight train wreck that had occurred there on October 4, 1923. She did not remember it, because she was only one month old at the time, but she had often heard her parents talking about the wreck. They had been living on Noah Burkholder's farm at that time. Mammi Shaub had been there to help Memm when they heard the terrible crash. Mammi had gone running out to the tracks with the Burkholders to see what had happened. Both of the motormen had been killed and nine other people injured.

What if a train comes while we're on this bridge? Sarah worried. She listened for the sound of an approaching train, but the clacking of the trolley was the only sound coming from the rails. She breathed a silent sigh of relief when they were safely across the short span and going on toward Ephrata.

Before long, the trolley came into town on Washington Street and stopped on East Main Street. After all the passengers who had come into Ephrata were off the trolley, and all those who wanted to go the opposite direction had gotten on, the motorman backed the trolley car into Washington Street. The trolley could be driven from either end, so the motorman stopped and walked to the other end of the car. Then, what had been the back of the car became the front as the trolley returned to Adamstown.

Sarah and Esther waited with Daed for the Conestoga Traction Company trolley car that would take them from Ephrata to Lancaster. It would leave Ephrata on Lake Street, go to Diamond Station east of Akron, across the Conestoga Creek at Talmage, then on to Leola, past the Lancaster Stockyards, and finally to Penn Square in the big city of Lancaster.

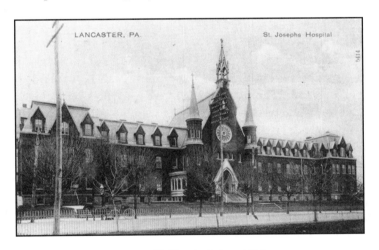

St. Joseph's Hospital, circa 1907.

The St. Joseph's Hospital, which had been in operation since 1883, was located on College Avenue a few blocks from the center of Lancaster. Tall crosses mounted on top of the steep, high peaked roofs and round towers of the red brick Gothic-style building were silent testimonies of the Roman Catholic sponsors of the institution.

"Yous will have to wait here in the sitting room while I go up to see Memm," Daed told the girls when they entered the hospital lobby. He was not afraid to let them alone in the lobby, for they were old enough to know how to behave without supervision and he knew the nun at the information desk would keep an eye on them. "Yous can look at the magazines on that there table."

Sarah and Esther looked where Daed was pointing and walked over to examine the magazines piled on the table. The Norman Rockwell painting on the cover of the *Saturday Evening Post* caught Sarah's attention. She sat on one of the big leather chairs and idly turned the pages of the magazine. The inside was not as interesting to her as the cover seemed to promise.

"Esther," Sarah whispered, "what do you have?"

"This here," Esther whispered back as she held up a *Farm Journal*. They were too intimidated by the atmosphere to speak aloud.

Watching the people who went in and out of the hospital was more interesting than the magazines, so they were soon laid aside. The girls were used to seeing women dressed in black at church on Sunday, but their dresses were nothing like the long flowing robes of the nuns who glided back and forth in the halls. Each nun wore a gold cross on a gold chain fastened around her neck. The crosses hung down on the gleaming white, high-necked bibs that were a stark contrast to the black long-sleeved, wide-skirted habits which reached to the floor and completely concealed the feet of the nuns. Stiff white headbands covered their foreheads and long black veils hung to their waists so that not a strand of their hair could be seen. They were so completely covered in their regulation clothing that only their hands and faces, from the eyes to the chin, were visible.

The girls jumped off their chairs and rushed toward Daed when they saw him returning at last to the lobby. "How's Memm?" they asked in unison.

"Much better," Daed smiled. "I think she might come home soon."

The worry lines in Daed's face relaxed and his eyes smiled at the girls as they rode home from Lancaster on the trolley. They were all happy to know Memm was getting well and would soon be home again.

Memm was still in the hospital when the month of May ended. On the fourth of June, Grandmother answered a knock at the back door and found a neighbor standing on the porch.

"I just got a call from the hospital," Harry Cooper told Grandmother. "They said to tell Barney that his wife can come home now."

"He's out in the barn," Grandmother said. "I'll tell him. Thanks for bringing the message."

When Daed heard the good news, he dropped all his plans for the day and used Harry Cooper's telephone to call his brother Eli. He agreed to take Daed to Lancaster in his automobile and bring Memm home.

"They told us she'll still have to take it easy when she comes home," Daed told Grandmother. "We had decided she should go to Daadi Shaub's until she's fit to come back here and have the children around again."

"If you can find places for the others, I'll take Anna home with me," Grandmother offered.

"We'll scatter them around among the Shaubs and the Aukers," Daed said. "It shouldn't be a problem. Sarah can go with us to Daadi Shaub's and help Mammi with her work."

Grandmother put each child's clothing in a clean, empty feed bag. When Eli came, he drove to the homes of Daed's relatives and dropped one or two children at each place until a temporary home had been provided for each of them. Then he took Daed to Lancaster and brought him and Memm back to Daadi Shaub's house.

Sarah stood on the porch watching as Memm walked slowly from Eli's car to the house. How weak and pale she looked!

"Sarah!" Memm said with a glad smile on her pale face. "Were you good while I was away?"

"Oh, yes!" Sarah's face lit up at the sound of Memm's voice. The familiar sound was beautiful to Sarah's ears, even if the voice was soft and tired.

Being at home with her loved ones was the extra boost Memm needed to recover from her near brush with death. Each day she grew stronger, until finally she was able to go back to their own home again. The children returned home by ones and twos as their mother continued to improve. Within a few weeks the entire family was once again at home and, as far as the children knew, back to normal. Memm did not speak to them of the grief she carried for her stillborn daughter, nor did Daed tell them the size of the hospital bill that had been added to his already heavy debt load.

Daed and his brother-in-law, Noah Auker, formed a partnership of sorts to earn money by logging. They hired Joe Gangaway, Christian Burkhart, and Norman Sweigart to help them cut the logs into firewood, using Noah's 10-horsepower engine to run the saw. If the buyer was not far away, they delivered the wood with their horse-drawn wagons. But sometimes Daed's cousin, David Wenger, delivered the wood in his truck. They cut firewood wherever they could find a patch of woods in the Ephrata area that someone was willing to let them log. A load of firewood was usually sold for about $5, but once when Daed was desperate to find a buyer, he sold a load to Butcher Albright for $2.50. Sometimes he traded a load of firewood for something the family needed.

Sawing firewood in the hot summer months was hard work, but Daed had so much debt he was willing to do anything to earn a little money. When silo filling time came in September, he took his team and went around the neighborhood helping Horace Martin, Casper Eberly, Jacob Shirk, and other farmers chop corn to fill their silos.

September also brought Sarah's ninth birthday and the beginning of another school year. She and Arthur once again braved the barking dogs and other animals as they walked back and forth to Mohler's School each day. Esther was six and old enough to be in first grade, but she was kept at home because of a condition the doctor called "a gland problem."

"Never, never give these pills to anyone else," the doctor warned Memm when he gave her the pills Esther was to take. "They would be poisonous to anyone else, but the only harm they will do to her is stunt her growth."

The pills were put safely out of the children's reach and doled out to Esther according to the doctor's instructions. She dutifully swallowed them, although they did not seem to be doing much to cure the problem.

At the dinner table one Friday, Daed told Memm, "Since it's raining, I think I'll take Davy to Ephrata to be shod this afternoon. I'll pick up Sarah and Arthur after school on my way home."

"Can I go with?" Esther asked eagerly.

"I don't care," Daed consented. "Frank might as well come along too."

When they got to the blacksmith's shop, Daed unhitched Davy and led him to the open door of the shop. It smelled of sulphur from the coal that burned all day long in the blacksmith's furnace as he heated the iron and hammered it into the shapes he needed. When he did not have horses to shoe, he made horseshoes in various sizes.

The children stayed in the buggy where they would be safe and dry but still be able to watch the blacksmith at work. He lifted each of Davy's feet in his hand, one after another, and cut away some of each hoof. Then he clapped an iron horseshoe on the hoof and fastened it in place by driving nails through the shoe into the hoof. The nails did not hurt Davy's hooves, so he stood quietly until his four new shoes were firmly in place. Daed decided not to put rubber pads on the horseshoes because they seemed to make the horse slip more easily on the wet roads and do more harm than good. When the blacksmith was finished, Daed backed Davy between the shafts of the buggy, hitched him up again, and climbed in the buggy.

The rain that had been falling steadily in the morning dwindled to a drizzle and stopped, but the road was still wet. Davy trotted swiftly from Ephrata to Mohler's School without slipping once on the wet road.

"Whoa," Daed called to Davy as he pulled on the reins to stop the horse in the schoolyard.

They waited until the door opened and the scholars spilled out, in a rush to get home. Sarah and Arthur were surprised and glad to see Daed waiting for them. For once, they would be spared the scary walk past the farm with the barking dogs. They climbed into the back seat of the buggy and dropped their empty lunch buckets on the floor.

"I'm going to stop at Burky's auction," Daed told the children when Davy pulled the buggy out onto the road. "I want to talk to Burky."

The Farmers Market & Auction[8] Noah Burkholder operated every Friday was housed in a building he had erected on his farm. Although people scoffed and said the business would fail, just like the garage and then the restaurant which had been in the building before, the market was thriving and growing rapidly ever since it had opened in April.

"Can we go along in?" Arthur asked for all of the children as Daed jumped out of the buggy.

"*Ya,*" Daed gave permission.

The children scrambled from the buggy while Daed tied Davy to the hitching rail. Then they trailed Daed to the market house which set close to the Reading Road. The narrow aisles of the dirt floor in the market house were crowded with shoppers who circled through the building looking for bargains. From the little restaurant at the front of the building came the mouthwatering smell of hot dogs cooking. The aroma helped whet the appetites of the shoppers and entice them to buy the farm-fresh products the local farmers had brought to the market.

As she wiggled through the crowd trying to follow Daed, Sarah's eyes were busy looking at the wares offered for sale on the market stands. In the corner near the back door was Elam Burkholder's fresh meat stand where his sons sold the cuts of beef and pork which had been prepared in the small butcher shop on his

---

[8] Known today as the Green Dragon.

farm. Dan Witmer sold smoked meats and cheese from his stand in the center of the building. Other stand-holders sold produce, baked goods, eggs, butter, socks, notions, brooms, and all sorts of merchandise usually found in the typical market house.

Daed threaded his way through the shoppers to the little office in the front corner of the building where he knew Noah Burkholder was most likely to be found.

"Wait out here," Daed told the children before he stepped into the little office. It had originally been a three-holed outhouse, but Noah had turned it into an office by replacing the seats with a floor and adding a 25-watt light bulb. The office was too small to hold many people, so there was no room for children who had no business to conduct.

Sarah could hear Daed in the office asking to borrow Noah's potato digger on Monday. As Daed and Noah talked, she watched the people eating at the little restaurant. The smell of the hot dogs tied her stomach in knots. The apple butter sandwich, jar of canned peaches, and fresh apple she eaten from her lunch pail at noon were long gone. How she wished Daed would buy some hot dogs for them to eat! But, at the same time, she knew such wishful thinking was useless for Daed never had money for such expensive luxuries. So she silently watched the people eating and grew more and more hungry.

"All right, *kinner* (children)," Daed said when he stepped out of the office. "Let's go."

"Can we get some hot dogs?" Arthur hopefully asked Daed as he started walking back through the building.

Then Sarah knew Arthur was hungry too. She held her breath for a split-second while she waited to hear what Daed would say.

"Memm will have supper ready when we get home," Daed answered without stopping. Sarah could not help being disappointed, even though she had known it was useless to ask Daed to buy hot dogs.

The children fell into line behind their father and wiggled their way through the crowds that blocked the aisles of the market house. Sarah dodged into an opening between two people and almost bumped into Daed. He had stopped at one of the stands and was talking to the man who stood behind the table. He reached for a brown paper bag and began scooping peanuts from a barrel into the bag as he talked. Sarah could hardly believe her eyes when Daed handed the man a nickel and took the bag.

"*Datt bischt* (there you are)," Daed said as he handed the bag to Arthur. "You'ns can eat these on the way home."

Daed had given the bag to Arthur because he was the one who had asked for something to eat, but Sarah knew he was being told to share the treat with his siblings. As soon as they were in the buggy, Arthur took a handful of peanuts from the bag and passed it on to Esther. When the bag came to Sarah, she took a handful of peanuts and dropped them into her lap. She cracked the shell of a roasted peanut, picked out the two nuts, rubbed off the paper-thin brown skins that covered them, and popped them into her mouth.

"Do you want some, Daed?" Frank asked as he generously offered to share his holdings.

"*Vy, danke* (why, thank you)," Daed said in a tone of exaggerated politeness. He grinned as he shifted the reins into one hand and took the two shelled peanuts from Frank's grubby little hand.

Inspired by Frank's generosity, Esther suggested, "Let's save some for Memm."

"And for Mary and Anna, too," Sarah added.

They rode home, blissfully unaware of the inevitable mess the peanut shells made on the buggy floor as they happily shared the nickel's-worth of wealth inside the brown paper bag. A handful of peanuts would never spoil their appetites for the supper Memm was cooking on her black enameled Columbian Choice range.

The kitchen smelled of rivel soup and raw-fried potatoes when Sarah stepped into the room. "Daed got us some peanuts!" she exclaimed as she handed the bag to her mother. "We saved some for you and the little girls."

"Well, that was nice!" Memm said, smiling as she looked in the wrinkled paper bag and then set it on the windowsill. "I'll put them back until after supper. Set the table, girls. We'll eat as soon as Daed comes in."

Sarah and Esther got the dishes from the cupboard and set eight places at the table. Memm hurried back and forth in the kitchen, finishing the simple meal. She scraped the fried potatoes from the black Griswold frying pan into a bowl. She set the bowl in the warming closet on the back of the stove where the food would stay warm until the family sat down at the table. Then she dropped a big spoonful of her homemade butter into the kettle of simmering rivel soup. As the butter melted, a beautiful yellow color spread through the hot milk and little white rivels, which were small balls of dough made with a mixture of egg, flour, and milk.

They were all so busy no one noticed what Anna was doing until Mary suddenly cried, "Memm! Anna's eating Esther's pills."

"Anna!" Memm gasped when she spun around and saw her almost two-year-old daughter picking up one of the little white pills she had spilled from the bottle. Memm did not know how many, if any, of the pills Anna had swallowed. The only way to be sure she was safe was to make her empty her stomach as quickly as possible. Memm grabbed Anna, rushed out to the back porch, held her over the dog's dish, and stuck her finger down Anna's throat to make her vomit. Sure enough! Some little white pills came up with the contents of Anna's stomach.

More frightened than hurt, Anna screamed as Memm carried her back into the kitchen and sank weakly into the rocker with the crying child in her lap. "It's good you saw her," Memm told Mary over the sound of Anna's crying. "She'll be all right. But after this, we must be sure those pills are *always* put away."

The pills had not been inside Anna long enough to dissolve. As soon as she recovered from the scare of being forced to vomit, she was fine. Memm put the pills high up on top of the Hoosier kitchen cabinet where they would be safely out of a little girl's reach and doled out only to Esther as they had been prescribed.

Memm told the story to her sisters and Mammi Shaub when the family gathered at Daadi Shaub's house on Sunday.

The women clucked their tongues and shook their heads as they thought of the near-tragedy that had occurred. But Anna, completely healthy and ignorant of the danger she had courted, played happily with her little cousins.

On Monday morning, Memm told Sarah and Arthur, "We're going to dig potatoes at Noah Auker's today. We won't be back by the time school's over, so yous go on home with the Sweigarts after school tonight. Daed will come and fetch you when we get back."

"All right," Sarah and Arthur nodded. They seldom stayed at the neighbor's house, but would much rather go there than be alone at home waiting for the rest of the family to return. They had not forgotten how frightened they had been once before when they had been alone until after dark. They had climbed up on the table for safety and lay there, crying and scaring each other as they named all the fierce creatures they imagined might come and get them. They did not want to repeat that terrifying experience.

At the end of the school day, Sarah and Arthur walked home with the four Sweigart children as usual. How strange it seemed to walk past their own empty house instead of turning in at the end of the lane! They walked on, past the woods to the place where the road met another road which came down over the mountain. The six children walked a short way uphill on this dirt road to reach the Sweigart's home. Sarah and Arthur had often passed the Sweigarts' place but rarely went into their house. They were not Mennonites. Daed wanted his children's friends to be from among their own church people.

Grace considered Sarah to be her company since they were nearly the same age. She took Sarah with her to the girls' bedroom while she changed her dress. Grace hung her school dress neatly on a hook where it would be easy to find the next morning when she dressed for school again.

"I have to feed the chickens," Grace told Sarah after she had put on an old dress. "You can come with me."

"Okay," Sarah agreed. She could not change her dress, because she had not brought an old one with her. She could put on a clean apron the next day if the one she was wearing got dirty, but she would have to be careful not to tear her school dress or make it too dirty to wear the next day.

Sarah followed Grace to the corn crib to get some ears of corn and then to the corn sheller that stood nearby in the corn barn.

"Do you want to turn it or shall I?" Grace asked politely.

"You can. I'll put the ears in," Sarah answered. She poked the ears, one by one, into the iron mouth on top of the corn sheller while Grace turned the handle on the side. A yellow stream of shelled corn flowed from a little wooden chute into a bucket Grace had set under it. The empty red-brown cobs which fell from an opening under the sheller would be saved to use as kindling to light the fire in the kitchen cookstove.

The chickens flocked around the girls as they scattered the corn on the ground in the chicken yard. The girls left the chickens contentedly pecking at the corn and ran off to play until they would be called to eat their own supper.

Two extra places were set at the supper table for Sarah and Arthur, who slid onto the bench behind the table just as they would have done at home. The inside of the humble house, which lacked electric and plumbing, was not vastly different from their own home. The food on the table was the same type of plain, ordinary cooking Sarah was used to eating, but she did not feel comfortable with this family and ate only small portions.

After supper, Sarah helped Grace dry the dishes as her big sister washed them. Although the chores Grace did after school were much the same as Sarah did at home, they were somehow more interesting when doing them in a different house. As she dried the dishes, she began listening for the sound of Daed's buggy wheels. She had expected to eat supper at the Sweigarts' house, but she did not want to stay there after dark.

As the sun went down and the light faded outdoors, Mrs. Sweigart lit the coal oil lamp in the center of the table. Shadows filled the corners of the room where the soft light did not reach. The clock cleared its throat and struck eight. Still, Daed did not come. There was no use in standing at the window and watching for him, because the outdoors was too dark to see anything.

"It's bedtime," Mrs. Sweigart said at last. "You two might as well just go to bed here," she told Sarah and Arthur.

Sarah wanted to go home. She did not want to go to bed at the Sweigarts' house, but she knew they would blow out the lamps and go to bed. She did not want to sit alone in the dark waiting for Daed, so she followed Grace to the girls' bedroom while Arthur went with the boys to their room. Grace put on her nightgown, but Sarah had not brought her nightgown. She took off her apron and dress, laid them across the foot of the bed, and lay down in bed wearing her slip.

What if Daed doesn't come, Sarah thought as she lay in bed beside Grace. *What if we're still here in the morning yet? What if he never comes for us?*

Sarah did not think she had fallen asleep, but suddenly Mrs. Sweigart was shaking her and whispering, "Get up. Your dad is here."

Sleepily, Sarah slipped her dress over her head and put her arms through the sleeves. She did not bother to put on her apron, but rolled it in a ball and carried it under her arm. She stumbled sleepily down the steps and went out to the wagon where Daed was waiting.

"What took you so long?" Sarah asked Daed as she climbed up and sat on the seat beside him.

"I didn't think it would get this late," Daed apologized as Arthur scrambled up into the wagon. "We were digging potatoes until the sun set, and then I had to take the potato digger back to Burky yet after we got home."

The night air was warm, because it was only the middle of September. Sarah leaned comfortably against Daed as the horse pulled the wagon down the hill and turned to go in the road that would take them home. She was so sleepy she could hardly keep her eyes open, but she could feel the warmth of Daed's body and the strength in his arms as he held the reins. She knew now how silly it had been to worry about being left at the Sweigarts. *I should have known Daed would come for us,* she thought as her eyes closed. *Daed would never let us with strangers. He will always come and take us home.*

Chapter 6

Sarah and Arthur trudged hesitantly up the steep hill toward the Lincoln Independent School. At the end of March 1933, the Wenger family had moved into the tenant house on Harry Wanner's farm which was located midway between the schoolhouse and the Red Run Mill.[9] Because they had moved, Sarah and Arthur had been forced to change schools and finish second grade at this one-room school. They did not know any of the children they saw in the schoolyard or the teacher who was standing on the porch of the red brick schoolhouse.

The other children stared curiously at Sarah and Arthur as they stepped onto the school grounds. From the way they were dressed, the children knew the new scholars were from a family that went to the Pike church. In the same way, Sarah and Arthur knew the other scholars were mostly from families of Groffdale and Weaverland Conference (commonly known as the Wenger and Horning) churches. All three groups were Old Order branches of the Mennonite church, but the differences between them were obvious to the trained eye.

One of the girls marched boldly up to Sarah and said, "My name's Esther Fox. What're your names?"

"Sarah and Arthur Wenger," Sarah bashfully answered for both of them.

"What grades are yous in?" Esther asked.

"We're both in second."

"Are yous twins?"

---

[9] The current address of this farm is 796 Gristmill Road, Ephrata, Pa.

"No. I'm a year older than him, but we started school together."

"Oh. Well, I'm in second too," Esther informed the new scholars. She went on asking questions and getting acquainted, chattering in such a friendly way that the knots in Sarah's stomach were beginning to relax by the time the teacher rang the bell.

The scholars marched into the classroom and took their seats. The teacher told Sarah and Arthur her name was Miss Minerva Ronick. She wrote their names in her record book and told them to take seats near Esther Fox. Sarah put the tablet and pencils she had brought with her in her desk. She did not have any school books, because the books she had studied at Mohler's belonged to that school.

Miss Ronick began the school day with Bible reading and prayer, just as Miss Royer had always done at Mohler's School. The teacher gave Sarah a Second Reader, but no other books. Then she began calling classes to recite their lessons and collected their lesson papers. She read the lessons from her books and copied things from them on the blackboard, but the scholars did not have many books of their own.

Sarah learned the names of a few more girls while they jumped rope at dinner recess. Although they spoke in her own familiar Pennsylvania Deutsch language when they were not in class, she was too shy to contribute much to the conversation. She was satisfied to trail Esther Fox and let her do the talking.

At the end of the school day, Sarah and Arthur walked down the hill from the school to the road that went to Red Run. The dirt road went up and down, following the rise and fall of the hills. It was muddy from the spring rains, so they walked in the mat of grass that covered the middle of the road like a strip of brownish-green rag carpet. The mild warmth of the afternoon sun verified the promises of spring found in the wild garlic and skunk cabbage growing on the road banks. Robins, recently returned from their southern winter homes, hopped across the newly plowed fields in search of earthworms.

"Where's Daed?" Arthur asked Memm when he and Sarah stepped into the kitchen.

"Still out in the woods," Memm told him as she took a loaf of bread from the oven. "He'll be home for supper soon."

Daed was not farming at the Wanner place. He was trying to earn a living by logging and day labor, working a day or two at a time for the local farmers when one of them needed an extra hand. He knew they could live in the tenant house for only one year, because one of Harry Wanner's children would be getting married then and moving into the house. Daed and Memm were not excited about the idea of moving again in a year. They were hoping to see some improvement in their finances by then, but had not made any progress yet. After Daed paid the man who helped him cut the wood and the driver who delivered it to the customer, very little was left of the $5 he got for a load of wood.

The spring woods were wet and muddy, just like the roads and fields. When Daed came home, his pants and coat were heavily splattered with mud. He took off his shoes on the porch and carried them into the kitchen.

"Get me some water to wash up for supper," Daed told Sarah as he set his shoes on a piece of newspaper to dry beside the cookstove.

While Daed hung his coat and hat on a hook behind the door, Sarah opened the door over the reservoir on the end of the cookstove and flipped down the water spout. Hot water ran by gravity flow into the enamel basin she held under the spout. The water had been heated by the coal fire that burned in the other side of the stove. When enough hot water had run into the basin, she simply flipped up the spout to cut off the flow of water.

While Daed washed his hands and face, Sarah helped Memm dish the *snitz un knepp* (dried apples and dumplings with bits of ham) she had made for supper. In addition to their serving of hot food, each child was required to eat a thick slice of home-made bread spread with homemade butter. This tradition, which was older than their Swiss/German immigrant ancestors, had developed because bread was both cheap and filling and was designed to "take the edge off" the appetite.

After supper, Sarah and Esther washed the dishes while Memm looked after the little girls and mended socks. Arthur and Frank sat on the floor working on a kite they were making from thin sticks and old newspaper. Daed cleaned his shoes so they would be ready to wear again the next day and then sat at the kitchen table to write in his big diary and record book.

"I want a horsey ride," little Anna said as she poked her head up under Daed's arm.

"Just a minute," Daed said as he pressed a small rectangle of soft, absorbent paper on the words he had just written. The blotter soaked up the extra ink so it would not smear when he closed the book.

"Horsey ride, horsey ride," Mary chimed, grabbing Daed's other arm.

"Now," Daed said after he had wiped his pen on a scrap of cloth and put the cap back on the ink bottle. "Anna asked first." He pushed his chair back from the table and crossed his legs. Anna seated herself on Daed's extended foot and held up her hands. Daed grasped each of her hands firmly in one of his and began bouncing her on his foot as he recited an old Pennsylvania Deutsch nursery rhyme:

> *Reide, reide Geile,*
> *Alle schtund en meile,*
> *Do un datt en Blockhaus,*
> *En wennich weider draus*
> *Gucke de schwatz boppa raus.*
> *Giddyap, giddyap, giddyap,*
> *WHOA!*

Anna shrieked with laughter as Daed's foot bounced higher and faster on the giddyaps and then stopped suddenly on the whoa. "Do it again," she begged. "Do it again."

Daed's foot started going up and down again, bouncing Anna as he recited another verse:

Reide, reide, Geile,
Alle schtund en meile,
Gehts iwwer der Schtumpe,
Fall'st Boppli nunner![10]

At the last words, Daed tipped Anna sideways and dropped her gently on the floor without losing his grip on her hands.

"Do it again!" she cried as she tried to climb back on Daed's foot.

"No, me," Mary clamored. "I want a horsey ride too."

"It's Mary's turn," Daed told Anna. "You can have another ride after Mary."

Memm smiled as she watched the little girls giggling and shouting with glee as they took turns riding the horsey. The other children could remember when they had been small enough to ride Daed's horsey. The cozy family atmosphere that filled the kitchen was taken for granted with every one of them unconsciously presuming things would always continue to be as they had always been.

The walk to school the next morning was not as scary as it had been the previous morning, because now Sarah and Arthur knew the teacher's name and a few of the scholars. Still, Sarah dreaded another day of being among strangers. She and Arthur slid into their seats when Miss Ronick rang the bell to begin another school day.

"Second grade Arithmetic," Miss Ronick called as she began their grade's first class of the day. "Hand in your papers."

Each second grade scholar handed the teacher a piece of tablet paper with the previous day's completed lesson.

"Where's your paper?" Miss Ronick asked Sarah.

[10] Ride, ride a horsey/Every hour a mile/Here and there a log house/A little further on/Black dolls (are) looking out./Giddyup, giddyup, giddyup, Whoa! Second verse: Ride, ride, a horsey/Every hour a mile/Goes over a stump/Baby falls down.

"I don't have any," Sarah almost whispered as she hung her head in shame.

"See you have one tomorrow," Miss Ronick warned as she turned and walked to her desk.

Sarah's face was red with embarrassment. She did not lift her eyes but was sure every eye in the school room was fastened on her.

"Don't you know how to do this?" Mabel Wise whispered across the aisle.

Sarah looked sideways at Mabel and shook her head.

"The teacher writes the lesson on the blackboard," Mabel explained. "You're supposed to copy the problems on a piece of paper and answer them."

Sarah had been used to working from a textbook at Mohler's School, but she quickly learned the new system of working without textbooks. She made sure she always copied the lesson on the blackboard to a piece of tablet paper before the teacher erased the lesson and wrote the next one for another grade. Never again would she be found without a paper to hand in when the teacher called for it!

The 1932-33 school year ended on Good Friday, just a few weeks after Sarah and Arthur began attending the Lincoln Independent School. They were not sorry to go home and forget about lessons until fall came again.

"There's a big pillar of smoke in the sky over toward New Holland," Daed said as he stuck his head in the kitchen door the next morning. "Come out and see."

The children rushed past their mother as she went out to look at the black column that rose up into the clear blue April sky.

"What's burning?" Memm asked.

"I don't know, but it must be something awful big," Daed said as he shook his head.

Later in the day, Harry Wanner told them someone had told him the pillar of smoke came from Elam Burkholder's tobacco warehouse. The enormous two-story 60-by-208-foot

frame building, which was one of the biggest tobacco warehouses
in Lancaster County, had burned to the ground during the night
of April 21. Although people gossiped and speculated for years
about the origin of the fire, it had been the work of an arsonist.

"That's an awful lot for such a time as this," Daed said when
he heard the loss from the fire was set at $75,000. "It's a terrible
thing any time, and being in this Depression makes it even worse.
It wonders me what this'll do to Elam."

Sarah did not know what Daed meant. As far as she knew,
Elam Burkholder had always been a big, rich farmer who took
charge and made things happen. She did not understand how the
fire could hurt him, especially since it was over and no one had
been burned.

The Depression which had begun three and a half years
earlier continued to deepen, robbing rich and poor alike. Daed
was unable to pay the doctor and hospital bills which had been
added to the load of debt he already carried. The few dollars he
was able to earn each week from logging and day labor did not
stretch far enough to cover all the needs of his growing family.

"Why don't I take Sarah home with me for the summer?"
Annie Auker suggested one Sunday when the Aukers were visiting the Wengers. "I'm not too peppy here of late and since Arthur
started walking he gets into everything now. I could use a girl to
help me for awhile, and you'd have one less mouth to feed."

"I don't know," Memm hesitated as she considered her
former neighbor's proposal. "I'll ask Amos and see what he says."

Daed told Memm it was up to her to decide if she could
manage without Sarah's help. Memm wanted to help her friend,
so she told Annie, "I guess you can have Sarah. I still have Esther
to help me here."

Sarah was surprised when she was told she was going home
with John Aukers to be their *maad* (maid) for the summer, but
she did not object. She understood this was only a temporary
arrangement. She knew John and Annie so well they almost
seemed like her uncle and aunt. In a way, she felt quite grown up
to be considered old enough to be Annie's *maad*.

Memm packed Sarah's clothes in a box which John put in the trunk of his car. The sporty coup had only one seat, but Annie held little Arthur on her lap so there was room for Sarah to squeeze in beside her. The five miles to the Aukers' home was quickly traveled in the smooth-riding coup.[11]

Annie showed Sarah the room in which she was to sleep. "You can put your clothes in the bureau," Annie said. "Hang your dresses on them hooks," she added as she pointed to a row of hooks fastened to a board on the wall.

Sarah's few belongings were soon in place and she settled easily into her new role of being Annie's *maad*. She did not expect more of Sarah than an almost-ten-year-old girl was capable of doing, but Sarah was kept busy. She helped to stem strawberries, shell peas, snap beans, pull weeds, hang up the wash, sweep floors, scrub the porch, gather eggs, and countless other chores that entered into the daily routine. There was no electric in the house, so Annie's methods and routine of housekeeping were basically the same as Sarah had been accustomed to at home.

John had grown up in the Pike church but had gone to his wife's Lancaster Conference church at Martindale when they were married. Now he found he did not feel comfortable there, so they had begun attending the Pike church. Sarah saw her family there at least every other Sunday. Since three of John's brothers had married Sarah's aunts, the families visited each other often. Sarah did not feel cut off from her immediate or extended family.

Annie cleaned the house every Saturday, for that was part of preparing for Sunday and the possibility of family or friends dropping in for a visit. As the months passed and the time for the birth of her new baby drew near, she assigned to Sarah the chores which were becoming increasingly difficult for her to perform.

"You can wash the kitchen floor," Annie told Sarah one Saturday after she finished sweeping it with the broom. "Then the cleaning will be done for this week."

---

[11] The current address of this property is 920 Glenwood Drive, Ephrata, Pa.

Sarah filled a metal bucket with water and got down on her knees to wash the floor with a rag. She did not feel like washing the floor. It looked enormous to her. She slapped the scrub rag carelessly across the middle of the floor and was soon finished.

"Sarah!" Annie cried when she saw the sloppy job Sarah had done. "This floor is not clean. Come back here and do it right."

Slowly, Sarah refilled the scrub bucket and got down on her knees to wash the kitchen floor the second time. *I'm tired of working all the time*, she thought sullenly as she scrubbed the oilcloth.

Just then, little Arthur came toddling into the kitchen. Sarah knew if he walked across the wet floor he would make dirty tracks on it. She did not want to wash the floor a third time. "Stay back!" she snapped as she held out her arm to block his path and pushed him away without looking up.

"Waaaaah!" Arthur screamed as he lost his balance and fell into the scrub bucket. Water splashed out over the side of the bucket, wetting Sarah's dress and making puddles on the floor.

"Now what?" Annie cried as she rushed into the room to see why Arthur was crying. "*Aie du liewer* (Oh my dear!)," she exclaimed as she snatched up her dripping son. Every stitch of his clothing was wet and he was soaked to the skin.

"I'm sorry," Sarah apologized. "I didn't push him in the bucket on purpose."

While Annie changed Arthur's clothes, Sarah bent guiltily to her task. She was ashamed of herself, and tried to make up for her meanness by washing the floor properly.

The hot weeks of summer melted away one at a time in rapid succession. Sarah turned ten on the first day of September and would enter third grade when school started the day after Labor Day.

"Can Sarah stay on a little longer?" Annie asked Memm. "She'll have to go to school, but she can help me evenings and Saturdays still. I'd like to keep her 'til sometime in December. I should be back on my feet by then."

Memm agreed to let Sarah stay with the Auker family a few more months, so on the first day of school she got on a big yellow school bus and rode to the huge four-room Bergstrasse School. Once again, she had to face a new teacher and meet a group of strange children. By the time she got to school on the first day, she was sick to her stomach from the combination of tension and motion sickness.

Both of the schools Sarah had attended were small schools with all eight grades in the same room. The Bergstrasse School was so big that each of the four rooms held only two grades. Sarah found her way to the third-and-fourth-grade classroom where she met the teacher, Martha Sturgis. The children who attended Bergstrasse had been bussed in from the surrounding community and represented a wide variety of families. Although there were some children from Mennonite homes in the school, she saw at a glance there were very few from Stauffer (Pike) Mennonite homes.

The school day followed the same familiar pattern, but Sarah felt lost in the crowd of strange faces. She filled her desk with the third-grade textbooks the teacher gave her and quietly tried to study her lessons. She went outside with the other scholars at recess, but did not speak to anyone unless she was spoken to. A great lonesomeness for her brother Arthur welled up within her, for they had always gone to school together. *I guess Esther went to the Lincoln Independent School with Arthur today*, she thought sorrowfully. Even though she had not liked the poor little one-room school, she could not help wishing she could be with her brother and sister.

As the weeks passed, Sarah became accustomed to the Bergstrasse School and riding the school bus twice each day. She gradually learned to know the names of all the children in her room. Anna Newswanger was a friendly, likeable girl, but Sarah did not develop a close friendship with her or any of the other girls. She usually trailed the girls, satisfied to be in the group and listen to them talk, but was too shy to contribute much to the conversation.

When Arlene Sauder came to school one morning wearing a frilly Shirley Temple dress, the other girls were instantly jealous. Although she did not wish for a Shirley Temple dress herself, Sarah could not keep her eyes from turning to look at Arlene's dress.

"She thinks herself so smart," the jealous girls whispered to each other as they watched Arlene walking down the hall.

But Sarah could tell Arlene was not a proud person. She wore the Shirley Temple dress because her mother had made it for her, not because she wanted to show off. Arlene was kind to everyone and proved her character by taking pity on a very poor boy at school whose shoes were falling apart. Arlene asked her mother to buy a pair of shoes for the boy, brought them to school in a brown paper bag, and gave them to him.

The plain dresses Annie was sewing for herself on these fall days were made from an entirely different pattern. She was also making a different style of head coverings for herself. Laying aside her own preferences, she had submitted to John's desires. She had agreed to leave her own Lancaster Conference church and join the Pike congregation of the Old Order Stauffer Mennonites in which her husband had been raised. Replacing his sporty coup with a horse and buggy was not as difficult for John as it was for Annie to part with the fine furniture she had bought when she married him. She did not want to have a split marriage with each of them attending separate churches, so she sold her living room suite, floor rug, and dining room suite. All these changes were made in preparation for the change of church membership, but the formalities would not take place until after their new baby was born. Annie did not want to stand up in church while she was "in the family way," nor did John want to embarrass her in public.

The new baby was born on November 15 and named James. Then Sarah knew her time of living with the Aukers would soon be over. In a few weeks Annie would be able to do her own work again and Sarah could go home to stay.

The weather was mild the week before Christmas. On Monday, Christmas Day, the mercury rose to fifty-seven degrees, making it feel more like Easter than Christmas. Sarah went to the Auker family Christmas dinner with John and Annie. His brother Ammon, who had married Memm's sister Mary, had taken over his father's farm at Hahnstown. Ammon and Mary lived double in the farmhouse with his parents, Benjamin and Lizzie. The Auker family filled the house and the children spilled out into the warm outdoors. Sarah was ignorantly unaware of the whispered conversations that took place behind her back as her three aunts, who had married the Auker brothers, discussed her mother's condition and what they should tell their niece.

At last, Aunt Mary drew Sarah aside and said quietly, "Sarah, you won't be able to go home after all right now. Your mother is in the hospital again."

"Oh?" Sarah's one-word question was a request for more information.

"Yes. She's in Lancaster at St. Joe's again," Aunt Mary said. "It's the same trouble she had before. I didn't hear anything how she is today, but you'll have to stay with Johns at least as long as she's in the hospital."

"All right," Sarah agreed. She knew going to the hospital was a serious matter, but she was not overly alarmed because Memm had eventually recovered the last time she had been in the hospital.

The north wind blew its icy breath into the county as Christmas Day drew to a close. Sarah lay in bed listening to the cold wind shriek as it rattled the windows, trying to come into the house so it could get warm. The temperature continued to fall, and the next day managed to rise only one degree above the freezing mark. The bitterly cold air that followed the winds brought six inches of snow which began during the day and continued falling into the night. By Wednesday the temperature had fallen to twelve degrees, making it hard to believe only two days earlier the air had been as warm as spring. The wind swirled the glittering white snow into drifts which closed many of the country roads. The whole world seemed to have frozen in three days time and still the temperature continued to drop.

Annie diapered baby James for the night while Sarah put Arthur's flannel pajamas on him. She had hung her own flannel nightgown by the stove to warm before going into the unheated upstairs. If she changed her clothes quickly, the nightgown would still be faintly warm when she crawled between the cold sheets in the cold bedroom. Knowing she had met her obligations for the day when Arthur was dressed for bed, she lit a small oil lamp to take upstairs with her. Then she took her nightgown from the back of the chair, crossed the room to the stairs, and opened the door.

"Sarah," Annie's quivering voice called.

With her hand still on the doorknob, Sarah stopped and turned to look back at Annie. The icy blast of cold air that rushed down the stairway to meet her somehow matched the sound of Annie's voice.

"Sarah," Annie gulped, and then forced herself to go on. "Your mother died last night. Daadi Shaub is going to come and get you in the morning. You'll be staying with them until the funeral's over."

Sarah stared speechlessly at Annie. She could not believe her ears, but the tears in Annie's eyes confirmed the words she had said were true. Too shocked to reply, Sarah only nodded numbly and stumbled woodenly up the stairs.

"Well, she took that better than I thought she might," Annie said to John. She sighed heavily with a hint of relief in her voice as she looked at the closed stair door. "I kept putting it off all day because it dreaded me so to tell her."

"I feel sorry for all of them, even if we kind of expected this when Amanda went to the hospital again," John groaned. "We know God don't make mistakes, but this is one I sure don't understand. Amos can't take care of six children without Amanda. I don't know how he'll ever manage."

Sarah's warm nightgown grew cold as she stood alone in the frigid bedroom staring into the blackness of an unknown future. In her mind, she ran screaming down the stairs and out the door. She bounded across the miles all the way home, flung open the door, and leaned panting against it. Memm turned from where she was standing at the stove and turned to look at Sarah.

"What scared you?" Memm asked.

Weak with relief, Sarah's legs turned to jelly. It had been a nightmare. Memm was still in the kitchen where she belonged. She was not dead.

Sarah shivered and came back to reality. She did not know how long she had stood motionlessly beside the bed holding the lamp. As her numb fingers fumbled with the buttons on her dress and then her nightgown, Annie's words echoed in her dazed mind. *Your mother died last night. Died? That means dead . . . Gone . . . When? How? Why?*

Sarah was shaking with cold when she finally blew out the lamp, crawled between the frigid sheets, and lay down. The warmth of the heavy comforters piled on top of her could not melt the icy fingers of grief that clutched her heart with a vengeance.

Your mother died last night. . . . Last night. . . . She was dead all day . . . Why didn't somebody tell me before now?

Sarah heard the Aukers come upstairs and go to bed. She heard the clock strike downstairs in the quiet house. She was too stunned to cry and too shocked to sleep. *Did Annie really say Memm died, or was I dreaming?* she wondered. She was sure she had not fallen asleep, but the idea that her mother could be dead was too unreal to be true.

Chapter 7

The sound of footsteps going down the stairs woke Sarah. She heard John riddle the cookstove to shake the ashes down into the ash pan; then the sound of the stove lids rattling as he stirred up and shoveled coal on the fire. She knew Annie would soon go downstairs to start cooking breakfast.

Sarah snuggled deeper into the heavy comforters and quilts that covered the bed for a few more minutes of comfort before she would have to leave the warm cocoon and get dressed in the cold room. *Your mother died . . .* The words suddenly stabbed her memory and she was instantly, fully awake. *Died? It can't be!* When she went downstairs she would find out it had all been a horrible dream. Or would she?

The abnormal silence at the breakfast table and the tears that shimmered in Annie's eyes whenever she looked at Sarah filled her stomach with a rock that left no room for food. Although no mention was made of the subject, she knew she had not been dreaming the evening before and Annie really had told her Memm was dead. Yet, it was too unreal for her to believe it was true.

After Sarah finished washing the breakfast dishes, Annie handed her a large paper bag and said, "Pack some clothes in here so you're ready when Daadi Shaub comes. You'll need your Sunday clothes for the funeral, so be sure you take them along too."

Sarah took the bag and went upstairs to pack her clothes. She had only enough clothes to last from one wash day to the next, so there was little to pack. When she went downstairs with the bag in her hand, Annie was putting on her shawl and bonnet.

"We have to go away this morning," Annie told Sarah. "I hate to leave you here alone, but we can't wait. I'm sure Daadi Shaub will be here soon. We'll come over there tomorrow."

After John and Annie drove away with their two little boys, Sarah stood alone at the window watching for Daadi Shaub to come. The clock ticked loudly in the silent house, but there was no solace in the sound. Tears of loneliness and the aching longing for her mother coursed down her cheeks as she waited alone at the window, but there was no one to hear her cries or comfort her in her grief.

The length of time Sarah waited for her grandfather to arrive was not actually as long as it seemed to her. How relieved she was to see his sleigh turn in beside the house! When he slipped out from under the buggy blankets, she hurried to open the door and let him in the house.

"Brr-r-r-r, it's cold out there," Daadi Shaub shivered as he stepped into the warm kitchen. "It was down to zero again this morning and didn't go up much yet. I must warm up first before I go back out in that." He took off his gloves and rubbed his hands together over the cookstove. His cheeks and nose were red from the cold. "Did Johns leave already?" he asked as he noticed the emptiness of the house.

"*Ya*," Sarah said with a nod. "They couldn't wait 'til you came." She could not tell him how much comfort his coming had already given her. Neither could she wait any longer to ask the questions that had been tumbling through her mind. "What happened to Memm?" she asked.

"Well," Daadi said. He stopped to clear his throat while he fumbled for words to tell his ten-year-old granddaughter about her mother's death. "Your Memm had the same sickness as before. She went to the hospital just before Christmas. Your brothers and sisters all came to stay with us. The day after Christmas your Daed was with her all day. That was the day we had such a snowstorm. He came back to our place in the evening but wasn't more than home 'til the hospital called the neighbors and told them to tell him to come back right away."

"The neighbors came and gave him the message, so he went and called Charlie Wentzel to take him to Lancaster in his machine. It was snowing something awful and they had a hard time getting there. It's a wonder they made it at all, but way late that night they finally got to the hospital. And then they were too late anyhow. The doctor told them your Memm had died at twenty after ten. Her heart gave out and she just fell asleep. There was nothing to do there, so Charlie brought Daed back to our place again. It was almost morning 'til they got back through all that snow."

Daadi pulled his cotton hankie from his pocket, wiped his eyes, and blew his nose. "The undertaker brought her to our house yesterday afternoon," he went on when he could speak again. "The funeral is on Friday."

Seeing Daadi's tears and hearing the story brought fresh tears to Sarah's eyes. She wiped them away with the back of her hand. She was too young to comprehend the grief Daadi was experiencing. She could only think of Memm as her mother, not as Daadi's daughter.

"*Ya, wohl,*" Daadi sighed as he stuffed his hankie back in his pocket. "I guess we better be starting back."

Sarah put on her coat and bonnet, pulled her black rubber boots over her shoes, and closed the four buckles tightly. She wound a hand-knitted muffler around her neck, pulling one layer up over her mouth and nose so that only her eyes showed. Then she pulled a pair of hand-knitted mittens over her hands and picked up the paper bag that contained her clothes.

Daadi pulled back the buggy blankets just far enough for Sarah to slip in under them. She set the bag at her feet while Daadi climbed in the sleigh beside her and tucked the blankets snugly around both of them.

The horse pulled the sleigh smoothly over the snow as they went from Hahnstown to Hinkletown and then on toward Daadi's farm. The sky was clear, and the snow sparkled in the sunshine. They rode without speaking, for the cold air that streamed around them made conversation nearly impossible. The only sounds were the squeak of the sleigh runners and the clop-clop-clop of the horse's hooves on the cold, hard snow.

Daadi stopped beside his house long enough for Sarah to jump out of the sleigh. She ran into the house while he went on to the barn to stable the horse.

"Sarah!" Mammi Shaub cried as she swept her oldest granddaughter into her arms.

Sarah was not used to open displays of emotion, but she clung to her grandmother now as they wept together. Her sisters watched curiously until Mammi released her after a long moment.

"Come over to the stove and warm up," Mammi said as she reached under her apron and drew a hankie out of her skirt pocket. "You must be almost frozen."

"It was cold," Sarah acknowledged as she sat on the wood-box and pulled off her boots, "but I'm okay." She would have gone through anything to be with her family that day.

When she began to be warm again, Sarah asked Esther, "Where's Daed?"

"In the parlor with Memm," Esther told her.

"Do you want to see her?" Mammi asked gently.

"Yes," Sarah nodded.

"I'll—go with you," Mammi choked as new tears sprang to her eyes.

Sarah followed Mammi into the parlor. When Sarah saw the coffin, she stopped and stood still. She wanted to see Memm, but not in a coffin. Yet, there it was; and she knew her mother's body lay inside the plain, tapered wooden box. Only now did Memm's death become reality. Sarah knew, without a shadow of a doubt, that Memm really and truly had died.

Daed saw them and stood up. He was glad to see Sarah, but the grief in his eyes drowned out the welcome he felt in his heart. He stood beside her, with his hand on her shoulder, while she looked at Memm's face. It was perfectly still and almost as white as her shroud. The only color in all the whiteness inside the coffin was the pale pink of Memm's lips and the color of her hair. She was only thirty-five years old and had not lived long enough for her hair to turn gray.

Daadi's house was the same as always and yet not the same at all. Mammi was always busy, but now she seemed strangely idle as she did nothing but meet the needs of the children. People came and went throughout the day, expressing sympathy with gifts of food and deeds of kindness, doing the work for Mammi. Daed did nothing at all except sit beside Memm's plain coffin in the parlor and speak quietly to the visitors who dropped by.

Mary and Anna were too young to understand the reality or comprehend the finality of death. They simply accepted each moment as it came. Esther was the only sister Sarah could ask about their mother's death.

"Charlie came and took her to the hospital in his machine," Esther told Sarah. "Daed went with them. I remember the machine lights shone into the house when Charlie came, so it was after dark. Memm put on her black Sunday dress to go. That's the last we saw her."

"Did yous stay alone?" Sarah gasped.

"No. Two of the Wanner girls came to stay with us over-night," Esther said. "The next day Daed brought us all here to stay with Daadi Shaubs. Daed went to the hospital every day. The day after Christmas he stayed there all day. Right after he got home that night, the neighbor came and said the hospital called. They said Daed should come in right away, so Charlie took him in. It was snowing fierce that night."

"That's what Daadi told me," Sarah nodded.

"All us children were sleeping in one room," Esther went on. "Mammi made a bed for some of us on the floor. During the night I woke up and heard somebody crying something awful. It really wondered me who it was. I found out later it was Daed. He had just got back from the hospital then and told Daadis that Memm died."

Friday, the day Memm's funeral was to be held, was another bitterly cold day as the winter weather continued to hold the county in its icy grasp. Memm's brothers and sisters and their families came to Daadi's house for the dinner which was served by church friends to the thirty family members. After the meal, the traditional short service would be held in Daadi's home before the funeral procession made its way to the Pike Meetinghouse for the burial and funeral service scheduled to begin at 1:30 in the afternoon. Sarah and her brothers and sisters stood in a small cluster beside Daed while relatives came into the room to look at Memm and speak quietly to Daed before the home service began.

"Where's the baby?" Sarah and Esther heard Aunt Leah whisper to Aunt Mary.

"At her feet," Aunt Mary whispered back.

The girls tilted their heads so they could peek into the closed bottom half of the coffin. No one had told them there was a baby. But sure enough! There was a little blanket-wrapped bundle at Memm's feet. They did not know their mother's death had been caused by what was known as toxemia, or severe pregnancy-induced hypertension, for such matters were never discussed in the hearing of children. The girls had no idea there was a connection between their mother's death and the unnamed prematurely-born baby girl they had seen lying at the foot of the coffin.

When it was time for the service to begin, Sarah sat beside Daed on one of the wooden folding chairs that had been provided for the family. After all of the chairs were filled, members of the extended family sat on the canvas seats of backless folding stools. When everyone was seated, quietness settled over the house. Then Uncle Jacob Stauffer stood up. "Uncle Check" (Jake) was married to Daed's sister, Magdalena, whom everyone called Lena. He was the bishop and also the grandson of the Jacob Stauffer who had started the Stauffer Mennonite group in 1845.

Uncle Jacob cleared his throat before he began speaking in his sing-song preaching voice. Sarah did not understand much of what he said, because he spoke in the German language which was always used in church services rather than the everyday Pennsylvania Deutsch dialect of German they spoke at home.

After the bishop finished speaking and led in prayer, the pallbearers picked up Memm's coffin and carried it outside to the black horse-drawn hearse that was waiting to carry it to the meet-inghouse. Everyone dressed warmly for the cold, slow ride behind the hearse. Then they went outside and got in their carriages. Daed and his motherless children, followed by Daadi and Mammi Shaub, were at the head of the line that formed and fell into place behind the hearse as it moved slowly toward the Pike Meetinghouse.

The buggy sheds and horse barn at the meetinghouse were nearly filled with teams of horses and buggies when the funeral procession arrived at the church yard. Those who could not find parking space in the sheds covered their horses with blankets and tied them at the hitching rails. The carriages in the funeral procession pulled into the stalls of the buggy sheds that had been reserved for the bereaved family. The people who had taken shelter inside the meetinghouse while they waited, now spilled out to prepare for the viewing while the coffin was unloaded and set on a pair of turned wooden legs. The women huddled together at one end of the building while the men formed a second group at the other end. The immediate and extended family stood in front of the crowd, slightly back from the coffin. The undertaker lifted and laid back the hinged lids that covered Memm's face. Then he stepped back and waited while the people filed by on both sides of the coffin, men on one side and women on the other, to view Memm's remains. Each man took off his broad-rimmed black hat as he passed by the coffin to pay respect to the young mother. The long line of black-coated arms jerked up and down, up and down, as the men took off and replaced their hats.

The biting cold air slipped easily through the bare tree branches in the church yard and snaked between the people huddled together beside the church building. Sarah shivered as she stood beside Daed, waiting until everyone had filed by the coffin. Then the immediate family stepped forward and stood in a circle around the coffin to look at Memm's face for the last time. Daed shook with sobs and, seeing his grief, the waiting crowd silently cried with him.

At last, Daed stepped back to signal he was finished. The undertaker closed the lids of the coffin and motioned for the pallbearers to come forward. They picked up the coffin and carried it to the cemetery, with the ministers and family following in order behind them. The pallbearers placed Memm's coffin on short planks that had been laid across the open grave and slipped two wide brown straps under the coffin. After the planks were removed, two pallbearers stood on each side of the grave, each holding one end of the straps, and slowly lowered the coffin into the hole that had been prepared for it.

No one spoke a word until the coffin bumped into the bottom of the hole and the pallbearers pulled up the straps. Then Uncle Jacob began to speak words of comfort to the mourners. Sarah's feet were numb with cold as she stood on the snow-covered ground in the open air beside the grave. She was so cold she could not even try to listen to the words the bishop was saying but merely endured the wait until they could all go into the warm church for the funeral service. Memm's brother, Uncle Christ Shaub, opened his overcoat and wrapped it around Mary to give her some added protection from the bitter cold. While the bishop was still speaking, the men who had been assigned to fill the grave began shoveling dirt into the hole. Clods of frozen ground thunked dully on top of the coffin and slid down its sides as the bishop committed Memm's body to the ground and her spirit to God who gave it.

At last, Uncle Jacob finished speaking and the crowd turned to go into the meetinghouse. Sarah's teeth were chattering and her heart felt as numb as her feet when she stumbled woodenly into the shelter of the meetinghouse. She thought she could not bear to leave Memm out in the cold, frozen ground, but had no choice.

The walls of the meetinghouse were covered with white plaster and lined with rows of coat hooks. More rows of hooks were screwed into long boards which hung from rods in the ceiling above the men's benches so the men could hang their hats above their seats. A coal-burning stove near the center of the room provided a welcome heat to the thoroughly chilled people who were finding seats and settling down to listen to the funeral sermon.

The benches inside the meetinghouse were made of bare wood, with one board across the back for support. The benches were divided into four sections, with two aisles that intersected in the middle. The benches were set in a U-shape to face the preacher's table which stood at the head of the center aisle on the side of the building nearest the road. The long singers' table, with a backless bench on each side of it, stood in the wide center aisle in front of the preacher's table. Men who were gifted in singing were appointed to sit at the singers' table and lead in the singing of the hymns as they were announced.

The seating pattern in the Pike Mennonite Meetinghouse is identical to that of this Old Order Mennonite church. The preacher's table stands at the head of the long singers' table in the center of the auditorium.

Arthur and Frank sat with Daed and Daadi Shaub on the first bench on the left side the singers' table where the men and boys always sat. Sarah, Esther, Mary, and Anna sat with Mammi Shaub and their aunts on the first bench of the women's section, on the right side of the singers' table.

When everyone was seated, Uncle Jacob rose from his seat on the bench behind the preacher's table and stepped forward to open the service. After making a few remarks, he announced the number of a hymn which he read and then sat down. The first minister rose to take his place and began speaking.

Mary and Anna fell asleep during the half-hour the first minister was speaking. After he sat down, Joe Brubaker rose and preached for another hour, using Philippians 1:21-23 for his text. "For me to live is Christ and to die is gain. But if I live in the flesh this is the fruit of my labour. Yet what I choose I know not, for I am in a strait betwixt two, having a desire to depart and be with Christ, which is far better."

Esther leaned against Mammi Shaub and fell asleep during the second sermon, but Sarah could not sleep. Her chilled body slowly grew warm as the service progressed, but her heart remained a frozen lump, for she was old enough to wonder about the future. The German words the preacher said swirled over her head without entering her mind. Although she had seen Memm buried and knew she was gone, Sarah could not imagine life without her mother.

What will happen now? Sarah wondered. *I didn't mind staying with John and Annie for awhile, but I don't want to live with them the rest of my life. I want to go home! I want Memm!*

Then, suddenly, the sermon was over and the congregation knelt for a prayer which ended with the Lord's Prayer. After everyone got up from their knees and sat down again, the bishop announced the number of a hymn which was to be sung. There was a small stir as people reached under the seat of the bench before them and took out the German *Unpartheyisches Gesangbuch* (Impartial, or Unbiased, Songbook). Pages rustled softly as people found the place in the little brown books which had been compiled and used by the Mennonite church ever since they were first printed in 1804. One of the singers "raised the tune" and the other singers joined him. By the second line, full volume had been reached as the congregation joined their voices to sing in unison the slow, often-slurred tune they knew without seeing any musical notes. After the hymn, Uncle Jacob rose to read Memm's obituary. He repeated the line stating her age, "Thirty-five years, six months, and two days."

The service concluded with a final prayer, and then everyone began getting ready to go home. Friends again provided supper at Daadi's house, serving the meal to the twenty family members who were able to be there.

"You can stay here for the weekend, Sarah," Annie Auker said as she and John prepared to go home. "John will come for you on Sunday evening so you can go back to school on Monday."

Sarah nodded, but did not speak. Her head felt too dull and heavy to think. She simply did whatever she was told to do and tried not to think about the future.

Sarah and Esther helped Mammi put things away and set the house in order again on Saturday. The bishop and his wife, Uncle Check (Jake) and Aunt Lena, invited Daed and the children, and Daadi Shaubs, for dinner on Sunday.

When they got home, Daadi picked up Anna and carried her over to the cupboard. "Now, let's see what Mammi has in here," he said as he opened the cupboard door.

Sarah and her siblings crowded around Daadi as he reached into the cupboard and drew out a paper bag. They all remembered when Daadi had said the same thing to them as he carried them to the cupboard. They knew he was about to dole out either some candy or cookies.

"Look what I found," Daadi smiled as he reached into the bag, pulled out a gingersnap cookie, and handed it to Anna. He filled the outstretched hands of all his grandchildren with some of the cookies he habitually ate as a tonic for his stomach.

Sarah took her share of the cookies and nibbled each one to make it last as long as possible. Daed and Memm never had money to buy cookies, but Daadi enjoyed sharing his cookies with his grandchildren.

As long as Sarah could be with her family and grandparents, she was able to ignore the future. But then, much too soon, John Auker was at Daadi's door, ready to take her home with him. She would have to stay with the Aukers until Daed decided what he was going to do, and how he would provide for his motherless children.

"I asked Harry Wanner if one of his girls would keep house for me," Daed told Daadi Shaub. "They're taking turns helping out for now, but none of them wants to stay."

"Then you have to find homes for the children and make sale," Daadi Shaub told him. "You can't take care of six children by yourself. Me and Mammi are too old to raise another family. You'll just have to sell out and find homes for the children."

"I don't have a lot of choices," Daed said slowly. "I guess that's the only thing I can do with the children if I can't find anybody to keep house for me. But maybe I could just store my stuff somewhere for awhile."

"You have to make sale," Daadi insisted. "You need the money. Elam Burkholder can't help you out this time. This Depression is robbing everybody, rich and poor."

"That's so," Daed admitted. Elam Burkholder had helped Daed when he had lost everything after the cows got Bang's Disease, but now Elam was also bankrupt. He had bought farms for his three oldest children just as the Depression was beginning. Then, in the space of three months in the spring and summer of 1933, the tobacco warehouse and two barns on his own farm had been totally destroyed by fire. In October, all his farms and properties had been sold on Sheriff Sale.

Too grief-stricken to think clearly, Daed finally agreed to accept Daadi's advice. Daed found an auctioneer and arranged to have a public sale on February 27, 1934. The auctioneer made a list of the things which were to be sold and had sale bills printed. Daed could not afford to have the sale bill printed in the Ephrata Review, so he simply distributed the thin paper fliers at various business places around town and hoped for the best.

Sometimes it seemed to Sarah as if Memm's death and the funeral had been a nightmare. She had gone back to school, and life in the Auker home had returned to normal. But whenever she saw her family at church or Daadi Shaub's house, Memm was noticeably absent. *If this is a nightmare, it's one that never ends,* Sarah thought.

When the morning of the sale day arrived, Sarah told Annie, "I want to go to the sale." It was a Tuesday, but she knew she could not sit in school and study while a sale was going on at home.

"Do you *have* to go?" John asked when Annie relayed Sarah's request to him. "It was down to zero again this morning."

PUBLIC SALE !

Tuesday, February 27, 1934

The undersigned will sell at Public Sale, at his residence, on the road leading from Red Run Mill to Independent School House, midway between the two named places, on the farm of Harry Wanner, the following, to wit.

 ## ONE HORSE

good driver and worker, 16 years old.

Carriage in good condition; Trotting Buggy, Set of Carriage Harness.

HOUSEHOLD GOODS

3 Beds, with Springs; Single Bed,

with Spring; Cot Bed, Large Kitchen Cabinet, Sink, Extension Table, 2 Sideboards, 2 Small Bureaus, 2 Washstands, Desk and Bookcase, combined;

MINNESOTA SEWING MACHINE

LARGE PARLOR HEATER

COLUMBIAN CHOICE, BLACK ENAMELED RANGE,

with Warming Closet and Reservoir, in good condition;

Couch, Lot of Carpet and Linoleum, Lot of Dishes, Glassware, Aluminum-ware, ½ Dozen Old-Fashioned Chairs, 3 Rockers, 2 High Chairs, 2 Stands, 250 Quarts of Canned Fruit, 5 Bushels Sweet Potatoes, Empty Fruit Jars, Crocks, Iron Kettle, Copper Tea Kettle,

HAAG TWIN TUB WASHING MACHINE,

1½ H. P. FAIRBANKS GASOLINE ENGINE,

Lot of Tools, Heavy Blacksmith's Vise, Small Forge, Anvil, Drill Press, Emery Grinder, Bale Box, Scalding Trough, Meat Grinder, with Pulley; Sausage Stuffer, Lard Press and many other articles too numerous to mention.

Sale to commence at 1 o'clock P. M., when terms will be made known by

Amos R. Wenger

B. W. Witmer, Auct.
H. G. Martin, Clerk.

"Yes!" Sarah cried as her eyes filled with tears. With all her heart, she wanted to be at the sale with her family.

"*Ya, wohl,*" John sighed. "If you must go that bad, I guess I'll take you."

The sale was set to begin at one o'clock in the afternoon. John hitched the horse to the sleigh and tucked the blankets snugly around himself and Sarah. Then they set out on the cold, five-mile ride from the Aukers' home to Harry Wanner's farm. The bitter cold came through the blankets, numbing Sarah's hands and feet long before the sleigh was anywhere near Red Run.

"Whoa!" John yelled as the sleigh rounded a curve and tipped at a dangerous angle. Before Sarah had time to think, the sleigh upset and rudely dumped both her and John in the snowbank.

Coughing and sputtering, Sarah clawed her way out of the snow and stood up. She brushed the snow off herself while John set the sleigh back on its runners and shook the snow from the blankets. Then they both crawled back into the sleigh, more chilled than ever, to finish their cold ride.

When the sleigh coasted to a stop at the farm, Sarah saw rows of Daed's tools, Memm's furniture, and household goods standing in lines across the snowy yard in front of the house. "Go in the house and warm up," John told Sarah when she jumped out of the sleigh.

Sarah ran to the house and opened the door.

"You can't come in here," one of the Wanner girls called when she saw Sarah standing in the open doorway. "Anna has the whooping cough."

Disappointed, Sarah turned around and went to look for Daed. She found him, but he was busy talking to the auctioneer and clerk.

"Sarah!" Mammi Shaub exclaimed when she saw her forlorn granddaughter. "What are you doing here? Why aren't you in school?"

"I wanted to come," Sarah said in a choked voice. She realized now how different the sale was in reality from what she had imagined. She had come to the sale, but she had not come home.

The house was empty. Daed was too busy to talk to her. She could not even be in the house with her sisters. The outdoors was bitterly cold, and there was nowhere to get warm.

When it was time for the sale to begin, the small crowd that had braved the elements gathered around the auctioneer. He went up and down the rows of Daed's tools and butcher equipment, selling each item to the highest bidder. His driving horse, carriage, trotting buggy, and harnesses were sold and taken away by their new owners. Sarah stood beside Mammi Shaub, watching as the strips of rag carpet, Memm's dishes, quart jars of canned fruit, crocks, tea kettle, and other household goods were sold. Then their beds, washstands, the kitchen table, Memm's Minnesota treadle sewing machine, and Daed's combination desk/bookcase were sold for ridiculously low prices. When the big parlor stove was sold, Sarah remembered the happy day Daed had bought it and the excitement of bringing it home to surprise Memm. The wicker baby coach in which all of the children had slept as babies would never be needed again and was sold for a pittance. The black Columbian Choice cookstove and Hoosier kitchen cabinet were each sold for $10, although they had been brand new when Memm and Daed set up housekeeping eleven years earlier.

As much as Daed needed the money to pay his bills, the weather and Depression had combined to make the sale a total failure. But it was too late for him to change his mind. Everything was sold and could not be returned.

"Are you ready to go?" John asked Sarah when he found the heartbroken girl standing on the porch watching people carry things away.

She was so cold her teeth chattered, so Sarah merely nodded her head and followed John to the sleigh for the long, cold ride home. She was so discouraged she intensely wished she had not come. She had learned Daed was going to go way up in the mountains somewhere for at least a year to cut wood for a stranger. The children were going to be separated and sent to various families who were willing to give them a home. She would stay with John and Annie until Daed found another place for her. She had no idea how long she would stay with the Aukers or where she would go from there.

Being at the sale had made Sarah feel worse instead of better. *There's nothing left to go back to*, her thoughts wailed with anguish at the shocking discovery. *My family is all broken up. I don't have a home anymore!*

Chapter 8

"I watched a happy little brook gliding gently on its way . . ."
Sarah muttered to herself in a sing-song voice. She stepped across
a puddle in the long muddy lane that led from Uncle Ammon and
Aunt Mary's farm buildings to the road. "Soft, enchanting, lovely
music . . ." she went on, reciting the poem the third graders had
been assigned to memorize. *The Song of the Brook* was such a long
poem Sarah thought she would never be able to say all sixteen lines
by the end of the school year.

Evening after evening, Aunt Mary had patiently repeated
the lines over and over as she helped Sarah learn the poem. "By
the time you know this poem, I'll be able to say it too," Aunt
Mary had once sighed.

As she stood at the end of the lane waiting for the bus that
would take her to the Bergstrasse School, Sarah recited all sixteen
lines of the poem to herself.

I watched a happy little brook,
Gliding gently on its way;
Soft, enchanting, lovely music.
It so sweetly seemed to play.
Then I noticed as I watched it,
That the song it sweetly sings;
Comes from only rocks and pebbles
As the water o'er them swings.
And I thought in love and wonder,
How the sweetest songs we sing;
Come from sorrows, trials, and heartaches,

> *Which this life does seem to bring.*
> *I bowed my head in meek submission*
> *In that quiet, shady nook;*
> *And I prayed, "Dear Lord, I thank Thee,*
> *For the lesson of the brook."*

Although Sarah did not understand all the big words or fully comprehend the meaning of the poem, she was finally able to recite all of the lines. If she could only remember them until she got to school, she would say them to the teacher and be finished with the grueling assignment.

Sarah repeated the words over and over until the arrival of the yellow school bus interrupted her recitation. She climbed aboard the bus, found an empty seat, and began the ride toward another day at the Bergstrasse School. She had gone to live with Aunt Mary and Uncle Ammon Auker soon after Daed's sale, but she had not been forced to change schools because her aunt and uncle also lived in the Bergstrasse School district.[12]

Uncle Ammon was a good father to his two children and kind to Sarah, but he could never take Daed's place in her life. Although Sarah was comfortable with Aunt Mary, she was not Memm. Sarah's aching longing for her own mother was like a deep, dry well that held no water for the thirsty soul. Aunt Mary's children were still babies. Lizzie Mae, who was always called Maude, would be two years old in May. Ed, who had just been born in January, did little other than eat and sleep. Sarah was homesick for her brothers and sisters.

Each of the Wenger children was living with a different family. Arthur had been taken in by Willie and Hettie Wanner, whose only child had died in infancy. Esther was living at Martindale with Daed's half-sister, Aunt Fannie and Uncle Dave Gingrich. Frank had gone to Terre Hill to live with the John B. Weaver family. Levi and Emma Zimmerman, a young couple who lived at Red Run and attended the Pike church, had taken

---

[12] The current address of this property is 332 Mohler Church Road, Ephrata, Pa.

Mary to their home. Anna was with Memm's sister, Aunt Barb and Uncle Milt Good.

Sarah was glad when the 1933-34 school year ended in April and she could forget about doing lessons until September. Helping Aunt Mary with her work was more to her liking than sitting in a stuffy school trying to learn things she did not understand.

As she had done the previous summer when she was Annie Auker's *maad*, Sarah helped Aunt Mary in the house and garden. She pulled weeds, picked and shelled bushels of peas, hung wash on the line, gathered eggs, tended the babies, churned butter, washed dishes, and did a multitude of chores that varied with the days of the week and the season. Living with Aunt Mary did not feel the same as being Annie Auker's *maad*, because she could not think of going home again someday.

I don't think Aunt Mary really wanted me, Sarah thought as she pulled weeds in the garden. Everybody wanted Anna because she is the cute little baby. But I'm too big to be cute. Nobody wants me. Aunt Mary just took me because somebody had to and she thought she should since she's Memm's sister.

As she slowly worked her way down the row, Sarah daydreamed of waking up to find out the whole thing had been a bad dream. She would go home and find everything the way it used to be. But daydreams could not change the truth. Memm was gone forever and would never come back.

Sarah had not seen Daed for months. He had gone far away to a place called Texter Mountain. He had made a contract with Frank Wartluft to do logging on his mountain property for one year. Daed's cousin, David Wenger, and "Blinky" (Aaron) Martin lived with him in half of a house on the mountain. Sometimes Rine Mitchell, Bob Witmer, Charlie Wentzel, and other men went to help them for a day or two. Sarah did not know if she would ever see Daed again.

One Saturday evening Aunt Mary told Sarah, "We're going to Daadi Shaub's for dinner tomorrow."

"Who else is going?" Sarah asked.

"Oh, just the family," Aunt Mary said in an offhand tone. "Sams and Milts and Weavers and us. Everybody but Christs." Sarah knew Memm's brother, Christ, and his wife, Lena, lived more than twenty miles away in the city of Reading. They could not be expected to make such a long trip every time the Shaub family got together.

As Sarah took her weekly Saturday night bath in the washtub, a growing eagerness for the coming day put a sparkle in her eyes. She had almost forgotten how it felt to be happy and looking forward to something. Daadi Shaubs had moved to a place in the Hahnstown area in the spring. Esther was staying with them now and Milts would bring Anna with them. She would get to spend the day with two of her sisters and play with Miriam, Irene, Vera, and Edna. The cousins would probably go up in the barn and play with the Aunt Ricky clothes. It would be just like old times again.

As Sarah stepped into Mammi's kitchen the next day, a familiar voice floated across the room. Memm's here! The involuntary thought flashed across her mind and was instantly followed by a sinking feeling when she realized the voice belonged to Aunt Lizzie. Her voice sounded like Memm's voice, but Memm was not there. She would never be there with the family again. Stuffing the hot tears of disappointment inside, Sarah went to find her sisters.

Anna was not yet five years old and had already adapted to the change in her life. She was happy to see her big sisters again, but not on the same level with Sarah and Esther. They filled each other in on what had been happening in their lives since they had last seen each other.

"I couldn't go to school when I was with Aunt Fannie," Esther said. "Lloyd had the whooping cough. They say it takes six weeks coming and six weeks going, so we were quarantined the rest of the school term. Aunt Fannie got some first grade books from the Martindale School and I learned every word in them. But 'til the quarantine was off, school was over. And then I came to Mammi Shaub."

"Where will you go to school next year?" Sarah asked.

"I guess Bergstrasse," Esther said.

"So will I," Sarah smiled. "We won't be in the same room, but we can at least see each other every day. At least if you stay with Mammi."

Although the sisters did not discuss their feelings of insecurity, they were keenly aware of the temporary nature of their living arrangements. They knew Arthur had also been moved into another home and was now living with Mr. and Mrs. David K. Martin on a farm in the Hinkletown area. The knowledge they could be moved to other homes at any time always lurked in the back of their minds.

The refreshing day Sarah spent with her sisters and cousins at Mammi Shaub's house was soon over. In like manner, the summer which had seemed to stretch far into the distance when it began, drew to a close before Sarah was ready to go back to school.

"Labor Day is early this year," Aunt Mary said as she lifted the August page of the calendar to look at the September page. "That means school starts a little earlier too. You'll go back to school on September fourth. That's only two weeks away."

Sarah dreaded going back to the big school and having to do lessons again. "At least Esther will be there this year," she said to herself. "That's the only thing about school starting I'm glad for."

The first day of September came on a Saturday. The house must be cleaned, the porch and walks scrubbed, and food prepared for Sunday. Because nothing was done to celebrate birthdays, and because Sarah was so busy, she almost forgot that day was her eleventh birthday.

As usual, Sarah went to the Pike church on Sunday morning with Uncle Ammon's family and came home again to eat a late dinner. After dinner, Aunt Mary put the babies in bed for their naps while Sarah washed the dishes.

An unfamiliar touring car came in the long, dusty lane and some strangers walked up the cement walk to the house. By the way they were dressed and the fact that they were driving a car, Sarah correctly guessed they were Weaverland Conference Mennonites. Uncle Ammon answered the knock on the door and invited the couple with two small children into the parlor. Aunt Mary soon came downstairs and joined them.

After she finished washing dishes, Sarah went outside, sat on the swing that hung from a tree branch, and gently swung back and forth. With her big toe, she drew little lines in the thick dust of the bare ground under the swing. She did not know the visitors, and they had no children her age, so there was no reason to meet them.

"Sarah," Uncle Ammon called from the porch. "Come here."

Sarah walked slowly toward the house, afraid she was being called to meet the visitors. She hated meeting strangers and never knew what to say to them.

"Come in here," Uncle Ammon said as he led the way to the parlor.

Sarah followed him without saying a word.

"This is Norman and Lizzie Nolt," Uncle Ammon told Sarah. "They are willing to give you a home. Shake hands with them."

Norman and Lizzie Nolt, 1930.
Courtesy: Mary Nolt Martin

What? Sarah thought as she felt a jolt like an electric shock go through her body. She put her hands behind her back and looked at the floor.

"Shake hands with them, Sarah," Uncle Ammon prompted.

Sarah put out a limp hand and let the strangers shake it, but she did not look up at them. She felt as if she was merchandise they were inspecting.

"We'll take her," Lizzie said after a long moment of silence. The way she said it made Sarah feel like an invisible gavel had fallen on the auction block and she had been sold into slavery.

"Well, I guess it's settled then," Uncle Ammon said and turned to Sarah. "You'll be going home with Normans. These are their children. Mary is two and the baby is just seven weeks old. His name is Melvin."

Sarah nodded, but did not say a word. She could not have spoken even if she had wanted to, for her throat was closed with terror.

"We must go pack your things," Aunt Mary said.

Sarah stood, rooted to the spot, and stared at her aunt. She could not believe what she was hearing. Surely Uncle Ammon and Aunt Mary would not send her away to live with total strangers; not right here and now!

But Aunt Mary was walking toward the stairway. "Come," she said as she stopped at the bottom of the stairs and turned around to look at Sarah.

Numbly, Sarah followed her aunt up the stairs to the bedroom.

"Norman and Lizzie's neighbors told them about you," Aunt Mary said as she folded Sarah's clothes and packed them in a wooden orange crate. "Lizzie can use a girl to help her. They thought they best come today, so you don't have to change schools after it already started."

Aunt Mary went on talking, but her words did not penetrate Sarah's mind. *Where do they live? Where are they going to take me?* She saw the old rag doll Great-aunt Maggie Reich had made for her. She did not play with dolls anymore, but she snatched it up and placed it in the crate with her clothes and the other things Aunt Mary was packing.

Sarah followed Aunt Mary down the stairs again and out the front door. She knew now she had not misunderstood. Her eyes filled with tears and she bit her lip to keep her chin from quivering.

Norman and Lizzie were standing by the car talking to Uncle Ammon. Norman took the crate of Sarah's belongings and put it in the trunk. He and Lizzie shook hands with Uncle Ammon and Aunt Mary. Norman sat little Mary in the middle of the front seat and took his place behind the steering wheel while Lizzie took her seat in the other side of the car with the baby on her lap.

"You must go now," Aunt Mary said gently. "They are waiting." She shook Sarah's hand formally, as if she was saying good-by to someone special. Her eyes were wet as she said, "Be a good helper for Lizzie."

Sarah felt like running away instead of going with these strangers. But she had been taught to do what she was told, so she climbed into the back seat of the car and closed the door. She looked at Aunt Mary and Uncle Ammon through the open side of the touring car. Her eyes begged to be called back, but her aunt and uncle had turned around and were walking slowly away as the car began moving out the lane toward the road.

Sarah closed her eyes to keep the hot tears from spilling out. She must not cry in front of these strangers. Her stomach churned and she gulped desperately to keep from throwing up. She opened her eyes and saw the cows grazing in the familiar meadows beyond Uncle Ammon's farm. She had ridden by that meadow and seen those cows many times during the months she had lived with Uncle Ammon and Aunt Mary. Now she was riding past them with strangers who were taking her far away to a place she had never seen. *Will I ever see anybody in my family again?* she wondered.

The car passed places she could not remember seeing before. She did not know where she was going. Could she run away when she got wherever it was they called home? How could she get back to Uncle Ammon and Aunt Mary? Would they let her stay if she did find a way to get back? Why did they send her away? What had she done wrong?

At last, Norman drove in a long farm lane and parked the car between the house and barn that stood at the other end of the lane.

"Here we are," Lizzie said as she opened her door. "This is where we live."

Sarah looked at the big, double farmhouse. She did not want to get out of the car and go in the house with Norman and Lizzie, but she had no choice. Norman lifted the crate of her things out of the trunk and carried it to the house. Lizzie followed him, leading little Mary by the hand and holding baby Melvin in her other arm. Sarah slowly trailed behind them, her feet dragging with dread of the unknown. She felt like screaming and running away, but she did not know where to run.

"Come with me," Lizzie said to Sarah when she stepped into the kitchen. "I'll take this box upstairs and show you where you'll sleep."

Sarah put one foot in front of the other as she slowly followed Lizzie up the stairs.

"This will be your room," Lizzie said. She opened the door to a small bedroom that smelled of moth balls and looked as if no one had ever used it. "You can put your things in the bureau awhile. When you're done, come down for supper."

Sarah did not feel like eating, but she thought she had better do what she was told. She sat at the table and spooned sugar over the diced fresh peaches, bread cubes, and milk Lizzie set before her. Although the bread was soggy from the milk, it stuck in her throat. She sniffed and wiped her nose with the back of her hand. She could not eat with these strangers. Summoning all her courage, she put another spoonful of the cold milk soup in her mouth and choked it down. She was the last one to empty her bowl, and could only hope what she had swallowed would not come up again.

The Norman Nolt farm. The current address of this farm is 181 Amsterdam Road, New Holland, Pa. Courtesy: Mary Nolt Martin.

"There's not many dishes," Lizzie said to Sarah, "but you might as well wash them. If there's anything I hate, it's getting up in the morning and having yesterday's dirty dishes staring me in the face. There's hot water in the teakettle."

Sarah looked out the window as she poured hot water into the enamel dishpan. The farm buildings were so far from the road she could not see the end of the lane from the kitchen. If anyone she knew happened to drive by, she would never see them or be able to run out the long lane fast enough to jump in their buggy. *How long will I have to stay here?* she silently wondered with a sense of hopeless desperation. *I got to get away somehow. But how can I ever manage to do it?*

When it was bedtime, Sarah went up the stairs to the strange room and the strange bed. She pulled out her old rag doll and laid it on her pillow. She had not slept with a doll for a long time, but it was one familiar face in this strange place. She blew out the light, crawled into bed, and lay very still. Through the open windows she could hear the sounds of the animals in the barnyard, the crickets in the grass, and the wind blowing through the leaves. She wondered how she could ever fall asleep in this strange bed.

She did not know where it came from or what it was, but something fierce and dreadful was suddenly chasing her through the darkness in the cemetery at the Pike church. She dodged around the headstones, twisting and turning to escape whatever it was that chased her. Her feet slipped on the wet grass and she was tumbling down into an open grave. "Help!" she screamed. "Help! I'm falling! I'm falling!"

A bright light shone into Sarah's face and she heard a stranger's voice. She opened her eyes into the blinding light and quickly closed them again.

"Are you all right?" the same voice asked as a hand gently shook Sarah's shoulder.

Sarah opened her eyes again. She was not in the cemetery after all. She was not at home. She was not with Annie Auker or Aunt Mary. She was in that strange room of that strange house. Lizzie was standing beside the bed in her nightgown with a flashlight in her hand.

"Did you have a bad dream?" Lizzie asked.

Sarah nodded and turned her head to the wall.

"You're all right now," Lizzie said quietly. "Go back to sleep." She went back to her own room, taking the light with her.

Sarah's fingers fumbled in the darkness and found the arm of her rag doll. She wanted to put on her clothes and run far, far away, but she could not. She was more afraid of the darkness of night outside than of the strange room. The pounding of her heart gradually slowed and after a long time she fell asleep again.

As soon as she woke up, Sarah reached for her rag doll. She did not want to get out of bed or leave the room but knew she had no choice. She dressed slowly and carefully made her bed, taking as long as she dared to accomplish both tasks. She sat her rag doll on the pillow where she would see its face as soon as she walked in the room again. Knowing she could no longer postpone the inevitable, she went slowly down the stairs to help Lizzie get breakfast on the table.

The work Lizzie expected Sarah to do was the same as she had done at the other places she had lived. This was Monday, so it was wash day. Sarah helped Lizzie get the wash on the line to dry, make meals, tend babies, and wash dishes. She soon learned Lizzie was particular with her housework. She was quick to correct Sarah if she did not do things just right. The dishes must be washed in a certain order and the wash hung on the line a certain way. The towels must be folded evenly, with the hem edges on the inside, and stacked with the folded end facing out. Sarah did not know how she could ever remember to do everything exactly the way Lizzie wanted it done.

At last the long day was over and Sarah could escape to the bedroom. She could not think of it as her room for she knew it was a spare room, kept empty for hired help or overnight guests. She was not being paid for her work nor was she a guest, but neither was she a part of this family. She did not belong here, but she would have to stay whether she liked it or not. That night she dreamed she was walking down a long hall at the Bergstrasse School. No matter how fast or how long she walked, she never got any closer to the end of the hall.

"You will be going to the Amsterdam School this morning," Lizzie said the next morning. She wound a brown rubber band around the pigtail she had just finished braiding with half of Sarah's naturally wavy hair and started combing back the other half to make another braid. "I'll show you where the field lane is. That's the quickest way to get there from here. You don't need a lunch because you'll come home for dinner."

Sarah walked out the field lane, past the chickens clustered around the range shelters, and on toward the little red brick one-room school. She pulled one of her pigtails over her shoulder and looked at the loose ends below the rubber band. Lizzie had not pinned the braids in a circle on the back of Sarah's head the way she had always worn them. How strange it felt to have her braids hanging loosely down her back! Her life had changed so drastically and quickly she felt as though she was not Sarah Wenger anymore, but someone else she did not know.

The Amsterdam School, located on Amsterdam Road, is still in use today as a one-room Amish school. Courtesy: John N. Oberholtzer.

Thoughts of her appearance disappeared and changed to worries as Sarah neared the school building. What was the teacher's name? Was she nice? Who were the other scholars? She was sure she would not know anyone. As she feared, the children in the school yard stared at her when she walked around the rail fence that surrounded the school yard and stepped inside. She could see the majority of the scholars were Amish children. Her stomach tied itself in a hard knot. Would they laugh at her?

Sarah did not speak to any of the scholars as she stepped up on the porch. She went into the school to meet the teacher and find out where she should sit.

"Good morning," the teacher said pleasantly.

Sarah saw the teacher was an older lady with a kind-looking face. The hard knot in her stomach relaxed slightly.

"My name is Mrs. Elizabeth Burkholder," the teacher introduced herself. "And what is your name?"

Sarah shyly told the teacher her name, age, and that she was in fourth grade. The teacher wrote the information in her record book.

"And what are your parents' names?" Mrs. Burkholder asked.

"Daed's name is Amos Wenger," Sarah said softly, desperately hoping Mrs. Burkholder would not ask about her mother.

"And your mother is . . ." Mrs. Burkholder said with her pen poised above the blank space for the mother's name in her record book.

Sarah looked at the floor and did not answer.

At the silence, Mrs. Burkholder looked up and saw the tears that threatened to spill from Sarah's eyes. "What's the matter?" the teacher asked gently.

Sarah sniffed. "I don't have a mother anymore," she said so faintly it was almost a whisper. "She died last Christmas."

"Oh! I'm sorry," Mrs. Burkholder said. Her voice was full of genuine sympathy.

Suddenly, Sarah found she could speak to this grandmotherly teacher. "I am at home with Norman and Lizzie Nolt," she said. She hated the sound of the words when she heard herself saying them. They identified her as a poor, homeless child, dependent on the charity of strangers for survival.

"I see," the teacher said. She wrote Norman and Lizzie Nolt in parentheses under Daed's name in her record book. "Well, I'm glad to have you in our school and hope you will like it here," Mrs. Burkholder smiled.

The teacher showed Sarah the desk where she should sit. She slid into the seat and put the tablet Mrs. Burkholder gave her inside the desk. The two, new yellow pencils fit nicely into the groove in the desktop. Then Sarah sat with her hands clenched in her lap and waited for school to begin.

The scholars trooped noisily into the classroom when Mrs. Burkholder pulled the rope that rang the bell on top of the schoolhouse. Some of the scholars looked at Sarah as they took their seats, but no one talked to her. She wondered who the girls were and if any of them would want to be her friend.

When the bell rang again, the noise stopped. The scholars in all eight grades turned to face the front of the room. They clasped their hands in front of them on their desktops. Sarah brought her hands from her lap to the desktop. All eyes were on Mrs. Burkholder. She stood up and looked at the rows of faces in front of her.

"Good morning, children," Mrs. Burkholder said when the room was perfectly quiet. "Welcome to another year at the Amsterdam School. We have a new scholar this year," she said as she looked at Sarah. "I want all of you to be kind to Sarah Wenger and make her feel at home with us."

All the scholars looked at Sarah. She felt her face grow hot and wished she could disappear. But then Mrs. Burkholder began talking again and all the children looked back at the teacher.

The school day followed the same pattern as all the other schools Sarah had attended, beginning with Bible reading, prayer, and singing before the first class was called. As the scholars in the other grades were called to class, Sarah worked on the assignments Mrs. Burkholder gave the fourth graders. She must not take any school work home, because she would have to help Lizzie with the housework after school.

"Fourth grade reading class," Mrs. Burkholder called. The fourth graders took their reading books from their desks and rose from their seats. "Alvin, please read the first two paragraphs on page six," Mrs. Burkholder said to the boy at the front of the line.

Sarah opened her book to page six and read the words on the page silently along with Alvin Weaver as he read aloud:

1. The North Wind and the Sun once began to dispute with each other about their power and influence.

2. Just then a traveler, wrapped up in his cloak, was passing, and they agreed to test their strength upon him to see which could first get his cloak off.

"Thank you," Mrs. Burkholder said, and called on Katie Ober-holtzer to read two more paragraphs.

3. So the Wind began to blow cold and piercing blasts, which made the poor man shiver, but he only folded his cloak more closely about him.

4. Next the Sun came out of the clouds and shone warm and bright upon the traveler's head.

"Thank you," Mrs. Burkholder repeated as Katie took her seat. "Sarah, read the last paragraph, please."

Sarah's face grew hot again. She was sure the eyes of every scholar in the room were on her. She cleared her throat nervously and began reading:

5. The man, fainting with the heat, quickly threw off his heavy cloak and sat down under the shade of a friendly tree to escape from the great heat.

When she reached the end of the paragraph, the teacher thanked Sarah. She took a deep breath and slid back into the safety of her seat. She had not made any mistakes and no one had laughed at her.

When school was dismissed for the one-hour dinner recess, Sarah's steps dragged as she walked back the field lane to the Nolt home. After dinner she washed the dishes and then walked back to school again. By the time she got there, recess was almost over.

Sarah tried to study geography and spelling in the afternoon. She did not enjoy school, yet she dreaded the end of the school day. All the other scholars would be going home to their mothers, but she would have to go back to Lizzie. She could not think of the Nolts' home as her home, nor did she want to go there. She wanted to go home. Home to Memm and Daed, Arthur, Esther, Frank, Mary, and Anna. But there was no such place. If she went to any of the places they had once lived, none of her family would be there. All seven of them were scattered and lived in different places. This was where she was told her home was now, but she was sure she could never feel at home there.

"Why did God let Memm die?" Sarah cried. Her throat was too tight to speak any more words, but her thoughts ran on with her tears. Didn't He know how much she still needed her mother? Did He know she was dreadfully homesick? Did He care?

Chapter 9

Tears of homesickness trickled down Sarah's cheeks as she trudged out the long field lane toward another day at the Amsterdam School. "I don't want to go to school," she wailed aloud. "But I don't want to be in the house with Lizzie all day either." She would have been embarrassed if anyone had heard her telling herself all about her troubles and how badly she felt. But she could say anything she wanted, for she was alone on the field lane and the tall cornstalks on both sides were stone-deaf.

As she neared the back corner of the schoolyard, Sarah wiped her eyes with her sleeve. She did not want the other scholars to see she had been crying. Even when she was able to stop the flow of tears, the crying inside her never stopped. Her head ached from crying all the time, but the well of tears that gushed from her aching heart never ran dry. The tears were always there, just under the surface, ready to spill over whenever she thought no one would see. Every night she burrowed her head into her pillow and cried with homesickness. But the life she had known in her first ten years was gone forever and the place she wanted to be no longer existed.

Sarah went to school because state laws required her to be there, but she could not concentrate well enough to learn her lessons. The impossible longings for her family and home filled her mind, leaving no room for spelling, grammar, arithmetic, or any of the other subjects Mrs. Burkholder taught in the little school. Sarah wished she could walk to school by the road instead of the field lane, even though it was twice as far. She thought maybe someone she knew would drive by and pick her up. But by the time she finished washing the breakfast dishes there was never enough time to walk to school the long way. So she always walked out the field lane, hidden from the road by the tall cornstalks, where no one could possibly see her.

Maybe I can go fetch the mail sometime, Sarah thought as she stepped up onto the school porch. A glimmer of hope arched like a faint rainbow above her rainy spirit. Norman Nolt's mailbox stood beside the road that went to New Holland. The end of the long lane was too far away to be seen from the house. Fetching the mail would be a legitimate reason to walk out to the road.

The idea of going for the mail grew into a wonderful daydream that comforted Sarah's aching heart all day. Her lessons lay half-finished on her desk while her imagination played the scenario again and again. She clearly saw Daadi Shaub driving by in his spring wagon while she stood at the mailbox. He recognized her and stopped. She jumped in the wagon and rode away with him. No one had seen her leaving with Daadi. She had escaped!

"Can I go fetch the mail?" Sarah eagerly asked Lizzie when she got home from school.

"Norman's dad fetched it already," Lizzie said.

Sarah's face fell. *Well, maybe tomorrow*, she thought, refusing to give up hope.

But the next day Lizzie's answer was the same. "Norman's dad fetched it already. He always does. Why do you keep asking?"

Sarah shrugged and did not answer. Her daydream faded around the edges. She knew Norman Nolt's parents and single sister, Annie, lived on the other side of the farmhouse. David Nolt was an old man who had retired and passed his farm on to Norman. David enjoyed the leisurely stroll to the mailbox every day and never guessed Sarah wanted to do the job after she got home from school.

Gradually, Sarah began to realize the truth. "If somebody did stop and pick me up, where would they take me?" she asked herself. "If I went back to Aunt Mary they would probably bring me right back here. Then I'd be in double trouble." She remembered the time Daed fetched her and Arthur at the Sweigarts after they were already in bed. *I thought Daed would never let us with strangers*, she remembered. *I thought he would always come and take us home. Now we have no home and he can't come to get me even if he wants to.* "You're stuck here," she told herself, finally facing the crushing truth. "You have to stay whether you like it or not. So *es is*. (That's how it is.)"

As the weeks inched along, Sarah became acquainted with her surroundings in the new neighborhood. She learned the farm was located about two miles north of the town of New Holland where Lizzie did her shopping. Norman's brothers, Eli and Sam Nolt, lived on two neighboring farms next to the home farm. Sam and his family went to a Lancaster Conference church, but Eli was the deacon of the Weaverland Conference congregation at Groffdale.

Norman and Lizzie were also members of the Weaverland Conference church at Groffdale, which met every two weeks. Of course, Sarah went to church with them. The inside of the building was arranged in the same Old Order pattern as the Pike church, with the singers' table in front of the preacher's table and the benches set in a U-shape around them. But the Weaverland Conference had switched from German to mostly English preaching and singing. They used a little black English songbook called *Mennonite Hymns.*[13]

On the "Off Sundays" when they did not have church, the Groffdale Conference group used the building. The two groups had divided in 1927 when they could not agree if their members should be allowed to own cars. Those who agreed with Bishop Moses Horning that cars should be permitted became known as the Weaverland Conference (or Hornings). Those who agreed with Joseph Wenger that cars should not be allowed, and continued to travel by horse and buggy, were known as the Groffdale Conference (or Wengers). The division was known as "the friendly split" because the two groups continued to meet in the

---

[13] This small hymn book is a newer version of the first English language Mennonite hymnal published in Virginia in 1847 which was originally titled *A Collection of Psalms and Hymns.* The tunes are designated by poetic meter and have no musical notations.

same building. One Sunday the church yard was filled with buggies and the next Sunday with cars when the *dei maschiene leit* (the machine people) had church.

"You'll have to get up a little early tomorrow," Lizzie told Sarah one Saturday evening. "We're going to my parents for dinner, so we'll go to their church at Meadow Valley."

Sarah did not know anyone at either Groffdale or Meadow Valley, so it did not make any difference to her where they went to church. She would be surrounded by strangers at either place. She did not know Lizzie's parents, so she would be in another group of strangers there. She would have preferred to stay at home, for she had never learned to enjoy meeting strangers, but she knew she had no choice. Wherever Norman and Lizzie went, she had to go with them.

"So this is Sarah," Lizzie's mother said in a friendly voice when they arrived at her door the next day. "We're glad to have you with us," she smiled as she shook Sarah's hand warmly.

As she had expected, Sarah did not know any of the girls who had come to John and Mary Martin's house for dinner. She trailed Lizzie to the kitchen where the women were helping their hostess finish the dinner preparations.

"Here," Lizzie said as she handed her baby to Sarah. "Keep Melvin out of the way so I can help Mom get dinner out."

Sarah sat on the settee with the baby on her lap. She looked up in surprise when she heard a friendly voice say, "*Wie geht's?* (How do you do?), Sarah. Do you remember me?"

Sarah looked up into a round, smiling face and nodded shyly. "You're Annie Burkholder," she said, and smiled in return. What a pleasant surprise to find someone she knew at this place!

In a flash, Sarah's memory replayed the day of the tobacco shed raising when the Wenger family had lived on Elam Burkholder's farm at Springville. She saw Annie rushing back and forth as she served a huge dinner to the volunteer workers. She heard Elam's booming voice calling out orders to the men. She could see the tobacco shed taking shape, the pig sty walking by on a row of men's legs, and the little Burkholder boys recklessly riding the children's wagon down the barn hill.

"Lizzie is my niece," Annie explained to Sarah. "Her dad is my brother, John. He told me you're living with Norman and Lizzie now. Where are your brothers and sisters at home?"

"Arthur's with David K. Martins, Esther's with Daadi Shaubs, Frank's with J. B. Weavers, Mary's with Levi Zimmermans, and Anna's with Uncle Milt Goods," Sarah answered quietly.

"It's just too bad things went the way they did," Annie said sympathetically as she gave Sarah's shoulder a little pat. "I hope someday things work out so yous can all be back together again."

Sarah felt hot tears rush to her eyes. She did not know what burdens Annie carried but felt she spoke as one who understood heartache. Sarah had never guessed that Annie and Elam Burkholder were Lizzie's aunt and uncle. *Why, Elam is one of Daed's friends!* Sarah thought with a warm feeling of surprise and gladness. Somehow, knowing the connection made Lizzie seem not as much of a stranger as before.

After dinner, Sarah joined the small group of visiting girls. Lizzie had combed and dressed her according to the Weaverland Conference patterns, so she blended in with the other girls. They accepted her among them, but she had always preferred to listen to what the others said when she was in a group and did not contribute much to the conversation.

Lizzie's treadle sewing machine had been humming ever since Sarah arrived at the Nolts. Seeing she needed new clothes, Lizzie had made some new Sunday dresses for Sarah and put away the Pike dresses she had brought with her. Her Pike bonnet had also been put away and replaced with a softer, smaller bonnet. It tied under the chin but seemed more like a cap than a bonnet since it was not made in the sunbonnet style. Lizzie also put away the white head covering Sarah had always worn to church. Lizzie told her the girls in their church did not wear coverings until they were old enough to join church. Now Lizzie was working on making some new school dresses for Sarah.

With a baby and a toddler to care for, trying to sew could be frustrating. Lizzie often did her sewing in the evening when Sarah was there to take care of the little ones. Now, while Sarah washed the stacks of supper dishes, Lizzie sat at the sewing machine. Her feet peddled up and down while her hands guided the maroon fabric under the needle. At the end of the seam, Lizzie cut off the thread and held up the width of fabric which would become the skirt of a dress. She pulled on one end of the thread and expertly gathered the fabric to fit the skirt piece to the waist.

Sarah looked at the stack of dishes still waiting to be washed and felt sorry for herself. She was stuck with the boring, thankless job of dish washing while Lizzie had the pleasure of sewing. She thought Lizzie should show more appreciation for her help.

"If I wouldn't be here washing your dishes, you wouldn't be able to sew," Sarah said boldly.

Lizzie took the pins out of her mouth and said, "If you wouldn't be here, I wouldn't be making this dress. A favor for a favor."

Lizzie was merely stating the facts as she saw them. She did not mean to hurt Sarah's feelings, but her face grew hot with embarrassment. She had not given any thought to what Lizzie was sewing. Washing dishes was a small favor in return for the much larger one Norman and Lizzie were doing in giving her a home. She had begun to become accustomed to living with the Nolts and was finally able to go to sleep without crying every night. Now she had been squarely put in her place. She remembered the time she had decided they were not poor children, even though the stockings they had hung up at Christmas remained empty, because they had a loving home and enough to eat and wear. But now she really was a poor child, dependent on the charity of others for survival. Instead of pitying herself, she should be grateful. But how could she be grateful for something that was so humiliating?

If only I could go home again, Sarah thought with renewed longing, while at the same time she knew it was impossible. She had no other home than this.

The pink sweater Lizzie bought for Sarah contrasted nicely

with the new maroon dress. The dress even had a collar on it. She had been taught to respect authority and do what she was told, so she could not tell Lizzie she was used to wearing black sweaters and collarless dresses. She wore whatever Lizzie provided, for to object would show a lack of gratitude.

The golden glory of October faded as the month faded into history. The corn was picked and hauled to the corn crib at the barn. Sarah no longer felt like a fugitive when she walked back and forth to school each day. She could look across the empty field and see the end of the road east of the schoolhouse. The mornings of early November were frosty, so she hurried to reach the warmth promised by the smoke rising from the school's chimney.

Classes were well underway for the day when someone knocked on the door. Visitors during school hours were rare, so everyone turned to watch as Mrs. Burkholder went to answer the knock. She stepped outside and closed the door of the classroom behind her. The scholars heard the teacher talking with a man, but they could not see who it was or hear what was being said. They looked at each other, wondering which of them would be called out and what had happened. A father coming for a child during school hours was a sure sign of serious trouble.

All heads turned when Mrs. Burkholder opened the door and came back inside the classroom. She was followed by a short, young girl wearing a Pike dress and apron.

Sarah's mouth fell open. She stared, unable to believe her eyes. *Esther! What's she doing here?*

Esther followed the teacher to her desk at the front of the room.

"Children," Mrs. Burkholder announced. "We have a new scholar who just moved into our neighborhood. This is Esther Wenger, Sarah's sister."

Instantly, all the scholars turned their heads to look at Sarah. Esther followed their gaze and stared at Sarah while the teacher went on asking everyone to make Esther feel welcome in their school. The teacher's words sailed over Esther's head while she stared at her sister. Sarah's pigtails were hanging down the back of the pink sweater she wore over a maroon dress. Esther could hardly believe her eyes. Her own sister was dressed so fancy she seemed like a stranger.

"Esther is in second grade," Mrs. Burkholder announced. "Since we don't have a second grade this year, I'll put her in third grade." The teacher assigned Esther a seat and resumed classes after she was settled.

Sarah and Esther looked at each other across the space that separated them. It was almost time for first recess. They could hardly wait to ask each other the questions that were burning in both of their minds. As soon as school was dismissed for recess, the sisters rushed outside to talk.

"I'm at home with Christ and Emma Good. They live out there at the end of this road," Esther said as she pointed to the right. "Where do you live?"

"On that place up there," Sarah said, pointing north to the farm at the end of the field lane. "With Norman Nolts. How's come you went to Christ Goods?"

"They don't have any children," Esther explained. "Emma wanted Anna because she's the baby, but Uncle Milts already took her. Christ told Emma I was big enough to help with the work, so she decided it would be all right to take me instead. They just fetched me this morning. I did *not* want to go with them. I hid under the bed, but they found me and made me come anyways."

"I didn't want to come here either," Sarah nodded with understanding. "I was homesick something awful at first, but it's starting to go a little better now."

"I didn't know you'd be here, but I'm glad you are," Esther acknowledged. "Where did you get such fancy clothes?"

"It's what Lizzie gave me to wear," Sarah shrugged. "What made you so late getting to school?"

"After we left Daadi Shaub's house we stopped at the Bergstrasse School to get my stuff," Esther explained. "Then we went to Christ's and unloaded my stuff from the pickup before he brought me up to school. That all took awhile."

The ringing of the bell, which signaled the end of recess,

interrupted the sisters' chat. Sarah and Esther took their seats and returned to their studies. Having a sister in the room made the school a much more warm and friendly place for both of the girls.

Esther loved to read and enjoyed learning, so she adapted well to the new school. In spite of the fact that she had attended school only half of first grade and a few weeks of second grade before she skipped to third grade, she was able to keep up with her classmates.

When Mrs. Burkholder called third grade spelling class on Friday afternoons, the scholars lined up along the side of the room. They had been studying their spelling words all week, but on Friday the best speller was determined by "trapping." Esther had been at the head of the class the previous week, so she took her place at the head of the line.

"Candle," Mrs. Burkholder gave the first spelling word.

"Candle," Esther repeated. "C-a-n-d-l-e, candle."

"Correct," the teacher nodded. She looked at John Oberholtzer, who was next in line, and said, "Infant."

"Infant, i-n-f-a-n-t, infant," John spelled his word correctly.

Mrs. Burkholder went on giving a new, or review, spelling word to each scholar. If one of them could not spell the word he or she was given, it was passed down the line to the next scholar. If he spelled the word correctly, he traded places with the scholar who had not been able to spell the word. If the word was passed down the line more than once, the successful speller might be able to take a big jump and trap several scholars in one move. Trapping was more exciting than a regular spelling bee when a scholar sat down after he missed a word, because there was the possibility of moving up toward the head of the line as long as the teacher gave spelling words.

"Cocoa," Mrs. Burkholder pronounced the next spelling word.

"Cocoa," Esther repeated the word slowly. She closed her eyes and tried to see the word in her book. She could not remember if the last letter was *a* or *e*. "C-o-c-o-e," she spelled.

Mrs. Burkholder shook her head. "John," she said as she passed the word on to him, "Cocoa."

"Cocoa, c-o-c-o-a, cocoa," John spelled.

"Correct," Mrs. Burkholder said.

John grinned triumphantly at Esther and took her place at the head of the line. She wrinkled her nose to send him a message of remorse mixed with challenge. If he missed one of the words the teacher gave him, she still had a chance to regain her position at the head of the class. John did not miss any words but maintained the place of honor at the head of the class.

"Ha-ha," John teased in a friendly way when school was dismissed. "I beat you."

"Just you wait 'til next week," Esther retorted in a good-natured tone. "I'll trap you then."

Neither of the twin Amish boys in third grade, Christ or Leroy Stoltzfus, could ever defeat Esther and John. The rivalry of trapping motivated both of them to study hard in order to defeat the other, making them stiff competitors for the honor of being head of the class.

After Thanksgiving, Mrs. Burkholder organized a winter hot lunch program in the back of the school room. Some of the children walked two miles back and forth to school each day. The teacher thought they should have something warm to fill their stomachs at lunch time. She told the scholars to ask their parents for any dishes or cooking equipment they could spare from their kitchens. One of the parents loaned a small table and another a two-burner oil stove. Other scholars brought dishes, spoons, or kettles.

"Now," Mrs. Burkholder told the scholars, "I would like everyone to bring a few vegetables along tomorrow. Bring carrots, potatoes, onions, celery, canned tomatoes, or whatever your mothers can spare. We'll put them all together and make soup for dinner."

The pot of soup bubbled and simmered on the oil stove all morning, filling the school room with a tantalizing aroma. Sarah's stomach twisted inside her as dinner time drew near. When school was dismissed, the scholars excitedly lined up to receive their share of the soup from the teacher.

How Sarah and Esther wished they could eat lunch at school! But they both had to hurry home to eat dinner. By the time they came back to school for the afternoon, the only thing that was left of the delicious soup was the good smell that lingered in the air. Every time the teacher made a hot lunch at school, neither Sarah nor Esther got to eat any of the food they smelled cooking all morning. They could hardly bear to go home and eat their ordinary dinners while the other scholars had something special at school.

When Mrs. Burkholder set up and decorated a spruce tree in the corner of the school room, Sarah knew Christmas was near. The teacher wrote each scholar's name on a slip of paper and put the papers in the hat she borrowed from one of the Amish boys. Everyone drew a name from the hat for the scholars' gift exchange. The teacher also planned a special Christmas program to which the parents were invited. Although the Amish and Old Order Mennonites did not participate in the worldly methods of celebrating Christmas, the non-Mennonite teacher was allowed to observe the holiday in her own way at school. Everyone understood their personal beliefs and school activities were two separate segments of life. To their way of thinking, that which would have been unthinkable for them to practice at home was permissible as long as it remained within the walls of the school room.

The last day of school before Christmas vacation was one of the most exciting days of the entire school year. After the usual morning exercises, Mrs. Burkholder directed the scholars as they practiced saying their pieces for the program they would give for their parents in the afternoon. Just before lunch, the scholars exchanged the small gifts they had gotten for each other after drawing names. The day reached its climax when the parents and younger brothers and sisters of the scholars arrived in the afternoon to listen to the program.

The adults squeezed themselves into the school desks until every seat was taken. Those who did not have seats stood along the sides of the room. The scholars were seated at the front of the room with Mrs. Burkholder. She would tell each scholar when to stand in front of the room and say his or her piece. The air in the warm, crowded classroom was thick with anticipation. Moisture fogged the window panes, from the bottom to the top, and then ran down the glass in tiny rivulets.

Sarah was both excited and scared but could not tell which feeling was greater. The teacher had dressed her and Esther in white robes made from old bed sheets. She opened their braids and combed out their hair to make them look as beautiful as angels. Sarah had never before worn her hair hanging loose. She could not see her own hair hanging down her back, so she looked at Esther's hair. It was so used to being braided it would not hang straight, but Sarah thought the kinks made it look curly. She knew her own brown hair was just as beautifully curled.

One of the beginners opened the program by lisping a four-line poem of welcome. The nervous scholars sang Christmas songs and recited Christmas poems. Mrs. Burkholder's grown sons had come to play their guitars and sing special songs. The program climaxed with reading the Christmas Story from Luke 2. One of the oldest scholars would read the passage to the hushed audience while the scholars spoke at the appropriate times.

A girl holding a doll took her place in the center of the platform with one of the boys standing behind her. The boys stood in a little clump on the left side, and the girls in another little clump on the right. Sarah's heart hammered as she took her place in the little group of girls and turned to face the audience that packed the school room. Her eyes darted back and forth from the teacher to the audience. She was looking for someone, but she must watch the teacher so she would not miss her cue to say her line.

"And there were in the same country shepherds abiding in the field, keeping watch over their flock by night," the narrator recited. "And, lo, the angel of the Lord came upon them, and the glory of the Lord shone round about them: and they were sore afraid. And the angel said unto them . . ."

The teacher nodded at the biggest girl. "Fear not: for, behold, I bring you good tidings of great joy, which shall be to all people," the girl recited. "For unto you is born this day in the city of David a Saviour, which is Christ the Lord. And this shall be a sign unto you; Ye shall find the babe wrapped in swaddling clothes, lying in a manger."

The narrator's voice began again. "And suddenly there was with the angel a multitude of the heavenly host praising God, and saying . . ."

Mrs. Burkholder nodded at the group of girls. Sarah's face glowed as she chanted in unison with the other girls, "Glory to God in the highest, and on earth peace, good will toward men."

Sarah's eyes traveled up and down the rows of desks while the narrator and other scholars finished the presentation. Fathers, mothers, sisters, brothers, and even a few grandparents had come to see the scholars speak their pieces. Emma Good sat in the middle of the third row. She had come to see Esther speak her piece. Sarah had not expected Daed to come, but she thought at least Lizzie, and maybe Norman, would come. She did not see them anywhere.

When the narrator finished reading, all of the scholars sang *Stille Nacht* (Silent Night) while the teacher's sons softly strummed their guitars. Then they took their seats and listened while Mrs. Burkholder thanked the guests for coming and closed the program. She gave each scholar a pretty little box of candy and an orange before school was dismissed for Christmas vacation.

The school room was suddenly filled with a babble of voices as the parents visited while they put on their coats. They stuffed their small children into woolen coats and leggings, collected their rosy-faced scholars, and headed home. Mrs. Burkholder would drive in her 1928 Model A Ford all the way to her Ephrata home across from the Mt. Zion Cemetery on Old Mill Road.

Sarah clutched her gifts as she walked home alone on the field lane. Someone had come to see all the other scholars, but no one had come to see her. Memm had been dead for a whole long year and Daed had gone away. Although she was deeply disappointed that Norman and Lizzie had not attended, she knew now she should not have expected them to come to see her in the Christmas program. They were not her parents. She was no one's child. No one cared about her.

Chapter 10

The old year of 1934 passed away, too worn and spent to make a sound when it was pushed out on the stroke of midnight by the new year of 1935. The weeks of dreary winter days dragged by so slowly it seemed to Sarah as if the season would never end.

At the first sign of spring in March, meticulous Lancaster County housewives were seized with an irresistible urge to clean their houses from the attic to the cellar. Sarah had learned Lizzie was a neat housekeeper, but the careful cleaning they had done each week was nothing in comparison to the annual ritual of spring housecleaning. Lizzie began by getting down on her hands and knees to scrub the board floor of the attic with a scrubbing brush and rag. Then she moved down into the bedrooms on the second floor, spending a whole day in cleaning each one. Every inch of every room, and everything in them, was washed, dusted, polished, or shined. The feverish housecleaning, which went on for weeks, would be finished only after every room on every floor was spick-and-span.

As the air warmed in April, Sarah walked home at the end of the school day more slowly than she had in the winter when the frigid temperatures had urged her to hurry. This afternoon she had spent a few minutes standing at the corner of the school yard talking to Miriam and Bena Lapp before they separated to go to their own homes. Sarah was slowly learning to know the other girls and starting to become friends with them.

As soon as she stepped inside the kitchen, Sarah knew she had done something wrong.

"There's too much work here for you to be wasting time standing around talking after school," Lizzie scolded. "When school's over, you shall come straight home and get to work."

Sarah flinched, as if she had been physically struck by the words, but Lizzie was too frustrated to notice.

"I was trying to houseclean the sitting room today and everything just went backwards," Lizzie rushed on as she handed Sarah an old broom handle. "The carpets are hanging on the washline. Go beat them so I can get them back on the floor today yet."

Sarah took the broom handle without saying a word and went out to the washline. She hit the first strip of rag carpet. *Thwack!* A small cloud of dust and dirt flew out of the carpet and sifted down. *Thwack! Thwack! Thwack!* the broom handle went as she beat the carpet.

"What's wrong with talking to the girls for a couple minutes before I come home?" Sarah asked herself indignantly. *Thwack!* "Ain't I allowed to have any friends?" *Thwack! Thwack!*

The dirt that had accumulated in the carpets in the past year flew out in choking clouds that covered Sarah with a thin film of dust. She beat on the carpets as if they had somehow disobeyed her and deserved the punishment they were getting. While she pounded on the carpets, she vented the hurt and angry feelings that had accumulated in her heart during the past year. Talking to herself did not change the situation, but it did help to relieve the stress. There was no one she could tell the deep, aching hurts in her heart. She was all alone in her world. Her own ears were the only ones which would listen to her problems. Her own heart was the only one that understood her feelings.

Thwack! Thwack! Thwack! "I'm sick of livin' here and bein' Lizzie's maid," Sarah complained to herself. *Thwack! Thwack! Thwack!* "I wish I could quit." *Thwack! Thwack!* "I wanna go home." *Thwack!* "I want my mother!" *Thwack!*

Sarah was panting from exertion when she finally threw the broom handle down on the ground and dropped on the porch to rest. The carpets were clean and ready to be laid on the sitting room floor. Lizzie would tack them down on the smooth boards she had thoroughly washed with a scrubbing brush and rag.

As she rested, Sarah faced the facts. Lizzie was not, and could never be, her mother. It was not Lizzie's fault that Memm had died. Although she had been directing her anger toward Lizzie, she was actually angry at the situation. Things simply were the way they were; no one could help or change what had happened. She could either make herself miserable by being angry and bitter, or she could accept things as they were and try to make the best of the difficult situation.

"It won't do any good to make yourself and everybody else miserable over something that can't be helped," Sarah advised herself. "You'll just have to brace up and make the best of it."

Having made up her mind to accept her home with the Nolts, Sarah gradually became accustomed to her environment as the months passed. Since Norman and Lizzie took Sarah with them wherever they went, she had begun to remember names and faces as she met their families on repeated visits. Lizzie was the third of ten children in her family, half of which were still living at home with her parents. Her brother, Mahlon, had married Vera Sensenig in January. His parents had hosted a wedding dinner for the newlyweds a few weeks later. Lizzie's married brothers and their wives added new babies to their growing families at regular intervals. Of course, the birth of every new baby must be honored with a visit and gift.

"We weren't over to see Noah and Anna's baby yet," Lizzie said to Norman one Saturday evening at the end of June. "Do you think it would suit to go tomorrow?"

"I guess," Norman consented.

After dinner on Sunday, Lizzie selected something appropriate for a boy from the drawer in which she kept her baby gifts and put the gift in a brown paper bag. Then the family got in their touring car and started the long drive to Noah and Anna's farm in the Millway area. Three-year-old Mary sat on the back seat beside Sarah, but Lizzie held baby Melvin on her lap. After they were beyond the *Katze Boucle* (Cat's Back) Hill at Fairmount, past

Farmersville and Diamond Station, the countryside they passed through was not familiar to Sarah. They drove through the little town of Akron and went on to Millway, but she did not recognize any of the houses.

When Norman finally drove in Noah Martin's farm lane, they found many other visitors had also come to see the new baby. Norman joined the men who had taken the wooden kitchen chairs out on the lawn where they could visit under the shade trees. The women sat in the house, but the children who were old enough to leave their mothers swarmed over the farm as they played together. Sarah did not expect to know anyone her age, so she followed Lizzie and Mary into the house.

"Aw," Lizzie cooed when she saw Noah and Anna's fourth son, Raymond. "He looks like his brothers." There was no doubt the boys had inherited their father's Martin features.

Sarah sat quietly in the corner, but Mary soon went off to play with the other little children and her Martin cousins. Harry was Mary's age and Roy just a year younger. The small children added their piping little voices to those of their mothers and created a small din in the crowded house. Anna drew out the box of baby gifts she had received from previous visitors. As she showed the gifts, she told who had given each one. The women admired all the lovely pieces of cotton and flannel fabrics, as well as the crocheted bibs, booties, and other things Anna had received as baby gifts.

The afternoon dragged on while Sarah sat and listened to the women talking. At last, Norman came into the house and asked Lizzie, "Are you ready to go?"

"I guess," Lizzie answered. She knew his question was more of an announcement than a request for information. He had evening chores to do, plus a long nine-mile drive home.

"It's your turn to come and see us now," Norman said to Noah as the family climbed into the touring car.

"We will," Noah promised his brother-in-law as he waved good-by.

The air that blew through the open sides of the touring car as they drove was often a cooling breeze, but today it was hot and muggy. The humidity level was so high the sky was a hazy gray color. The moisture in the atmosphere frizzled Sarah's naturally wavy hair and her clothes stuck to her skin.

"It'll give a thunderstorm yet," Norman predicted.

"I almost wish it would," Lizzie sighed. "That's the only thing that'll clear the air and cool things off again."

When they went to bed that night, the upstairs felt like a bake oven. Sarah threw back the covers and lay on the bare sheet, but the heat was so oppressive she could not sleep. A rumble of thunder in the distance hinted that relief might be on the way. The thunder grew louder as the storm approached. Then a little cooling breeze blew through the open window. The wind strengthened as jagged streaks of lightning preceded the drum rolls of thunder. Tree branches rattled their leaves and bent their branches as the wind forced them to bow to its power. Sheets of rain swooped down on the valley.

Sarah jumped out of bed and ran to the window. She pulled out the wood-framed metal screen that fit into the window opening and let the window fall down with a bang. Too frightened to lie down, she sat huddled in the middle of the bed and hugged her knees while she watched the storm. There was no one to share her fear, so she kept company with herself. She heard Norman go downstairs and knew he was watching the barn in case it was struck by lightning.

The storm did not pass over quickly as many storms did, but it hung over the Weaverland Valley for a long time. Lightning zapped, striking nearby again and again. The storm seemed to last for hours before it finally moved on. At last, Norman came back upstairs and went into his bedroom. The danger was over and they were safe. Sarah lay down again and finally fell asleep.

In the morning, the air was clear and the sky was blue. The storm had chased out the humidity and brought in dry air. The corn in the fields had been flattened by the wind and the ground around the farm buildings was littered with branches that had fallen from the trees.

"A lot of the locust trees were struck," Norman reported after he had inspected the damage the storm had done on the farm. "But, once again, they saved the place."

Sarah knew what he meant without further explanation. Many farmers planted locust trees around their buildings as protection from lightning. Because the trees grew higher than the buildings, lightning would strike the trees first and spare the buildings.

The flattened corn slowly straightened itself in the sunshine and went on growing, not defeated by the beating it had taken from the storm. The broken tree branches were picked up and tossed on the brush pile to be burned at a later date. Norman's farm was soon neat and tidy again, making the violent storm nothing but a memory.

The summer marched on across the rows of weeks on the calendar. Sarah did not see Esther every day as she had during the school term, because Esther was kept busy helping Christ and Emma raise the produce they sold at market. But the sisters saw each other regularly at church on Sunday mornings. Emma had made new clothes for Esther, too. The sisters were both dressed according to Weaverland Conference patterns, but Sarah's dresses were a little fancier because they were sometimes made from brighter colored fabrics and had collars.

Sarah had gone barefoot at home all summer. She found it increasingly difficult to force her feet into her shoes on Sundays. She knew she had outgrown her shoes in the year she had lived with Norman and Lizzie but did not have the courage to ask Lizzie to spend money on her for shoes. So she endured the pinching shoes until church was over and took them off again as soon as possible.

"Why do you walk so funny?" Lizzie asked Sarah one Sunday morning.

"My feet hurt," Sarah told her.

Lizzie looked at Sarah strangely, then bent down and pressed her thumb against the toes of her shoes. "No wonder!" Lizzie exclaimed. "Your toes are up against."

The next time Lizzie went shopping in New Holland, she took Sarah with her. Sarah often had to stay in the car and watch the little ones when Lizzie went to town, but this time she told Sarah to come along. They walked down the street to Rubinson's Store on the southwest corner of Main Street and Railroad Avenue. Sarah followed Lizzie up the cement steps, across the porch, and into the store. The three-story building had been the Styer Hotel until 1924 when it was purchased by the Jewish peddler, Sammy Rubenstein. He had changed his name to Rubinson, parked his gray peddler's wagon, and opened a department store in the brick building. In addition to a full line of clothing, fabrics, and housewares, Mr. Rubinson carried the plain clothing worn by the large number of Amish and Mennonite people who lived in the area.

Lizzie walked down the center aisle between the women's clothing and fabric departments to the shoe department, which was located on the right side of the building between the office and men's clothing department. The clerk in the shoe department was wearing shiny black dress shoes, sharply creased trousers, white shirt, and black bow tie. Elastic sleeve garters on his forearms held up the long sleeves of his shirt.

"May I help you?" the clerk asked Lizzie.

"Yes," Lizzie replied. "This girl needs a pair of shoes."

"All right, young lady," the clerk said to Sarah. "Suppose you sit on this chair and let me see what size you need."

Sarah sat down and put her foot on the cold metal plate the clerk placed in front of her. He moved the sliding pointer down to the top of her big toe and announced, "Size 4." He turned to Lizzie and asked, "And what kind of shoe did you have in mind, ma'am?"

"Just regular oxfords," Lizzie told him.

"Yes, yes," the clerk agreed. "A good choice. Sturdy, sensible shoes that will wear like iron." He hurried to the shelves that reached nearly to the ceiling and pulled out two shoe boxes.

Sarah could hardly believe what was happening. She had never imagined Lizzie would buy a pair of brand new shoes for her. Daed had always bought box-lots of used shoes, or seconds, at auctions for the family. They would root through the assortment until they found something that fit.

The clerk sat down on a stool in front of Sarah and used a metal shoe horn to carefully slide her feet into the black tie shoes. He tied the laces and told her to stand up. Then he tilted his head to look up at her as if she was someone important and asked, "How does that feel?"

"Good," Sarah almost whispered.

"Try walking in them," the clerk encouraged.

Sarah stepped carefully around the shoe box on the floor and walked gingerly to the edge of the shoe department. The smell of new leather wafted up to her nose at every step.

"What do you think?" the clerk asked Lizzie. "Will those be all right? They are a good buy at only $2.98."

Lizzie bent down and pressed her thumb on the front of the shoes to see how much empty space there was in front of Sarah's toes. "Hm-m-m-m," Lizzie murmured. "Let's try the next size bigger. I want her to have plenty of grow room."

The clerk had anticipated this move and took a pair of shoes from the second box. They were identical to the first pair except for the larger size. The fitting and testing of the shoes was repeated. This time Lizzie nodded her head when she pressed her thumb on the empty space at the toes of the shoes. "We'll take them," she said.

"Do you want her to wear them now or shall I wrap them up?" the clerk asked.

Sarah held her breath, hoping with all her heart she could wear the shoes right away, but Lizzie said, "Wrap them up."

They followed the clerk to the counter. He wrote out a sales slip and put it into a little round container with the three $1 bills Lizzie handed him. He fastened the container to a metal holder on a cable and pulled on the end. The container went zinging to the office where a man opened it and took out the contents. He put two pennies and the sales slip back in the container and sent it zinging back on the cable to the clerk in the shoe department. While they were waiting for the change, the clerk wrapped the shoe box in brown paper and tied it with string. The ceiling fans that circled rapidly overhead created a breeze which circulated the hot air but did not cool the inside of the store.

The clerk handed the sales slip and pennies to Lizzie, but he gave the shoe box to Sarah. "Here you are, young lady," he said cheerfully as he wiped his forehead with his white cotton hankie. "Enjoy wearing your new shoes and come see us again when you outgrow them."

Sarah was too shy to speak, so she smiled her thanks. She hugged the precious shoe box as she followed Lizzie through the store and waited patiently while she bought some things in other departments. Lizzie finished her shopping in the basement housewares department. They went out through the basement door, into the hot summer sun, and walked up the sidewalk toward Main Street.

Daed! Sarah's heart leaped when she saw a short man, dressed in plain Pike clothes, standing on the corner. *What's he doing in New Holland?* she wondered as she began running toward him.

"Where are *you* going?" Lizzie called after Sarah.

Just then the man turned and crossed the street.

Sarah stopped quickly and stood still on the sidewalk. "Nowhere," she muttered as her heart fell with a thud and her face flushed with embarrassment. The man was not Daed. He was a man Daed's size, but no one she knew. He must have been from Snyder County.

"Why did you start running like that?" Lizzie probed.

"I thought it was Daed," Sarah choked, feeling foolish. She looked at the sidewalk so Lizzie would not see the hot tears that rushed to her eyes.

How could I have been so wrong? Sarah wondered as she followed Lizzie down the street. *Did I live with Normans so long I forgot what Daed looks like? What if that man had really been Daed? Would've he taken me with him?* Even though the man had been a stranger, the disappointment was almost more than she could bear and spoiled the exciting shopping trip.

The next Tuesday, Sarah put on her comfortable new shoes and walked slowly out the long field lane toward the Amsterdam School. She had just passed her twelfth birthday and come to the first day of the 1935-36 school term. She dreaded having to study lessons again but was glad Mrs. Burkholder was teaching another year. The mature, experienced teacher had wisely mixed proper proportions of love and kindness with firm discipline, tamed the rowdy boys, and turned the Amsterdam School into a place of real learning.

After they were back in school, Sarah and Esther were able to see each other every day again. The trees had turned all colors, as if embarrassed at the thought of losing their leaves and standing bare in the cold all winter, when Esther brought shocking news to school.

"Christ's cousin, Nathan, came and told Christs that Daed is getting married," Esther whispered the astonishing secret in Sarah's ear.

Sarah stared at her sister in disbelief. "I don't believe that!" she exclaimed when she could find her tongue.

"It's so," Esther insisted. "The woman Daed's going to marry is Nathan Good's sister. Her name's Lydia."

"Well, maybe" Sarah said slowly. "But I'm not gonna believe it 'til Daed says so."

As the days passed, the leaves fell from the trees and covered the ground under them with a dry brown carpet. Neither of the sisters heard anything from their father.

"Do you know the man that's coming in the walk?" Lizzie asked Sarah one Sunday afternoon in mid-November.

Sarah looked out the window and stared. *Daed! It's Daed!* she thought in astonishment and was surprised to find herself suddenly bashful. She stood against the wall with her hands behind her back as she watched Norman open the door and welcome their visitor inside.

Daed stepped into the kitchen and took off his broad-rimmed black hat. His bowl-cut hair was totally gray. Sarah had often daydreamed of seeing Daed somewhere, but now that he had suddenly and unexpectedly appeared he seemed like a stranger. He had never come to see her before.

"Well, Sarah," Daed said after he had taken the seat Lizzie offered him. "What's the matter? Did the cat get your tongue?"

Sarah twisted her hands behind her back and looked at the floor. She did not know what to do. She was too big to run to Daed and sit on his lap as she had done when she was a little girl, but she thought it would be awkward to walk up to him and shake his hand as if he was a stranger.

"I brought you a present," Daed said as he patted his pocket. "But since you're afraid of me I guess I'll have to find some other girl to give it to."

"I'm just so surprised you came that I don't know what to say," Sarah murmured at last as she tiptoed to Daed's chair.

"Well, now. Since you found your tongue I'll see if I can find my present," Daed grinned as he reached into his pocket and brought out a beautiful cotton hankie.

"Thank you," Sarah said faintly as she took the hankie. It had pink roses all over it and a perfectly scalloped pink edge.

"I was just over to see Esther," Daed said. "She tells me you go to the same school."

"Yes," Sarah nodded. "We go to Amsterdam." She could not line up the words to ask or tell him all the things she could have said, so she only gave short answers to his questions. When the conversation stalled, Daed began talking to Norman again and she went quietly upstairs.

Sarah got the hankie box Daed had made for her so long ago and sat down on the bed with the box in her lap. She took out all the hankies she had collected from friends and relatives. As she looked at each hankie, the memories of by-gone days came back to haunt her. This one was from Aunt Fannie . . . *Aunt Fannie and the penny candy at the huckster stand when Daed had to sell out after the cows got sick* . . . this one from Great-aunt Maggie Reich . . . *Great-aunt Maggie and her homemade rag dolls* . . . this one from cousin Miriam . . . *Miriam and the other cousins playing with the Aunt Ricky clothes* . . . Had all those things really been a part of her life? The last two years had been so long that the first ten years of her life seemed as if they were a story she had read about someone else.

At last, Sarah put all the hankies back in her box. She carefully placed the newest one, which Daed had just given her, on top of the little stack and closed the lid. Then she went down the stairs and crept into the room where Daed was still sitting. She slipped quietly onto a chair and listened to the adults talking. She did not know that while she was upstairs Daed had told Norman and Lizzie he was going to be married to Lydia Good on Thanksgiving Day, November 21. He had made arrangements with the Nolts for Sarah to meet his new wife the following Sunday.

"Guess what!" Esther cried when she met Sarah at school the next morning. "Daed came to see me yesterday. He gave me this box of colors." Her eyes sparkled as she held out a box of eight crayons.

"He came to see me too," Sarah nodded. "He gave me a pretty hankie. I was really surprised."

"So was I," Esther admitted.

The sisters soon found more and bigger surprises were waiting for them in the following days.

"Your Daed married Lydia Good on Thursday," Lizzie told Sarah on Saturday evening. "Tomorrow afternoon Christ Goods are going to take you and Esther to your Grandfather Wenger's place. Your Daed is taking his new wife there and wants all you children to come meet her."

The fact that Daed had remarried was so unreal to Sarah and Esther that the sisters did not discuss the subject as Christ Good drove to Grandfather Wenger's house. Sarah was glad she was not alone when she stepped out of the car and went in the house to meet Daed's new wife. Lydia Good was a stranger to his children, because she had been a member of the Weaverland Conference until just before she married him. She had sold her car, changed her dress patterns, and joined the Stauffer Mennonite church so they could be married in the home of his bishop, Jacob Stauffer. Lydia had never met Daed's children and they did not remember ever seeing her before.

Daed stood up when Sarah and Esther followed Christ and Emma Good into the room. The woman who was sitting beside Daed stood up too. She was taller than Daed and slender. Her dress and the white head covering that tied under the chin were neatly made from the patterns the Stauffer Mennonite women always used. Although she was actually two years older than Daed, she looked younger than him because his hair was gray and hers was not.

"*Maed* (girls)," Daed said after he had shaken hands with the Goods, "this is my new wife, Lydia." He was smiling and looked happier than he had been for a long time. "Lydia, these are my two oldest girls," he continued with the introductions. "Sarah is my oldest child. How old are you now?" he asked Sarah.

"Twelve," Sarah answered as Lydia shook her limp hand.

"And this is Esther," Daed said as Lydia reached for Esther's hand.

"I'm nine," Esther said boldly. "I'll be ten in February," she added, wanting to make sure Lydia knew she was no youngster. The medicine she took for her gland problem had nearly stopped her growth. She grew weary of people guessing her to be much younger than her age.

"Arthur is between Sarah and Esther," Daed told Lydia. "After Esther is Frank, then Mary, and Anna's the youngest. She's five."

"I'm glad I got to meet all of you," Lydia said as she sat down again. "You're all scattered so far around Amos never could get yous all together before." She smiled at them and then at Daed.

Amos, Sarah thought. *She calls him Amos!* Memm had always called their father *Daed*. She had never called him *Amos* when she talked to them.

Sarah sat down and looked around the room. All of her brothers and sisters were there. Daed was there. They had not all been together since Daed went far away to work on the Texter Mountain. For the first time, the whole family was in the same room at the same time. Everyone but Memm. Sitting at Daed's

Teacher: Miss Mary R. Martin. First row: Ivan Zimmerman, Lydia Weaver, Etta Martin, Lucy Horst, Alma Horst, John Kurtz, Aaron Hoover, Esther Remick, Katie Sensenig, Mary K. Martin, Aaron Rissler, Melvin Rissler. Second row: Melvin Ludwig, Mary Horst, Alta Martin, Mervin Shirk, Anna Hoover, George Ludwig, Paul Martin, **Arthur Wenger,** *Martha Sensenig. Third row: Paul Sweigart, John Z. Martin, Fannie Weaver, Edna Fox, Ella Hoover, Lena Weaver, John K. Martin, Titus Hoover. Fourth row: Ralph Auker, Anna Horst, Amos Hoover, Martha Fox, Alta Hoover, Louise Ludwig, John Sensenig.*

CROSSROAD SCHOOL - ABOUT 1936

side, in the place that belonged to Memm, was this Lydia woman. Sarah did not like the way Lydia looked at Daed and smiled at him. The children sat stiffly on chairs, looking at each other and the stranger beside Daed. None of them knew what to do or say. Since Christ and Lydia were cousins, they knew each other well. As the children listened to the Goods and Grandfather Wenger visiting with Daed and Lydia, they learned she was the oldest of John and Sarah Good's ten living children. Lydia had been born in Lancaster County, but she remembered when her family had lived in May City, Iowa, and later in Dover, Delaware. The Good family had moved back to Pennsylvania when Lydia was twenty-five years old. One room of the house she owned at Farmersville was used for a small shirt factory. She employed five or six girls who sat at sewing machines all day making shirts. Her parents had lived in her house until her father learned he had cancer. Then they had moved to Bowmansville and lived double with Lydia's brother, Aaron and his family. Her father had died in February, but her widowed mother continued to live in Aaron's house.

Lydia's younger sister, Sarah, had married Amos Hahn the previous day, just three days after Daed and Lydia were married. The mother of the two brides would have a wedding dinner for both couples the next Sunday. The contract Daed had signed with Frank Wartluft to log his property on the Texter Mountain would not be fulfilled until May. Daed would make the long fourteen-mile trip home from the Texter Mountain as often as he could during the winter to spend the weekends with Lydia, but they would not begin housekeeping until spring came.

Bored with the adult conversation, the children wandered off to spend the short time they had together in ways that were more interesting to them. They had done their duty and met Daed's new wife. They would have to attend the wedding dinner the next Sunday, but his marriage had not made any major changes in their lives. They would all continue to live with the families where they were at home. Sarah had become accustomed to living in Norman Nolt's home and refused to think about the possibility that her father's marriage would have an effect on her future.

Teacher: Elva Mae Gutekunst. First row: Christian Zimmerman, Harvey Zimmerman, Lloyd Martin, James Burkholder, Catharine Burkholder, Anna Zimmerman, Ella Newswanger, Anna Martin, Frances Horst. Second row: Daniel Brubacher, Walter Hoover, Evelyn Miller, Paul Zimmerman, Frank Wenger, Mary Zimmerman, Lizzie Horst, Esther Zimmerman, Fannie Newswanger, Rebecca Brubacher. Third row: Paul Hoover, Harry Martin, John Miller, Mabel Zimmerman, Lydia Hoover, Emma Zimmerman, Anna Horst, Annie Brubacher.

Chapter 11

The home of the Good family was already filled with wedding guests when Sarah and Esther arrived at Daed and Lydia's wedding dinner on December 1, 1935. The aromas of home cured ham and browned butter mixed with all the other tantalizing smells of the homemade feast which was about to be served. The twisting of Sarah's stomach was not as much from hunger as from the anxiety of being among the crowd of strangers at the double wedding dinner Sarah Good was providing for her two daughters and their new husbands.

The mother of the two brides dropped what she was doing to meet Sarah and Esther at the door. "You'ns can put your coats in *de kammer* (the downstairs bedroom)," Mrs. Good said after she shook hands with the girls. Sarah followed Esther as she wormed her way through the crowd in the direction their hostess had pointed. The sisters piled their coats and caps on top of the mound of coats, caps, and shawls lying on the bed. Black bonnets and hats adorned the top of the bureau or were hung on wall hooks where they could not be smashed. Then the girls joined their two younger sisters in the *schtupp* (sitting room).

"Me and Anna came yesterday already," Mary told Sarah and Esther as the four sisters waited together to be called to the table. "And Frank," she added. "We all slept here."

"Is Arthur here?" Esther asked.

"Not yet, but he's coming soon," Mary said.

When Sarah Good announced the meal was ready to be served, the six Wenger children were surprised to have the unaccustomed privilege of being seated at the first table of dinner guests. Because their father was one of the grooms, they were guests of honor and seated in a row next to Daed. Newlywed Amos and Sarah Hahn, and all the other most important guests, were also seated at the first table. Sarah was glad she was sitting far enough down the row from Daed so she would not have to look at Lydia sitting beside him.

After the customary silent prayer, a stream of platters and bowls heaped with steaming hot foods were passed from hand to hand around the table. The small portions Sarah timidly ate were dwarfed by the huge amounts of food the Good brothers shoveled into their mouths. She hardly dared to look at those seven jovial men who talked and laughed among themselves as they ate. They had assumed their forty-three-year-old sister, Lydia, would remain unmarried all her life. Now she had found a husband and been married only three days before her twenty-two-year-old sister. Celebrating two weddings on the same day doubled the festive spirit in the Good family.

When the honored guests finished eating, the table was cleared and reset with clean dishes for the next group of guests. Again and again, the table was reset until everyone had eaten.

"Now it's time to play games," one of the Good brothers declared after the meal was over. Playing games after a wedding dinner was a long-standing tradition, but the games the Good brothers wanted to play were not the traditional type.

"First, we're going to give airplane rides," John Good announced.

The Wenger children watched incredulously as each blindfolded person was led out to take a "ride" on a table board and tricked into leaping from the board. After the airplane rides ended, the Good brothers selected players for the next "game." Arthur was eventually coaxed to participate in one game in which he unwittingly finger-painted black streaks on his face from the smoke-blackened bottom of a saucer.

This isn't funny! Sarah thought as she watched the poor young people being tricked. *It's awful playing tricks on people like that.* Her family had never done such things and she had never seen grown people acting so foolish.

"Now Sarah," John grinned. "It's your turn. We're gonna play Chicken."

"No!" Sarah shook her head emphatically.

"Come on," John coaxed. "Everybody else had a turn."

"Yes, yes, Sarah," the crowd of young people urged. "It's your turn to play. Arthur did."

"I don't want to," Sarah protested. She looked wildly toward the door. Where was Daed? What were he and Christ Good doing outside that took so long? *If only Daed would come in and tell them to let me alone!* she thought in desperation.

"It won't hurt," John promised. The crowd continued to coax and beg until Sarah was embarrassed to continue to refuse. Finally, she gave in and allowed herself to be blindfolded. Just as she feared, she wound up being the object of a practical joke.

Tears rushed to Sarah's eyes as the crowd laughed. They had taken their turns in the silly games without offense, but she felt small enough to crawl in a mouse hole. She had never been so mortified in her life! *What kind of a woman did Daed marry?* she wondered. *Is Lydia as rude and mean as her brothers? Would she be a wicked stepmother?*

Spending the day with Daed and his new wife in the houseful of strangers had been a chore in itself for Sarah. Having the guests make sport of her added insult to injury. Both she and Arthur struggled to keep back their tears of humiliation. Sarah was relieved when Christ Good finally came and told her it was time to go home. She had not enjoyed the wedding dinner one little bit. She was glad to go back to Norman Nolt's home, where she felt comfortable and secure, and try to forget about the depressing wedding dinner.

Sarah soon learned the wedding dinner Lydia's mother had hosted was only the first of many which would be held during the winter. According to the tradition, a newlywed couple was invited to the homes of their friends and relatives all through the winter to be honored with a wedding dinner and gift. In this way, the couple received many of the things they needed to begin house-keeping in the spring.

Although Daed's children were not always invited to accompany him and Lydia to the wedding dinners held in their honor, Mammi and Daadi Shaub naturally included their grand-children in the wedding dinner they hosted for their former son-in-law and his new wife.

Mammi's kitchen was full of good smells when Sarah and Esther arrived for the wedding dinner the Sunday before Christ-mas. Mammi had also invited Harvey Snyder to join them for the meal. His wife's funeral had been held that week and Mammi knew he needed to be in the company of friends. The kitchen windows were fogged with moisture from cooking and the warm breath of the family who gathered there. A fresh gust of cold winter air came inside every time someone opened the door, but it could not overcome the rich aromas of Pennsylvania Dutch home cooking.

"Sit yourselves down onct on the bench," Mammi told the children when the meal was ready.

Daadi sat at one end of the table and Daed sat at the other. Sarah took a seat on the bench behind the table and bowed her head for the silent prayer that preceded every meal. The conversa-tion that circulated around the table as the heaping platters and bowls were passed from hand to hand was comfortable and friendly. But every time she looked up, Sarah could see Lydia sitting at the corner of the table next to Daed. When the last piece of pie had been eaten, the toothpick holder made the final lap around the table.

"Let us return thanks," Daadi Shaub announced. Every head bowed for the silent prayer that ended every meal as they thanked God for the food they had eaten. "*Aamen*," Daadi intoned.

Chairs scraped on the oilcloth-covered floor as people pushed back their chairs and stood up. Sarah stacked the plates that were within her reach, piled the knives and forks on top of them, and carried everything to the dry sink where Lydia was already pouring boiling water from the teakettle into the enamel dishpan. Although she was the guest of honor, Lydia had helped Mammi put the meal on the table and was now helping to clean up afterward. Sarah had been watching Lydia shyly all through the meal. She seemed quite normal and had not done anything to indicate she was a wicked stepmother or rude and mean like her brothers. Still, Sarah did not know what to say to her.

"Lydia said she needs a dishrag," Mary relayed the request to Mammi Shaub.

"Here," Mammi said as took a clean dishrag from a drawer and handed it to Mary. "Why don't you ask her if you can call her *Memm* (Mom)," Mammi suggested.

Sarah and Esther watched as Mary and Anna promptly ran to Lydia and asked eagerly, "Can we call you Memm?"

"Yes," Lydia smiled. "You may."

How can they do that? Sarah wondered in shock and dismay. *She doesn't look a bit like Memm! I could **never** call her Memm!*

Anna and Mary had been three and four years old when Memm died. During the past two years, while they had been living with other families, they had nearly forgotten their mother. But Sarah and Esther were old enough to clearly remember how their mother had looked and the kind of person she had been. She was still a very real person to them. No one would ever be able to take her place in their hearts. Lydia was their lawful stepmother because she had married Daed, but mere law could not create any warm feelings for her in Sarah's heart. She felt more comfortable with Lizzie Nolt than she did with Lydia.

Uncle Weaver and Aunt Lizzie Auker, with their four little boys in tow, came after dinner to visit with Daed and his new wife. Of course, they had already met Lydia because she had joined the Pike church. Yet, they felt obliged to learn to know her better since she had married their former brother-in-law. The afternoon passed pleasantly and darkness fell early, making the day seem shorter than ever. Mary went home with Weaver and Lizzie, where she was currently staying. Aunt Barb came to fetch Anna, and the other children drifted away in various directions as they were taken back to the homes in which they were living. Sarah went home with Norman and Lizzie Nolt and resumed her normal routine, for nothing had changed in her personal life.

The day before the end of 1935, Lizzie asked Sarah, "How would you like to go over to Christ Goods and spend the night with Esther?"

"Can I?" Sarah asked in surprise.

"Yes," Lizzie smiled. "Get your nightie and run along. I'll call and tell them you're coming."

Sarah could hardly believe her good fortune. She had never before been allowed to spend the night with her sister. Even more amazing was the fact that she had not even asked to go. The overnight visit had been Lizzie's idea.

Sleeping together in Esther's bed was almost like old times for the sisters. As Sarah walked home the next day, she was deeply grateful for Lizzie's kindness. Then she found another surprise waiting for her when she got home. While she had been with Esther, Lizzie had gotten a new baby girl!

"Her name is Alta," Lizzie told Sarah when she took the baby in her arms for the first time.

"Alta," Sarah nodded with a happy smile. But she could not help wondering how it always happened that babies came when she was not there. The one and only time she had gone to spend the night with Esther was the very night Lizzie got a new baby.

Sarah had long ago ceased to play with dolls, but caring for a live baby was more appealing than any doll could ever be. Cute and cuddly though the new baby was, she added to the work load. Lizzie's single sister, Katie, came to help with the housework while Lizzie spent the standard two weeks in bed after Alta's birth. When Sarah came home from school in the afternoon, she was the live-in babysitter and Katie's right-hand helper.

With a new baby and two youngsters in the house, the winter flew by faster than Lizzie thought possible. The muddy month of March arrived before she had accomplished all she had hoped to do in the "slow" winter months.

"I still didn't have Amos and Lydia for a wedding dinner," Lizzie fretted to Norman. "Next they'll be ready to set up housekeeping before I get around."

"Well, pick a day once and send Lydia a card to see if it suits," Norman advised sensibly. "Then it'll get done."

Lizzie sent a penny postcard to Lydia, extending an invitation to a wedding dinner on a Sunday in early April. Lydia responded by returning a postcard with a short message accepting the invitation. The date of the wedding dinner became Lizzie's self-set goal for finishing the annual spring housecleaning. She scrubbed, dusted, and polished everything on every floor of the house.

On the day before the wedding dinner, Lizzie worked at a feverish pace to prepare the food she would serve. There was butter to churn, a goose to dress, butterscotch pudding and sweet potatoes to cook. She baked several kinds of pies, a tall frosted cake, and fresh loaves of bread. Then she peeled potatoes and covered them with cold water to keep them from turning an unsightly black before they were cooked the next day. Lizzie did not trust Sarah with the actual cooking, but she was assigned an endless round of smaller tasks to help ensure the food was perfectly prepared and the house was spotlessly clean by Saturday night.

"Go wash the walks yet before it gets dark," Lizzie told Sarah late in the afternoon.

The white chickens and ducks that roamed free on the farm constantly dirtied the cement walkways to the house. No matter how often the quacking ducks were chased away, they always waddled back to the same spot outside the door. Washing off the mess they made on the walks was a never-ending job.

Sarah set a metal bucket under the spout of the iron pump and lifted the handle up and down to pump buckets of water from the well beside the house. She threw bucket after bucket of cold water on the walks and scrubbed them clean with the corn broom. A root from the shade tree in the yard had pushed up one section of the walk, creating a low spot at the other end of that section. Although she swept it out, the muddy water promptly rushed back in the low spot again. Seeing the little brown puddle would not be persuaded to leave, Sarah gave up and hung the broom on its nail in the wash house.

"Sarah!" Lizzie called when she went outside and saw the muddy spot. "Come once here."

From the sound of Lizzie's voice, Sarah knew she had done something wrong. She walked slowly out of the house toward Lizzie.

"Look at this!" Lizzie scolded as she pointed to the muddy spot on the walk between them. "You left a mud puddle on the walk. Now get the broom and make this walk clean. Wouldn't you be ashamed if your mother saw it like this?"

No, I wouldn't! Sarah thought stubbornly as she turned to go fetch the broom. The lump in her throat was so big she could not say, even to herself, what she was thinking. *She is **not** my mother. I wouldn't care.*

Sarah was slowly growing accustomed to seeing Lydia with Daed, but the woman was still a stranger whom she could not begin to think of as her mother. Daed had been gone so long he had also become a stranger to Sarah. She could hardly believe he was the same man who had been her father for the first ten years of her life. As long as she was at home with the Nolts, she was able to pretend Daed had not remarried and nothing had changed. He was still on the Texter Mountain finishing the logging contract he had made with Mr. Wartluft. *But what will happen in May when the time is up?* the little questions nagged. *Will he come and fetch me? Do I want to go live with him and Lydia?*

Sarah wondered where Daed and Lydia would live if they set up housekeeping in May. He did not own a home. He had sold everything he owned after Memm died. Even if he took all six children back to live with him, it would not be *home*. Everything would be different. Sarah was torn between wanting to be with her family and wanting to stay with the Nolts. The only thing she truly wanted was for life to go back to what it had been before Memm died. But since that was impossible, she did not know what she wanted.

"I'm leaving Christ Goods," Esther abruptly told Sarah at school on Monday morning.

Sarah's heart skipped a beat and then dropped to her toes.

"Where are you going?" she asked quickly.

"To Christ's brother, Dan Goods."

"How's come?"

"I don't know. They just told me Daed said that's where I must go."

"Where do they live?"

"Somewheres up closer to Hinkletown. I won't come here anymore. I'll have to go to the Hinkletown School."

Mrs. Burkholder's tender heart was touched with compassion when she heard Esther was being moved to another home. The teacher decided to do something special for Esther.

"Go sweep out the outhouse," Mrs. Burkholder told Esther near the end of the school day.

Obediently, Esther took the corn broom and walked to the girls' outhouse at the back of the school yard. While she was gone, Mrs. Burkholder told the scholars about Esther's situation and her own plans for a surprise.

"I would like each of you to bring a little gift for Esther by next Friday," the teacher said. "Bring your gift in a paper bag and give it to me. I will keep it in my desk until . . ." The teacher stopped abruptly when Esther opened the door and stepped inside.

"Are you done already?" Mrs. Burkholder asked Esther.

"Yes," Esther nodded.

"Well," Mrs. Burkholder hesitated as she thought rapidly, "go sweep out the boys' outhouse."

*Sweep the **boys' outhouse?!*** Esther was astonished. She could not believe her ears. The girls never, ever went in the boys' outhouse. But, no matter how strange the order seemed, she saw the teacher was serious. Esther shrugged, grabbed the broom and went outside again. All the boys were sitting in their seats in the school room, so she knew their outhouse was unoccupied.

While Esther swept the dried mud and leaves from the boys' outhouse, Mrs. Burkholder quickly finished telling the scholars about her farewell party plans. When Esther came back in the school room, the scholars were busily preparing to go home. There was nothing to indicate Mrs. Burkholder had shared a big secret with them while Esther was out of the room.

In the days that followed, Esther never noticed the secret little exchanges that took place between the scholars and the teacher. No one breathed a word about the surprise that lay in store for her on the appointed day.

"You may put your books away now," Mrs. Burkholder announced suddenly on Friday afternoon. "We have something else to do before its time to go home."

The scholars looked knowingly at each other and grinned. Only Esther had no clue why the teacher had ended the school day early.

"Sarah and Bena," Mrs. Burkholder called. "You may come and help me." She opened the bottom drawer of her desk and began taking out brown paper bags. "Put these on the table," she told the two chosen girls.

Sarah and Bena piled the paper bags on the table at the side of the room where Mrs. Burkholder served the hot lunches she made in the winter.

"Now Esther," Mrs. Burkholder said with a smile, "we don't want you to forget us, so we decided to have a little going-away party for you. Come and open your gifts."

Esther's mouth dropped open. As she walked to the gift-laden table, she thought she must be dreaming. Never in her life had she been made to feel so special! One by one, she opened the brown paper bags and reached inside to pull out each new treasure. There were beautiful cotton hankies, a brand new notebook, a little china cup and saucer, a pocket comb and mirror set, and so many more things she could hardly believe they were really all hers to keep.

The joy of giving was painted on the smiling faces of the scholars who savored the pleasure of watching as Esther opened her gifts. The effort of keeping the secret and springing the surprise had been building ever since Mrs. Burkholder had hatched the plan. When the moment finally arrived, the suspense burst like a dam and overflowed to surround Esther with a flood of affection and good wishes. John Oberholtzer knew he would miss Esther, even though she was a girl, for her departure would end the good-natured competition between them to be at the head of the class.

No one missed Esther more than Sarah. Although she had not expected to see Esther every day after school ended on Good Friday, knowing she had moved from the neighborhood made it somehow seem more empty and friendless. Since Dan Goods and Norman Nolts were members of the same Groffdale congregation, the sisters were still able to see each other every two weeks at church. Sarah was glad Esther was there, for although she had learned to know some of the other girls her age at church she was too shy to develop a close friendship with any of them.

After Daed's contract with Mr. Wartluft expired in May, he and Lydia moved into a house he had rented near the town of Terre Hill. The day they moved in, Daadi and Mammi Shaub took Mary and Anna back to Daed. Mary sat on the back of the wagon, singing at the top of her voice. She had lived with Levi and Emma Zimmerman for over a year, but when they were expecting their second child Mary had been returned to Daadi Shaubs. For months, she had been shuffled between her grandparents and aunts, never staying in one place more than a few weeks at a time. Mary was so glad to be going to live in a real home where she could stay. To think of having a father and mother like other children was a dream come true.

I wonder how long I will stay here with Normans, Sarah thought when she learned Mary and Anna had gone home. Why had Esther been sent to Dan Goods instead of going home? Did Daed not want the rest of his children? Or was it Lydia who did not want them?

Although Sarah did not speak of it, the fear constantly lurked in the back of her mind that she might suddenly be uprooted again and sent to some strange place to live. She had been moved without warning once before and knew the same thing could happen again at any time. The two years she had lived with Norman Nolts was about as long as she had lived at any one place in her whole life. Her family had moved from house to house every year or two while Memm was still living. Was she destined to spend her whole life moving from one home to another? Would she never have a home where she could stay forever?

Chapter 12

When the bell on top of the Amsterdam School sent its tones ringing across the countryside to announce the opening of the 1936-37 school term, Sarah found Mrs. Burkholder had been replaced by a new teacher. The board members of the Earl Union School, north of New Holland, had heard how Mrs. Burkholder tamed the rowdy boys at the Amsterdam School. The Earl Union School, which was having similar discipline problems, had hired her to work her wonders with their scholars.

"My name is Mildred Myer," the new teacher introduced herself to the Amsterdam scholars. She was a young, pretty girl from the Church of the Brethren who wore a plain, cape dress and a large head covering. The Amish boys had already inspected her 1934 Chevy Standard car, with modern glass windows, which was parked at the edge of the school yard.

Although Miss Myer did not have the advantage of Mrs. Burkholder's years of experience, she was a good teacher. Building upon the foundation Mrs. Burkholder had laid during her years of teaching, Miss Myer was able to maintain order in the school and provide a favorable environment for learning. Sarah soon learned to appreciate the new teacher, but she missed seeing Esther at school this year.

The golden weeks of autumn faded into the increasingly cold, gray month of November. Sarah hurried home from school under the leaden skies that threatened to produce either an icy rain or the first snow of the season. Her fear of being moved from the Nolts' home had faded into the background as the weeks of summer and fall passed by with no indication of change.

When Sarah stepped inside the kitchen, baby Alta came crawling to meet her. Sarah stooped and scooped up the baby. None of the three little Nolt children could remember the time before Sarah had lived with them. As far as they knew, she had always been there and was their big sister. She had learned to feel at home with the Nolts and accepted as part of the family.

After Thanksgiving, Miss Myer planned the annual Christmas program and assigned special parts to the scholars. They would have to memorize their lines and regularly practice saying them aloud before the big day of the program arrived.

"Miss Myer gave out the parts today for the Christmas program," Sarah told Lizzie when she got home from school.

"Oh?" Lizzie questioned. "What are you doing?"

"Just helping sing," Sarah said.

"You're not saying a poem or anything?" Lizzie asked.

"No," Sarah gasped. "I'd faint if I had to stand up in front of everybody and say a part by myself."

"You could do it," Lizzie encouraged.

"Well, Miss Myer said I don't have to," Sarah declared. "Are you coming to the program?"

"Wait and see," Lizzie said secretively.

The excitement level rose, as it did every year when the scholars practiced for the annual Christmas program. For many of them, the school program was the highlight of Christmas and the only place they would receive gifts. As the parents and siblings of the scholars crowded into the school room on the day of the program, Sarah watched hopefully for Lizzie. She had come to the program the second year Sarah was a student at Amsterdam School, so she expected Lizzie to come again this year.

Just before the program was to begin, Sarah saw not only Lizzie but also Norman and all three of their children slip in the back door. The entire family had come to see her program! The well-practiced songs that came from Sarah's lips were enhanced by the feeling of security and acceptance communicated simply by the presence of her foster family.

When the program was over, the classroom was filled with a buzz of voices as friends and neighbors greeted each other and shared mutual good wishes.

"We're ready to go home," Lizzie called to Sarah some time later.

"Just a minute," Sarah answered. She hurriedly collected her gifts, put on her coat and cap, and climbed in the back seat of Norman's new *glaas maschien* (glass machine—car with glass windows) between Mary and Melvin. Although the closed car was not as cold as the old touring car had been, it had no heater. Sarah spread the car blanket over her lap and tucked the ends snugly under the children. The ride through the thickly falling snow was so short they were home before their noses grew cold.

"I hate to tell you this," Lizzie said to Sarah after supper. "Your Daed talked to Norman and said we must take you back to your own people."

As much as she had longed to hear such words two and a half years ago, they came now like an unexpected bolt of lightning from a clear blue sky. Sarah stood, rooted to the spot, and stared speechlessly at Lizzie.

"We're supposed to take you to Weaver Aukers by Sunday," Lizzie sighed. "You're going to live with them. It don't suit me, but that's how it is." She had come to depend on her school girl's help and did not know how she would manage without Sarah. But she was not their child, and if her father said she must leave they had no right to keep her.

Well, Sarah thought with a small measure of relief, *I guess it could be worse. At least this time I don't have to go live with total strangers.* Although she had not seen Uncle Weaver and Aunt Lizzie Auker very often since she had been living with Norman Nolts, Sarah had many good memories of Aunt Lizzie. She knew the Aukers lived in a farmhouse snuggled between the Conestoga Creek and the sharp turn of the road at the foot of the *Katze Boucle* (Cat's Back) Hill at Fairmount. The farm belonged to Daadi Shaub, but the Aukers had always lived there. They had five boys from one to eight years of age.

The Weaver Auker family lived on this farm along the Conestoga Creek. The current address of this farm is 320 Cat's Back Road, Ephrata, Pa.

"Come along," Lizzie sighed as she opened the upstairs door on Saturday evening. "I guess we might as well pack your things tonight."

Lizzie led the way up the stairs. Sarah looked at the room which had been hers for more than two years. She found it hard to believe she would be leaving it and not coming back. *Why is Daed sending me to Weaver Aukers?* she wondered. *If he don't want me to live here anymore, why can't I go home? Mary and Anna did.*

"Take everything out of the top drawer and put it in this box," Lizzie interrupted Sarah's thoughts. "Keep out what you need to wear tomorrow."

Upset and annoyed by the sudden turn of events, Lizzie jerked open the bottom bureau drawer where she had stored the old clothes Sarah had brought with her. Although they were badly worn and also outgrown, Lizzie would send them back with Sarah. Lizzie plunked the little pile in the bottom of the box. Then she lifted Sarah's black Pike bonnet from the drawer and held it up. She had not worn it since the day Lizzie had made her a cap like the Weaverland Conference girls wore.

"Are you going to wear this thing again?" Lizzie blurted without thinking how Sarah must be feeling.

Sarah shrugged wordlessly as the realization dawned on her, *I'm going back to being Pike!* She would not be allowed to let her braids hang down her back anymore or wear any of the dresses and other Horning-style clothing Lizzie had made for her. She would go to the Pike church and ride in a buggy again instead of a fine *glaas maschien.*

Sarah knew Norman Nolts had not sent her away of their own choosing. But when they drove away from Aunt Lizzie's house to go home, leaving Sarah behind, she felt forsaken.

"Aunt Lizzie doesn't really want me," Sarah told herself after she had gone to bed. "She just took me as a favor to Daed, because she thought it was her duty." She felt like a box of Aunt Ricky clothes—a shame to throw away but not worth enough to keep. She was convinced people took her in for whatever use she could be to them, not because they wanted or loved her. *I don't belong here,* she thought. *But where do I belong? Nowhere! I'm a misfit.*

The Pike lifestyle was not foreign to Sarah, but she had become accustomed to the way the Nolts lived. When she found herself dressed in Pike clothes, carrying a metal lunch pail, and walking toward Pleasant Valley School with Ralph and Clarence Auker on Monday morning, the change was so sudden it seemed unreal. She felt as if she was a stranger to herself.

The school was more than a mile from the Auker farm. Eight-year-old Ralph was in third grade this year and Clarence was a beginner. To reach the school, the scholars walked through the covered bridge built across the Conestoga Creek. On the other side of the bridge stood the old mill which old-timers called Fiandt's Mill, because it had once been owned by Martin Fiandt. The mill was now owned by Nate Eberly. Every fall, people for miles around brought their apples to Nate Eberly's mill to have them made into cider in his big cider press.

The snow and ice that now covered the creek had silenced its voice, but Sarah remembered the times she had gone swimming with her cousins in the creek. She knew when spring came the ice would melt and the creek would sing again as it tumbled over the rocks that lay in its path while it went on its way to becoming a bigger creek.

I watched a happy little brook, Gliding gently on its way, Soft, enchanting, lovely music, It so sweetly seemed to play . . .

Sarah did not know why the words of the poem she had learned in third grade should suddenly pop into her head, but once the words of *The Song of the Brook* had started rolling through her mind she could not stop them.

Then I noticed as I watched it, That the song it sweetly sings, Comes from only rocks and pebbles As the water o'er them swings . . .

The words which had been so difficult for Sarah to memorize in third grade now made sense. The creek was silent at the moment because the water was frozen. But its voice would come back in the spring when the water was once again free to rush over the rocks and pebbles that lay in it. The rocks and pebbles were the voice box that created the soothing music of running water in the creek.

Sarah tried to remember the rest of the poem, but the words would not come. She silently repeated the first eight lines to herself.

And I thought in love and wonder . . . the words started coming again . . . *How the sweetest songs we sing, Come from sorrows, trials, and heartaches, Which this life does seem to bring . . .*

Suddenly, Sarah understood. If all of the rocks and pebbles were taken out of the brook, it would have no music. The sorrows, trials, and heartaches of life are like the rocks and pebbles in the brook. The hard things God allows to come into our lives teach us to sing sweet music we would never learn in any other way.

"I had my share of rocks and pebbles," Sarah muttered wryly to herself. "And this morning there's some more in my way. I dread going to a new school again and meeting a bunch of strangers. If there's any sweet music in that, I sure don't hear anything!"

The road turned sharply to the left about one-half mile beyond the covered bridge. At the bend of the road Sarah and the Auker boys turned right onto another small country road. A girl about Sarah's age had seen them coming and stopped to wait for them. By the way the girl was dressed, Sarah could tell she was from a Weaverland Conference family.

"Are you coming to school?" the girl asked Sarah.

"Yes," Sarah answered shyly. "I had to change schools. I am at home with Weaver Aukers now."

"Then we're neighbors," the girl smiled, and went on without asking nosey questions. "I live at the mill. I'm Susanna Eberly. What's your name?"

"Sarah Wenger. Ralph and Clarence are my cousins," Sarah explained.

The neighbor girls became acquainted as they walked on toward the Pleasant Valley School. Sarah learned she was a year older than Susanna, but they were in the same grade because Sarah had not gone to school until she was eight. Becoming acquainted with a girl her age before she reached the school yard helped to soften the ordeal of meeting all the strange children.

Ignoring the little clusters of scholars scattered around the room, Sarah followed Susanna to the teacher's desk at the front of the room.

"Miss Wertsch," Susanna said. "This is Sarah Wenger. She just moved in with Weaver Aukers and is going to finish the school year here."

"Glad to have you," the teacher's friendly voice greeted Sarah. "And what grade are you in?"

"Sixth," Sarah said softly without looking directly into the teacher's eyes. She was glad she had met Susanna on the road and had someone to introduce her to the teacher.

"I see," Miss Wertsch said. She pulled out her record book and entered the necessary information as Sarah responded to the teacher's questions. Miss Wertsch replaced the book in her desk and scanned the rows of desks in front of her. "I'll put you with Eva Burkholder," the teacher decided. "She's about your age and doesn't have a seat mate."

Miss Wertsch led the way to one of the double desks on the left side of the room. "Eva," she said to the round-faced girl standing beside the desk. "This is Sarah Wenger. She's your new seatmate. Sarah, this is Eva Burkholder."

"Make yourself at home," Eva gestured cordially toward the desk. "I use this side; you can have the other."

"All right," Sarah nodded shyly as she put her school tablet and pencils in place. She had never had a seat mate before. This was the fifth school she had attended, but the only one that still used the old-fashioned double desks. Eva was big for her age and used her full share of the seat, but Sarah was thin. She had enough room to sit and work in the part of the seat that was left for her.

Miss Wertsch returned to her desk and rang the bell to announce the beginning of the school day. The scholars scrambled noisily to their seats and sat down. As silence gradually settled over the room, Sarah saw this school observed a strict segregation unlike any she school she had attended. The boys and girls were seated at double desks on opposite sides of the room. Clarence Auker sat in the row of smaller, single desks reserved for the beginners in the middle of the room.

Although Sarah had not known Eva Burkholder before, she saw now that she knew some of the scholars after all. All of the scholars, except one girl, were from Mennonite families. The Pleasant Valley School was in the part of the county where the Stauffer Mennonite population was centered, so quite a few of the scholars were children from the Pike church. Uncle Check (Jake) Stauffer's children, Martha, Jacob, and William, were there. Sarah also knew Eli Stauffer's youngest daughters, Mary and Susie, although they were several years younger than herself. While she had been out of the community, they had grown up and become school girls. Sarah did not waste her time looking at the boys and knew none of them would bother to look at her, for they were at the age when each gender avoided the other. As she looked at the familiar faces of the girls she already knew, she decided the Pleasant Valley School was not going to be as strange and unfriendly as she had feared.

In the weeks that followed, Sarah learned to know the other girls near her age. Eva Zimmerman lived on the farm next to Weaver Auker's place and sometimes walked to school with Sarah. Emma Hoover was a cousin to Anna Martin and her twin brother, Henry. The girls told Sarah that Miss Wertsch was about eighteen years old. The oldest scholars were just a few years younger than their teacher. Her father was J. R. Wertsch, the jeweler whose store was next to the Ephrata National Bank on the main street of Ephrata.

When she walked the snowy winter road to school, Sarah wore over her shoes a pair of second-hand black rubber boots which Daed had bought for her at the Noah Burkholder's market. When the earth tilted in the spring, the boots were needed more than ever, for the snow melted and turned the rich limestone soil into a brown sea of mud. The clumsy boots were designed to be practical, not fashionable. The four buckles snapped tightly in place to close the high tops of the boots. Sarah could safely wade through deep puddles without getting her shoes wet.

Just as they reached the corner of the school yard one morning, Sarah and her Auker cousins met Eli Stauffer's three children who were coming from the opposite direction. During the winter months, Sarah had learned to know Mary and Susie's older brother, Phares. He was in seventh grade. Sarah thought he was one of the most obnoxious boys she had ever known. He watched her struggle to do a math problem on the blackboard which he could have worked out mentally in a flash and wondered how she could be so dense. Miss Wertsch and the other scholars were aware neither of them appreciated the other.

"Now, Sarah," Uncle Weaver laughed when she complained at home about her schoolmate's annoying behavior. "You better be careful what you say. Someday you'll fetch him yet."

"I will not!" Sarah vehemently declared.

"The thing you throw the furtherest away is what you go fetch again," Uncle Weaver prophesied.

"I'm not going that far to bring anything back," Sarah retorted.

The next morning, Phares watched enviously as Sarah sloshed through the puddles to the schoolhouse. As he carefully stepped around the puddles, he looked at the old-fashioned gum shoes on his feet and felt sorry for himself. The low canvas tops above the gum soles closed with only one buckle and did almost nothing to keep out moisture. But he was not allowed to wear modern four-buckle Arctics. His father's brother, Jacob, was the bishop of the Pike church and lived on the neighboring farm. Phares and his sisters walked past their Uncle Check's (Jake) house every day on the way to school. He would see if they wore fancy four-buckle Arctics instead of gum shoes.

How come such a poor little girl can wear fancy boots like that and get away with it? Phares thought jealously. *It isn't fair!* She and other scholars with four-buckle Arctics could wade through deep puddles at recess, but he could only watch and wish to join in their games. He knew he would get a scolding if he went home with wet shoes, for dampness would ruin the leather and make the shoes come apart at the seams.

As the increasing warmth of the sun dried the mud and turned the earth a lovely shade of green, Sarah's boots were no longer needed. She was glad to stuff the clumsy boots in a corner of the wash house and walk to the last days of school on light feet that wore only black cotton stockings and sturdy black oxford shoes. After school ended on Good Friday, the shoes and stockings were also soon set aside for the summer. Sarah welcomed the summer with no tiresome lessons to think about and no shoes to slow her steps. She ran barefoot all day, wearing shoes only to go to church or to town.

"I can't go to town this week," Aunt Lizzie told Sarah one warm summer morning. "You'll have to go for me. I'll give you a list and you can go with Weaver."

"All right," Sarah quickly agreed. She liked to go to town.

The town of Ephrata was full of shoppers every Saturday. In the evening, young people would walk up and down the sidewalks, but the Aukers did their shopping during the day. Aunt Lizzie's shopping basket grew heavy with the things Sarah purchased as she walked from store to store to find the best prices on the items on her aunt's list. She knew Mammi Shaub was sure to be found at the Bazaar watching for bargains.

The Great Depression was slowly easing as President Roosevelt's economic recovery policies began to take effect, but a great majority of the population still stretched their scarce dollars by purchasing used items whenever possible. The auctions which were held at Noah Burkholder's market on Fridays and the Bazaar in Ephrata on Saturdays were two of the best places in the area to find bargains. Mammi always watched for bargains on useful household goods she or her daughters could use. She never spent a great deal of money, but bought mostly small items that sold cheaply.

Jakey Bemesderfer auctioned the items rapidly in his sing-song chant. He made up little jokes as he tried to keep the crowd in a good mood so they would be more willing to buy things. The uncouth Pennsylvania Dutchman sometimes went too far and said things that were off-color, but the lure of the bargains continued to draw Mammi Shaub to the Bazaar each week.

Sarah crossed the street and walked along the railroad tracks to the parking lot in back of C. P. Wenger's mill where the Bazaar was held. She could hear the chanting of Jakey Bemesderfer's voice as he auctioned off each item to the highest bidder. She joined Mammi who was standing at a place among the crowd where she could see the auctioneer. The hot sun beat down on the parking lot, making Sarah wish for shade. But Mammi stood, rooted to the spot, watching things sell and waiting for bargains. "Now here we have a Bible," the auctioneer announced as he held up a large, old German Family Bible which was to be sold. He repeated a silly German rhyme which he claimed were the words of Jesus.

"*Ich glaabt sell net!* (I don't believe that!)," Mammi Shaub declared boldly.

"Why, Lizzie Shaub!" the auctioneer said in a shocked tone. "*Bischt du umglaawich?* (Are you an unbeliever?)"

The crowd roared with laughter.

"Come on," Mammi Shaub said to Sarah in disgust. "We're getting out of here." She would not stand there any longer and listen to Jakey's crude jokes—*especially* if he was going to make sport of Holy things. He ought to be ashamed of himself!

Sarah helped Mammi carry the things she had purchased to Daadi's wagon. A talk with Mammi was as close as Sarah could get to being with her mother, so they sat in the wagon and visited until Daadi came. Then Sarah jumped out and went to Weaver's wagon to wait for him to come.

The busy summer was full of work from sunrise to sunset. Sarah mowed the grass in the yard with the muscle-powered push mower. She helped Aunt Lizzie work in the garden and stock the can shelves in the cellar with rows of green jars filled with fruits and vegetables. From peas and strawberries in June to apples and pumpkins in October, each month produced its own bountiful crop which must be preserved for the coming winter when nothing could grow. When the day's work was finished, the swimming hole in the Conestoga Creek just behind the house provided cooling relief from the heat and humidity.

Although she had no reason to complain of the way Aunt Lizzie treated her, Sarah could not shake off the feeling she was not really wanted there. Aunt Lizzie thought Daed should have taken all of his children home as soon as he remarried. She could not accept the reasons why only Mary and Anna had gone home and the older four children remained with other families. When Sarah weighed the options, she could not decide if she would rather stay with Aunt Lizzie or go home to live with a stepmother.

In March, Daed had managed to buy a small farm between Ephrata and the village of Murrell. Sarah and Arthur sometimes went home from church with Daed and Lydia for a Sunday. Esther joined them occasionally but Frank never came. The nine-mile distance between Murrell and Terre Hill where he lived with the John Weaver family was too far to travel. Sarah was glad to be with her family for a day but knew she was only a visitor. The place was not really her home.

Norman Nolts came to Weaver Auker's farm several times to see Sarah. She had lived with the Nolts so long they had considered her a part of their family and missed her after she left their home. She was glad to see them, but when they left she was more confused than ever. She half-wished she could go home with them, and yet she did not want to. She did not fit there anymore either.

"I'm so mixed up I don't know myself what I want," Sarah said, resorting to her habit of relieving stress by talking to herself. "How long must I stay with Aunt Lizzie? Where will I get sent next? Does Lydia have something against me that I can't go home? What did I do wrong? Where do I belong?" She could not answer any of the questions she asked herself.

When the 1937-38 school term began, Sarah was still living with Aunt Lizzie. Three of the Auker boys were scholars now, for little Paul was a beginner this year. *And this is my last year,* Sarah thought with a great measure of relief as she walked through the covered bridge to go to Pleasant Valley School. *At the end of this year I'll be old enough to quit and I'll be glad.*

Sarah had never enjoyed school. The frequent changes and disruptions of her life had not been conducive to learning. Having no mother to help her with the things she did not understand, she had struggled alone through most of her school years. She had long ago given up trying to be at the top of the class and was satisfied simply to make a passing grade.

"Are you gonna be my seat mate again?" Eva Burkholder asked when Sarah arrived at school.

"If you want to," Sarah smiled, pleased to be asked.

"Sure," Eva nodded. "Let's go pick out our seat."

The two girls put their lunch pails on the shelf provided for that purpose and staked their claim on a desk at the back of the room. The scholars were seated by order of seniority, with the youngest ones in the front seats and the oldest ones in back. Because Eva and Sarah were some of the oldest scholars, they were entitled to a back seat. Sarah liked having Eva for a seat mate. The seventh and eighth grades had separate arithmetic classes but were combined for Reading, Spelling, and Health classes. Eva was kind and patiently helped Sarah when she did not understand her lessons.

Miss Wertsch had pushed up the windows on both sides of the school room and propped them open with sticks. She let the door stand wide open so the fresh September air could come into the stuffy room. The smell of Lancaster County air varied with the seasons. In September the air carried the scent of ripening grapes and drying tobacco into the schoolroom.

The bright, sunny skies of October painted a beautiful backdrop for the crimson and gold leaves that shouted a last hurrah before they fell lifelessly to the ground. The dry, brown leaves of the cornstalks rustled in the crisp breezes which sent warnings that cold winter weather was waiting around the corner. On every farm, hard yellow ears of corn were being picked and stored in corn cribs. Some farmers used mechanical pickers pulled by tractors to pick their corn, but picturesque corn shocks still dotted the fields of Pike farmers such as Weaver Auker, Uncle Check (Jake) and his brother, Eli Stauffer. They continued to pick their corn by hand and haul it to their corn cribs in horse-drawn wagons. In the winter, the corn would be ground into chop as it was needed. Eli Stauffer used a Letz mill to grind his corn. The combination mill could chop hay and cornstalks on one side and grind corn on the other side. The engine of an Overland car he had bought at the junk yard provided the power to run the mill.

On the last Friday morning in October, Phares Stauffer came running across the school yard and slid breathlessly into his seat just as school was being called. At recess, he could talk of nothing but the brand new 14-horsepower John Deere B tractor and single bottom plow that had been delivered to the Stauffer farm that morning. His father owned a steel-wheeled Waterloo Boy tractor which they used to provide power for big jobs such as threshing, but the Pike church did not allow members to use tractors for field work.

Phares' older brother, Aaron, was not a member of the church. He had decided to buy a tractor a month after he turned twenty-one and start earning his living doing custom work for other farmers. He had made an agreement with the dealer, A. B. C. Groff in New Holland, to make a $100 down-payment on the tractor and plow. The balance of the $940 purchase price had been placed on a promissory note. Phares wanted to be at home when the new tractor was delivered that morning. He had waited until the last minute and then dashed to school, although he would much rather have stayed at home.

"The B has rubber tires," Phares crowed to the admiring audience of school boys. "They're much better than steel wheels. Yes, sir! Before long, all tractors will have rubber tires."

Every recess, Sarah heard Phares talking about the wonderful John Deere. *Humph!* she thought disdainfully. *What makes him such a tractor expert? He's just a Piker boy like the rest of us. What does he know?* She was not impressed.

When Phares went home from school that afternoon, his father told him and his brothers to bring in the corn that had been picked from the shocks that day. Eager to try out the new tractor, Phares figured out a way to hook the horse-drawn wagon to the tractor. By Monday morning, the story of what had happened on the way back to the barn with the first load of corn had reached the ears of the other boys.

"Hey!" young Jacob Stauffer called out when Phares stepped into the school on Monday morning. "How much of a load can a John Deere tractor haul?"

"Yeah, anyhow," Clarence Hoover chimed in. "I heard you got the tractor stuck."

"Who told you?" Phares grunted.

"Ah, things get around," Henry Martin laughed. "Milt Stoner seen the whole thing. Didn't he?"

"*Ya,*" Phares sheepishly admitted. He could still hear the laughter in the neighbor man's voice as he called out, *Grike die geil* (Get the horses!) He could not deny he and his brothers had gotten the new tractor stuck in the mud with its first load of corn, but he was still an ardent admirer of the green and yellow machine. "It wasn't the tractor's fault," he declared. "It was just too muddy there beside the crick."

"Yeah, yeah," the boys laughed.

"You said those rubber tires were so much better than steel wheels," Clarence reminded him. "So they don't go through everything after all? What do you think went wrong?"

"We just loaded the wagon too heavy," Phares said, taking responsibility for the trouble and defending the John Deere.

"Well, keep the horses handy," Henry teased. "You might need 'em again."

"It wasn't that bad," Phares protested "We got it out without the horses."

Sarah could not keep a smile from spreading across her face when she and the other girls heard the boys teasing Phares about his misadventure. "Serves him right!" she told the girls. "He oughta eat crow after he talked so big about that tractor all day Friday. He thinks he's so smart. If he ever gets married someday, I sure pity his wife!"

Chapter 13

The cold winter months seemed endless as they marched by at a slow day-by-day speed. But God kept His promise that the seasons would always follow in their proper order as long as the earth exists. Eventually, the spring of 1938 came in the front door and ushered the tired, old winter out the back door. Once again, the muddy month of March was followed by warm April showers that brought the earth back to life.

"Your Daed told Weaver he wants you to come home when school's over," Aunt Lizzie told Sarah as the school year reached its final weeks. The sudden warm feeling of being wanted at home spilled from her heart and crashed to the floor as Aunt Lizzie went on. "He's going to have a truck patch to raise market stuff and they can use your help."

There it was again! *They can use your help.* For years, Sarah had been shuffled from home to home, earning her room and board by the work she could do for the people who took her in. Did her own father want her now only for the work she could do for him? Did no one want her simply for who she was, rather than for the work she could do for them? She could not tell anyone the thoughts of her heart, so she kept them to herself.

"I'm going home to stay," Sarah told Esther at church on Easter Sunday morning.

"For real?" Esther could not keep a small note of excitement from her voice.

"*Ya*," Sarah nodded. "Daed said I shall come home when school's over. Friday was the last day, so I'm going home today."

"Maybe I'll soon go home too then," Esther said wistfully. "You think?"

"I don't know," Sarah said. "But I hope so. I hope yous can all come home soon."

After church was over, Sarah stashed her box of belongings under the back seat of Daed's buggy and climbed in to sit between her little sisters. Mary and Anna chattered gaily, excited to know their big sister was coming home to stay, but Sarah only half-heard what they said. She could not help comparing this home-going with the one her imagination had produced during those first months of acute homesickness when she had lived with the Nolts. She was glad Daed wanted her to come home, but it was not the home of her childhood memories. Her brothers and Esther were still "at home" with other families, Mary and Anna were school girls instead of babies, and the woman who sat beside Daed was not Memm. Sarah had been gone so long that Daed himself had become a stranger to her. Time had not stood still during the past five years, nor could it be rolled back to restore what had been lost. She was no longer an innocent, trusting child, but a sensitive adolescent longing for acceptance and security in an unstable world that constantly changed.

The twenty-eight-acre farm Daed had bought the previous spring from the heirs of Jacob and Mary Pfautz was a poor place by Lancaster County standards. The deteriorating buildings stood on poor quality soil which was overgrown with weeds and brush. But it was the best Daed could do, because he was still deeply in debt from the reverses he had suffered during his first marriage. Even then, it was the money Lydia had saved before she married Daed that made it possible for them to buy the $4200 farm and old, worn equipment to begin farming again. Daed had paid old Dan Stauffer half of the $1000 he had borrowed to buy the cows when he lived on the Miley place and was trying to pay off the balance of that and other debts. He was slowly crawling out of the deep hole of debt into which he had fallen during the Great Depression, but it was taking a long time. He hoped to build a new barn on his farm someday and make other improvements

Amos Wenger's farm was located on what is now East Fulton Street, Ephrata, adjacent to the New Life Fellowship Church. All of the buildings were razed in 2003 when the property was purchased by the Ephrata Public Park.

after he was out of debt. But for now, he still did not have "two nickels to rub together."

"Take your box up to the girls' room," Lydia told Sarah when they stepped inside the kitchen of the brick farmhouse. "Then come help me get dinner."

Sarah had visited often enough to be familiar with the house. She carried the box of her belongings upstairs and set it on the bed which was to be hers in the girls' room. The little girls slept together in one of the two double beds, but she would have the other one to herself until Esther came home.

Deciding to wait until later to put her clothes in the bureau, Sarah turned and ran down the stairs. "What shall I do?" she asked when she stepped into the kitchen.

"Set the table," Lydia said as she turned the raw potato slices she was frying in a black pan. The lard in the pan popped and snapped, covering the surface of the black cookstove with a thin layer of grease.

By the time Daed came in from stabling the horse, Sarah had set five places at the table, sliced a loaf of homemade bread, and set out a plate of homemade butter.

"Dinner soon ready?" Daed asked as he washed his hands in the enamel basin.

"Just about," Lydia answered.

When they sat down to the table, Daed looked at Sarah and smiled. Although he did not speak any words of welcome, the smile told her he was glad to have her at home again. Lydia did not make Sarah feel unwelcome, but her eyes did not have the same light Sarah saw in Daed's eyes when he looked at her.

After the customary silent prayer, the family of five filled their plates with the plain, nourishing fare Lydia had prepared. She knew how to turn ordinary ingredients into a well-balanced, tasty meal. From the bread and butter to the shoo-fly pie, everything they ate was home-grown or home-made.

"Memm, can I have more applesauce?" Anna asked after she had eaten everything on her plate.

"I guess," Lydia nodded and passed the dish of applesauce to Anna.

Memm! Sarah thought. The word had rolled off Anna's tongue without any effort. *She don't feel like Memm to me. I still can't call her that! But it wouldn't seem right to call her Lydia either. I don't know what to call her.* Unable to find a solution to the problem, Sarah simply avoided the issue by not addressing Lydia by any name.

The spring planting season had begun before Sarah returned home. Daed was busy preparing the fields for planting in May. He had dug and raked the vegetable garden where Lydia had planted the early things. Thin spears of onions, twin leaves of peas, and tiny leaves of cut lettuce were already peeking through the ground and stretching toward the sun.

Daed had also plowed a large truck patch where he planted the things they would raise for market. The fresh produce season began with lettuce and radishes at the end of April. They would be followed by sugar peas, green beans, cabbages, corn, tomatoes, potatoes, and turnips as the months of the year passed by in their proper order.

"It looks like this will be a good day to work in the truck patch," Daed said as he pushed his chair back from the breakfast table on a sunny May morning. "Sarah, you can start hoeing potatoes while I get ready to plant beans and corn."

"Can I hoe?" Anna asked eagerly.

"No," Daed shook his head. He knew a seven-year-old girl was likely to chop off the young potato plants along with the weeds.

Anna's face fell. She had hoped Daed would say yes so she could get out of her normal chore of washing the breakfast dishes. Hoeing sounded much more interesting than washing dishes.

"Your day will come soon enough," Daed promised. "By the time you're as big as Sarah, you'll be hoeing too."

"You got dishes to wash," Lydia unnecessarily reminded Anna. "Then you can help Mary churn butter for market."

Sarah got a hoe from the shed while Daed went to the barn to hitch up the horse. She walked to the truck patch and sighed inwardly as she looked at the long rows of potatoes waiting to be hoed. In the portion of the truck patch where Daed had already run the horse-drawn cultivator between the rows, wide brown stripes of soil alternated with the narrow green ribbons where weeds and potatoes were competing for growing space.

Sarah's hoe made a scratching, chopping sound as she began hoeing carefully around the little potato plants, setting them free to breathe the fresh air and grow bigger. "Once Anna's big enough to do it, she'll find out hoeing is more work than washing dishes," Sarah said, nodding her head to indicate full agreement with her own statement.

In spite of the tedious work, Sarah found it was impossible to feel sorry for herself on such a beautiful day. Puffy white clouds sailed gaily overhead in the clear blue sky. The air was perfumed by the pink and white blossoms of the peach and apple trees in

Brossman's orchard, directly across the road from the farm. Sarah had been strictly warned never to set foot in Morse Brossman's orchard, for he guarded it very jealously. But he was powerless to prevent the sweet smell of the blossoms from riding the spring breezes that went wherever they pleased.

Hoeing potatoes was back-breaking work. After all the weeds had been eliminated from the row, the ground must be hilled up on both sides of the plants to bury the little potatoes growing underground. Any part of a thin-skinned new potato that was not covered with soil would be "sunburned." It would turn green and not be fit to eat.

Sarah stood up and looked back to see how far down the row she had come. She thought the leaves of the little plants seemed relieved to be released from the clutches of the weeds. Looking across the truck patch, she could see Daed discing the section of ground where he would plant corn for market. In just a few weeks the corn would be up and need hoeing too.

"I'm going to spend the whole summer either working in the truck patch or helping butcher chickens for market," Sarah told herself. The routine of the few weeks she had lived at home so far told her what lay ahead. Mary and Anna were in the house with Lydia most of the time, but Sarah would be outside working with Daed more than in the house with her stepmother. "But that's okay," she decided. "I don't really want to be in the house with 'her' anyways."

Every Monday and Friday Sarah helped to dress chickens for market. Lydia's brother, John Good, sold the chickens every Tuesday and Saturday on a stand at a farmers' market in Philadelphia. He lived in the village of Lincoln and did not raise chickens himself. He bought eggs and chickens from local farmers and brought the chickens to Daed's farm to dress them.

A portion of the building behind the farmhouse was equipped for butchering. The end nearest to the house was called "the pump house," because it contained the pump from which they got the water they used in the house. The second room of the building was "the wash house" where the family laundry was done in the wringer washing machine powered by a gas engine. The last section of the unpainted building was the butcher shop.

Early in the morning of butchering day, Daed pumped water into metal buckets and carried them into the wash house. He dumped the water into two huge, black iron kettles that set in holes on the top of the iron furnace. Back and forth he went, carrying buckets of water and pouring them into the iron kettles until both of them were filled. Then he opened the little doors beneath the kettles and started a wood fire under each one. The water would heat to boiling while he ate breakfast.

"Here comes John," Daed said as he swallowed the last spoonful of his oatmeal on Friday morning. The words were not necessary, for the sound of John's truck and the cackling of the chickens had already come through the open screen door to announce his arrival. "Come out as soon as you're done," Daed told Sarah as he took his summer straw hat from the hook beside the door.

Sarah finished her breakfast at a leisurely pace and helped to clear the table before she went out to the butcher shop. She knew Daed and John would not be ready for her help until they had relieved the first batch of chickens of their heads; and she was not sorry to be excused from the first step of the butchering process.

By the time Sarah got to the butcher shop, the headless bodies of the chickens had stopped flopping around on the ground. She picked up several chicken by their feet and carried them to the wash house. The water in the iron kettles turned red as she plunged the chickens into the boiling water to scald them. A few seconds in the boiling water was enough to loosen the feathers so they would come off easily.

Sarah grabbed the legs of two chickens with each hand, pulled them out of the kettle, and carried them to the back of the building. White feathers flew in the air and sifted down to form a drift on the floor as she pulled handfuls of feathers from the chickens. Every little pin feather and stubble must be carefully picked from every chicken.

"Come with me," Daed told Sarah when they had filled a metal tub with naked chickens. "You're old enough to learn to dress a chicken."

Daed carried the tub of chickens to the work table in the butcher shop and filled the tub with cold water. He dipped a chicken up and down in the water to rinse it and then placed it on the table. "Now watch," he instructed.

Sarah watched as Daed's sharp knife swiftly sliced a hole in the chicken's underside. With swift motions, he removed the entrails and set aside the heart, liver, and gizzard. With another quick flick of the knife, he opened the gizzard and emptied the contents of this second stomach. Then he thoroughly rinsed the reserved organs and the empty cavity of the chicken with fresh cold water before he stuffed the giblets inside the opening.

"That's it," Daed declared as he placed the chicken in a galvanized garbage can and laid another one on the table. "Nothing to it. You do the next one."

Sarah gingerly picked up the knife. The stench from the still-warm entrails of the chickens filled the air. "This *gristles* (gags) me," she retched.

"You'll get used to it," Daed encouraged. "Don't stick the knife in too deep," he cautioned. "You don't want to slice the innards. Just cut through the meat and make a hole big enough to get your hand inside."

Sarah poked the point of the knife into the chicken and cautiously cut a shallow line down the underside of the chicken. She had not cut deeply enough.

"Here, I'll show you," Daed said. He placed his work-roughened hand over Sarah's thin one and guided the knife to make the necessary cut. "You'll soon get the feel of it," he reassured her. "Practice makes perfect. Now clean it out."

Sarah swallowed mightily to keep from gagging and bravely went on cleaning the chicken. At last, her first attempt at dressing a chicken lay in the can of cold water with Daed's chicken.

"Try another one," Daed said as he lay two more chickens on the table. "Just watch me and do what I do."

Sarah clumsily followed Daed's swift, practiced motions and dressed a second chicken with a little less help than she had needed the first time.

"You'll soon be able to do it as fast as I can," Daed encouraged her.

Sarah found Daed's statement hard to believe but could tell she was working faster after she had dressed a few dozen chickens. She was glad to stop for dinner, but she had no appetite. The smell of raw chicken on her hands would not wash off even though she scrubbed them in a basin of warm water with a gray bar of Lava soap.

Late in the afternoon, John loaded the galvanized cans of dressed chickens on his truck and went home. The cold water that covered the two hundred chickens would keep them cool and fresh until the next day when he would sell them on his market stand in Philadelphia. Daed spread the garbage on the back field where it would eventually be plowed under. Butchering was done for another week.

The work in the truck patch changed with the months and seasons, but dressing chickens was always the same. Twice a week, month after month, Sarah helped to dress chickens. Although she did not believe it was possible when she had started, Daed had been right. She was able to clean a chicken almost as fast as he did, and had gotten used to the smell. Her mind could be occupied with other thoughts while her hands mechanically cleaned chickens.

In September, Sarah watched Mary and Anna get ready to walk to the first day of the 1938-39 term at the Bethany School. Mary was in fourth grade and Anna in third. Mary had started school at Fairmount when she lived with her Shaub relatives, but by the next year the two little girls were back home to stay. Anna had been in first grade that year. She and Mary had walked up the hill from their rented house to the West Terre Hill School. The next year they had moved to the place where they now lived and started going to the Bethany School.

How strange it felt to Sarah to stay at home while Mary and Anna went back to school! But at the same time, she was greatly relieved to know her school days were over forever. She had turned fifteen on the first day of September and was no longer compelled by law to be in school. She would never have to go to another new school or study baffling school lessons again.

Although she had gone to the Bethany School the previous year, Mary dreaded going to school again. She was sick on her stomach every morning. If Daed said she did not have to go to school that day, she would quickly recover. If he insisted she must go to school, she was so sick the teacher soon sent her home again. Then, before long, she felt fine.

"My belly hurts," Mary complained at the breakfast table once again.

"You're not sick," Daed said knowingly. "You just don't want to go to school."

Sarah knew Daed was right, but she also knew how Mary felt. Fear and dread could tie themselves into tight knots in one's stomach and cause actual sickness. After weeks of battling the intermittent sickness, Mary finally grew accustomed to going to school and the sickness abated.

Although her formal education in the classroom had ended, Sarah continued to learn new things. She had once told Lydia she would like to learn to sew her own dresses, but Lydia had told her to wait until winter when they had more time to sew.

"I guess this would be as good a day as any for you to try to learn to sew," Lydia said after the little girls had gone to school one cold winter morning in late December. "Did you ever use a sewing machine before?"

"No," Sarah said with a shake of her head. "One time Mammi Shaub helped me make a slip for my doll, but that was just by hand."

"Well then," Lydia said, and paused to think. "The first thing you need to learn is how to run a sewing machine. We'll cut some squares you can sew together to practice. After that, maybe you can make a slip. That would be easier than a dress for your first piece and won't show if it gets a little *versuddelt* (messed up)."

Lydia brought her scrap box to the kitchen table and helped Sarah cut some squares from fabrics that had once been feed bags. Like all farmer's wives, she saved the colorful bags and turned the "free" fabric into a multitude of useful household linens and articles of clothing.

"Now," Lydia instructed as Sarah sat down at the sewing machine in front of the window, "lay the patches with the right sides together. Like this. Match the edges. Lay it right here, just so far from the needle, and put the foot down."

Lydia reached around the back of the machine and moved the lever that allowed the pressure foot to come down on the material. "Now turn the wheel at the end to start the needle and then pedal," she said. "Not too fast or you'll sew your fingers."

Sarah gave the wheel on the end of the sewing machine a little push with her hand and then slowly moved the foot pedal up and down. The needle of the machine went up and down to stitch a seam. Keeping the cloth straight with her hands under the moving needle while trying to pedal at an even pace with her feet was not as easy as it looked.

"Lift the foot, pull it out, and cut the thread off," Lydia said when she got to the end of the short seam. "Turn the wheel first so the arm is at the top, or else the needle will unthread."

Sarah did as she was told and held up the patches for Lydia's inspection. The seam was crooked, becoming more narrow at the end than it was at the beginning.

"Try another one," Lydia said. "Try to keep the seam straight."

All morning, Lydia hovered over Sarah as she sewed patches. The way Lydia watched Sarah's every move made her nervous. But she could tell Lydia was uneasy about allowing a girl to use the valuable sewing machine she had bought when she had a shirt factory in her house. Yet, she knew it was her duty to teach her stepdaughter how to sew, for every girl must know how to sew before she married and had to keep a family in clothes.

It would go better if she'd just go away and do something else for awhile, Sarah thought in annoyance. She wanted to do some real

Bethany School 1938

Teacher: Esther Becker. First row: Jack Wingenroth, Eleanor Kockhart, Jeanne Hauck, Ivan Good, Amelia Brossman, Celia Brossman, Lorraine Fry, Henry Weaver, Gladys Zimmerman, Elva Martin, Harold Martin. Second row: Anna Good, Winifred Connor, Luke Hollinger, Robert Mellinger, Evan Brossman, Harvey Ensinger, James Stahl, **Anna Wenger**. Third row: Jay Brossman, Clarence Sweigart, Richard Garman, Jean Wingenroth, Harvey Hersh. Fourth row: Charles Buckwalter, Eugene Wanner, Elizabeth Martin, Betty Jobe, Homer Hollinger, Ruth Weaver, Luke Musser, Harold Nolt. Fifth row: Harold Herman, Eleanor Fry, Clara Messner, Lloyd Stoner, Marion Ensinger, **Mary Wenger**, Norman Lentz. Sixth row: Wilbur Mohler, Ruth White, Roy Sensenig.

Courtesy: Mrs. Lorraine Kochel.

sewing, not just stitch patches together. But she knew Lydia would not teach her to sew a piece of clothing until she had proven she knew how to operate the sewing machine properly.

After dinner Lydia cut some muslin feed bags into the pieces Sarah needed to make a slip. *I never thought sewing would be such hard work*, Sarah thought when Lydia made her rip out a crooked seam and do it over. Her neck ached and she almost wished she had not asked to learn to sew. But, once started, she dared not quit and leave the project unfinished.

A gust of cold air rushed into the kitchen ahead of Mary and Anna when they came home from school in the afternoon.

"Look what I got!" Mary exclaimed.

Sarah turned from the sewing machine to see Mary holding up a little coin purse. "Where did you get that?" she asked.

"Betty Burkholder gave it to me," Mary crowed. "She had my name." There was no need to explain, for Sarah knew Mary meant Betty had drawn her name in the name-exchange for Christmas gifts at school.

"Is that so?" Sarah asked, although she did not doubt her sister's word. "It's really pretty," she said as she opened and closed the little purse.

"I can't believe Betty had my name," Mary said, awed at her good fortune. She greatly admired the dark-haired, sixth-grade neighbor girl who was the youngest daughter of Ez Burkholder. He was not poor like Daed. Betty had more and nicer things than the Wenger girls. Her cousins and friends called her *Boppe Betty* (doll Betty), because she had so many dolls.

"Well, take care of it," Sarah said as she handed the purse back to Mary.

"Oh, I will!" Mary breathed. She knew she would treasure it forever, simply because Betty had given it to her.

Lydia's family always gathered for a Christmas dinner. Although their mother had died in the spring, the Good brothers and sisters planned to gather for Christmas as usual. Sarah dreaded the day. She remembered the long-ago days when they had gone to family dinners at Daadi Shaub's house and would

A Home for Sarah

Hinkletown School - 1938

Teacher: John Wenger. First row: Wayne Martin, Edmond Morgan, Harvey Brubaker, Lawrence Weaver, Paul Martin, Lester Good, J. Christian Fox. Second row: Edith Fox. Third row: Anna Nolt, **Esther Wenger,** Charles Good, Mary Sensenig, Susie Good. Fourth row: Ivan Nolt, Rufus Hoover, Lloyd Fox, Annabelle Weaver, David Morgan, Clayton Snyder, Cloyd Good. Fifth row: Edna Good, Raymond Weaver. Sixth row: Betty Leisey, Annie Shirk, Mary Brubaker, Mary Dieler, Betty Nolt.

much rather have spent the day with her Shaub cousins. But Lydia was not related to the Shaubs and, of course, wanted to be with her family. Daed's responsibility to his current wife outweighed his connection to the Shaubs. His children had no choice but to spend the day with the Goods.

When the Wenger family arrived, the Good home was full of people, the noise of multiple simultaneous conversations, and tantalizing smells of home cooking. Lydia unpinned her black woolen shawl and hung it over her arm. "Give me your coats and bonnets, girls," she said to Sarah, Mary, and Anna. "I'll take them in with mine."

Lydia deposited their wraps on the bed in the downstairs bedroom and set their bonnets safely on the bureau where they would not be smashed. Then she swept into the crowded kitchen to help the women finish getting the meal ready to serve. Sarah and her sisters stood against the wall, not sure what to do with themselves.

"Coming along?" Emma Good's question invited Sarah to join the girls her age.

Sarah followed the Good cousins up the stairs where they would pass the time in girl-talk while waiting to be called for dinner. She had met the girls before and knew them well enough to remember their names were Kathryn, Dorothy, Emma, and Martha. But they were not Sarah's cousins and still basically strangers to her. She listened to the girls' lively conversation but did not speak unless she was spoken to. Painfully aware that she was an outsider brought in by circumstances beyond her control, it was impossible for her to consider herself a part of the Good family. She was glad when the day was over.

Ahh, it's good to be home, Sarah thought with a sigh as she lay down that night in the safety of her own familiar bed. The thought had come so naturally she surprised herself. Did she really feel at home here? *It's not like it used to be. "She" is not Memm, but I'm getting used to being around her. Even if it seems like a different family, I guess I'm starting to feel like I belong here.*

Chapter 14

During the first months of 1939, Daed earned a few dollars by helping neighboring farmers strip their tobacco. It was a dependable cash crop for many Lancaster County farmers but required much hard work from one spring to the next. Farmers who did not have a large family at home to help with the tedious hand work often hired day laborers to help them with the job. The standard rate of a dollar or two for a day's labor helped Daed pay the bills during the months when there was no produce to sell on market.

"I'm going to strip tobacco for Ez Burkholder today," Daed said one February morning. "Sarah, you might as well come along and help too. You won't learn any younger."

Sarah had never helped to strip tobacco. She was not sure she wanted to learn, but she had been taught to obey orders. If Daed said she must help strip tobacco, she would have to go with him. She knew their next-door neighbor was a self-employed carpenter who farmed his few acres on the side. His three oldest children were married. Betty, who was a "tail-ender" born thirteen years after her siblings, was still in school. Ez did not have the time or help he needed to strip his tobacco himself. He knew Daed needed the money and was glad to hire him to do the job.

Ez had moved the dried tobacco down from the top of the barn and moistened it so it would become as limp as rags. He had started a fire in the stripping room stove before he went to work. By the time Daed and Sarah stepped into the stripping room, it was warm enough to be comfortable. Gas lanterns hung on the wall gave a cheerful light which made up for the lack of natural light.

"You strip and I'll sort," Daed told Sarah. He showed her how to tear each leaf from the stalk without making any tears or holes in the leaf itself.

All morning, Sarah stood at the long table helping Daed strip leaves from the stalks. He sorted the leaves by size, laid them on piles, and tied the piles in bundles. Then he stacked the bundles in baling boxes, to be bound and wrapped before they were hauled to the warehouse for sale in the spring. The work was not difficult, but it was monotonous. Every motion was repeated over and over, all morning long.

Sarah was glad when it was time to go home for dinner, but as soon as they finished eating Daed was ready to go back to work. The afternoon seemed even longer than the morning had been. The longer Sarah stripped tobacco, the more she detested the job.

Sarah looked up when she heard a rattle at the door latch late in the afternoon. The door creaked as it swung open on its rusty hinges to allow Betty to enter the room.

"Hello," Betty said as she crossed the room to the feed bin.

"Hello," Sarah softly returned the greeting. She knew who Betty was but did not know her well enough to be able to think of anything else to say.

"I need to get some wheat for the chickens," Betty explained as she lifted the lid of the feed bin. She dipped an old blue agate kettle into the grain and brought it up, filled to the brim. Then she scurried out the door again and scattered the wheat on the ground in front of the barn. The chickens flocked around her, making contented little clucking sounds as they ate their supper.

Since Betty was home from school, Sarah knew she and Daed would soon be going home for supper. She hoped she would never have to strip tobacco again.

The next month, spring peeked hesitantly into the county several times before finding the courage to march boldly across the threshold in April. When school ended, Arthur had finished the eighth grade and came home to stay. He would not have to go back to school again in the fall. Of course, since he was a boy, he worked with Daed in the barn and fields. David Martin had trained Arthur so well in the occupation of farming he was able to pitch in and help Daed without needing much instruction.

Daed again planted a large patch of produce to sell on John Good's market stand in Philadelphia. Sarah saw she would be kept busy from spring through fall preparing produce and dressing chickens for the market stand. Then an unexpected development entered the picture.

"I could use another girl to help tend the stand," John told Daed while they were dressing chickens one Monday in May. "Could Sarah go along?"

"*Ach*, I don't know," Daed said slowly as he considered the idea.

"I'll pay extra," John promised. "I'm paying you $2.50 a week now to help dress chickens, but if Sarah goes along to market every Tuesday and Saturday, I'll pay $5 a week."

Sarah held her breath, waiting to see what Daed would decide. Going to market in the big city of Philadelphia sounded like an adventure. The extra money made no difference to her, for she knew anything she earned belonged to Daed until her twenty-first birthday when she would be "of age."

"All right," Daed agreed. "I have Arthur to help me in the truck patch now, so Sarah can go."

"I'll swing in here on my way down the Pike (Route 322) tomorrow morning and pick her up," John promised.

When Lydia gently shook Sarah's shoulder at three o'clock the next morning, she sat up groggily.

"Time to get up," Lydia whispered. She set the lighted oil lamp on the bureau and went back to her own bed for a few more hours of sleep.

Sarah poured some lukewarm water from the white ironstone pitcher into the matching big bowl that set on top of the washstand. Hurriedly, she splashed the water on her face and then dried herself with the linen towel that hung on the bar at the back of the washstand. She dressed quietly to keep from waking her sisters, picked up the lamp, and went downstairs. By the time

John Good's truck turned in the short lane, Sarah had eaten breakfast and packed a small lunch to take with her.

A mixture of excitement and fear churned within Sarah as she climbed in the truck beside Martha Martzall and closed the door. Although Sarah dreaded waiting on the crowds of strange city people who shopped in the market, the trip to the big city was a new and exciting experience for her.

"Good morning," Martha greeted Sarah politely while John loaded the lettuce and radishes Daed had prepared to be taken along to market. "Do you have enough room there?"

"Yes," Sarah answered. She had learned to know John Good's sixteen-year-old neighbor girl who sometimes came to the farm to help dress chickens. Although the two girls were nearly the same age, they were too opposite to become close friends.

Martha chattered gaily with John on the long drive through Honey Brook, Downingtown, and West Chester, to Philadelphia. Sarah had always preferred to be a listener rather than a talker, but she was appalled by the familiarity she observed between John and the young girl. *His wife is in a mental institution, but he's still a married man,* Sarah thought in disgust. Turning a deaf ear to the conversation between her traveling companions, she shrank against the door hoping desperately to become invisible through her silence.

After traveling east for more than two hours, the big city of Philadelphia lay just ahead. John gave his full attention to driving his truck through the city traffic toward the Upper Darby market house on 69th Street. The city of Lancaster, which had always seemed large to Sarah, was small in comparison to Philadelphia. Even at this early hour the city streets were busy with traffic. Cars and delivery trucks made way for the trolleys that swayed by with a swish and a hiss. Sarah heard bells clanging, traffic drumming, whistles blowing, and a siren wailing. The sounds mixed together in a confused noise with neither rhythm nor harmony.

Not one horse and wagon was to be seen anywhere. A maze of electric and telephone wires were strung from pole to pole above the streets. On some street corners, small booths held coin-operated telephones for public use. Rows of buildings crowded against each other, lining both sides of every street with no open spaces between them. Sarah saw no green lawns to give her eyes a rest from the concrete and asphalt that covered all the earth in the crowded city. It pressed in from all sides, squeezing fear from the hearts of country people such as Sarah who were accustomed to the wide open spaces.

John had made the bi-weekly trip to Philadelphia so often it had become routine. He drove fearlessly through the traffic to the market house and backed up to the door at the rear of the building to unload his merchandise. There was no time for foolish talk while he and the two girls set up his market stand. John unloaded the cans of dressed chickens and crates of eggs while Martha showed Sarah how to arrange the goods attractively on the wooden table which John rented in the market house.

"Lay the chickens out like this," Martha told Sarah as she lifted the dripping dressed chickens from the ice-cold water and lay them in rows in the center of the market stand. "Save room at each end. The flats of eggs go on the one end and the produce on the other."

Following Martha's instructions, Sarah helped arrange the market goods on the open market stand. It was tilted slightly down toward the shoppers so they could easily see the merchandise on display. A wide board at the bottom of the table kept the merchandise in place and caught the water that dripped from the chickens. The green and red of the bunches of lettuce and radishes added color to the display of pale yellow chickens and white eggs, making the stand more attractive.

All over the market house, other stand holders were busily arranging their products as the hands of the clock seemed to fly toward opening time. Food cooking in a small restaurant in the front left corner of the building sent mouth-watering aromas into the air.

By the time the doors opened at seven o'clock, a tempting array of country-fresh food was attractively displayed on the market stands. Fruits, vegetables, baked goods, fresh and smoked meats, cheeses, butter, and every kind of food country folks could grow or make was ready to be sold to city folks. Crowds of shoppers carrying empty market baskets over their arms surged into the market house. Most of the shoppers were women eager to get the best products on the market to feed their families. They were "English women" who spoke nothing but English. They wore hats rather than sunbonnets. Some of them had cut their hair short and let it hang loose around their faces, making them look as if they had just gotten out of bed.

Sarah stood back watching John and Martha wait on customers. She did not know if she had the courage to speak to the strange women who poked and prodded the merchandise before deciding if they wanted to make a purchase.

"C'mon!" Martha urged as she pointed to an old lady. "You wait on that one. I'll help you."

Sarah summoned her courage and timidly asked, "May I help you?"

"Yes, dearie," the old lady said as she pointed to a chicken on the table. "I'll take that one."

Sarah picked up the chicken and tore a piece of brown paper from the roll on the worktable behind the stand. Martha helped Sarah wrap the old lady's chicken neatly in brown paper and tie the package with string.

"Something else?" Sarah asked the old lady.

"No, thank you," the lady answered as she gave Sarah some money.

Sarah put the old lady's money in the cash box and took out her change. "Thank you," she said as she dropped a dime into the old lady's hand.

The old lady put the dime into her change purse and the wrapped chicken into her market basket. When she walked away, her place in front of the stand was immediately filled by another woman. This time Sarah needed no prompting to wait on another customer. After successfully waiting on her first customer, she found it was not as difficult to speak to the second English woman.

The first rush of early customers was soon reduced to a steady flow. Later in the day, when business dwindled to a trickle, Martha and Sarah took turns waiting on customers. At last she had time to look around the market house to see what the neighboring stand holders were selling. John's semi-circle stand fanned the end of the two rows of stands that were placed back-to-back in the center of the building. Behind their stand was a table loaded with all kinds of bread and other homemade baked goods. Directly across from them was Alderfer's lunch meat and cheese stand. Across the aisle, along the right side of the building was Zook's honey stand. John's main competitor, Paul Neidermyer, sold dressed chickens at a stand across the aisle on the left side of the building.

The pace of business rose and fell throughout the day, but when closing time approached the aisles were nearly empty. Daed's lettuce and radishes had been sold long ago. Only a few dozen eggs remained unsold and a few scrawny chickens still lay on the table. A bargain-hunter bought the chickens for a reduced price and went away as happy with the purchase as John was with the sale.

After the market closed, Sarah helped Martha clean the stand while John loaded the empty cans and crates on the truck. Darkness fell as they drove west toward Lancaster County. The lights of the oncoming cars blurred and crossed as Sarah's tired eyes refused to focus. Her head nodded and then jerked as she drifted in and out of sleep.

"Do you need toothpicks to keep your eyes open?" Martha teased.

"Aw, let her sleep," John said. "It's been a long day."

Sarah slept so soundly it seemed only minutes later when she awoke to find she was at home. "See you," she mumbled as she let herself out of the truck and stumbled to the gate in the picket fence. The clock in the corner of the deserted kitchen struck ten as she staggered up the stairs to her bed. The rest of the family was already asleep and her long nineteen-hour day had finally ended.

"How did you like going to market?" Arthur asked Sarah the next morning.

"It was okay," Sarah replied. "It's not hard work, but it makes for an awful long day."

The summer passed more quickly than ever. Every Monday and Friday Sarah helped dress about 200 chickens. Every Tuesday and Saturday she went to the market at Philadelphia. The two days in the middle of the week she helped Daed in the truck patch or Lydia in the house, depending where she was most needed. The whole family worked from early morning until bedtime.

There was no noticeable change in the weather on the first day of September, but it marked a major milestone in Sarah's life.

"Sarah's sixteen today," Mary announced grandly when John Good came to dress chickens.

"Is that so?" John chuckled as his eyes twinkled. "Sixteen! Now she can *rumschpringe* (run around). Next thing you know she'll have a beau."

"I will not," Sarah declared. Reaching her sixteenth birthday qualified her to socialize with the young people at singings and crowds on the weekends, but Daed would not allow her to date anyone before she was seventeen.

"There's no rush," Daed said as an expression Sarah could not interpret passed over his face. He suddenly saw in his rosy-cheeked daughter a marked resemblance to her mother. The knife of grief twisted once more in his heart as the memories of his eleven short years of marriage to Amanda and her death flashed through his mind. He had missed so much of his daughter's life. During the years she had been "at home" with other people she had changed from a girl to a young woman. Now she stood on the threshold of life, poised to make decisions in the next few years which would determine the course of her life.

Seeing Sarah blossom into a young lady reminded Lydia of a mother's responsibility to have at least one or two quilts finished and ready to give each daughter when she married. Quilting parties were a winter activity, for busy mothers had no time to quilt in other seasons of the year.

"I'm having a quilting next Wednesday," Lydia told Sarah the week after Thanksgiving. "I made it on a day you're home so you can help."

"I don't know how to quilt," Sarah objected.

"You can learn," Lydia replied. "But I mostly want you to take care of the dinner and dishes. Quilters come to quilt, not to cook and wash dishes."

Lydia brought the four boards of the quilting frame down from the attic and set them up in the *schtubb* (sitting room). After the four corners were clamped together, she basted the quilt backing to the strips of pillow ticking that were nailed on each board. She spread the cotton quilt batting on top of the backing and then lay the solid-color quilt top over the batting. In keeping with the desire for a plain lifestyle, Pike women always made solid color quilts. Elaborately-pieced quilt tops could become a vain display and cultivate pride. Lydia had sewed together two lengths of solid-color fabric and spent days carefully marking the top for quilting with intricate patterns of latticework, birds, flowers, and feathers. The backing was a darker color than the top, making the finished quilt reversible.

The friends and relatives Lydia had invited to the quilting sat on all four sides of the quilt frame, patiently hand-stitching the three layers together with tiny stitches. The women talked as fast as they stitched, sharing the news and discussing the details of housekeeping that filled their lives.

Sarah could hear some of the conversation while she worked in the kitchen. But after dinner was over and the dishes were done, she joined the women in the *schtubb*.

"Come on, Sarah," Lydia's sister, Mary, urged, "put some stitches in the quilt."

"I don't know how," Sarah protested.

"Then it's high time you learn," Mary declared as she stood up. "Here. Take my needle."

Seeing she could not politely refuse, Sarah took Mary's place at the quilt. She put the thimble on her middle finger and awkwardly pushed the needle up and down through the quilt. She was sure she would never be able to make the needle fly in and out like the other women were doing.

"That's not too bad," Mary encouraged as she bent and examined Sarah's work.

"My stitches are too big," Sarah said as she compared her stitches to the small ones Mary had made.

"Not big enough to catch your toenail in," Mary laughed as she repeated the standard quilting pun. "My stitches aren't as fine as some people's either."

"Don't you make ten stitches to an inch?" one of the other women asked with a grin.

"No!" Mary exclaimed with a chuckle.

"Mattie Bauman could," Lydia declared. "I was only nineteen when we left the Iowa settlement, but I still remember how fine she could quilt."

"That was before my time," Mary admitted. "I don't even remember living in Delaware."

Sarah gave her place back to Mary and then sat back to listen as the women talked about the Iowa settlement. Those who had not lived there had heard plenty about it. A group of Mennonites in Waterloo, Ontario, who were dissatisfied with their church had joined forces with the Stauffer Mennonite (Pike) church in Pennsylvania in 1883. The Canadian group soon began looking for a place to begin a new settlement. In 1887, three families and two single men moved to Osceola County, Iowa, where they had purchased land for $10 per acre in an area called May City. They wrote letters urging others to join them in the new settlement in the northwestern corner of the state. The rich, flat land was covered with prairie grass and well suited to farming. The next year, fifty people from Ontario and several families from Pennsylvania moved to the Iowa settlement. By 1900, more families had moved in from Ontario, Michigan, Indiana, and Lancaster and Snyder Counties of Pennsylvania. The church had grown to a membership of forty, plus a large number of children and young people who had not yet been baptized.

"We lived right on what they called Business Corner," Lydia remembered. "David Auker's saddler shop was across from us. On the other corners were Frank Gregory's blacksmith shop and David Weaver's store. Elias Gingrichs and Amos Baumans were our closest neighbors. It was such good farmland. Jesse Bauman claimed he got 500 bushels of wheat the first year he farmed out there. Besides that, he had 1000 bushels of oats, 600 bushels of corn, and 250 bushels of flax. If only the people would have got along with each other, we could've done good out there," she sighed.

"The way I heard, the bishop was part of the problem," Mammi Shaub commented.

"Well, yes," Lydia admitted. "He had his faults, but it was more than just him. Everybody agreed on beliefs, but they couldn't agree where to draw the line on the rules. They came from too many different places and had too many different ideas how things should be done. We left in 1911, and by 1915 everybody else moved away."

"Where is everybody now?" Aunt Lizzie asked.

"Scattered all over the country," Lydia answered. "Old Dan Stauffers lived in Snyder County for awhile before they moved back to Lancaster County. The Gingrich families and some of the Baumans and Lehmans came back to Pennsylvania, but they went to Lebanon County. Some families went to Michigan and Indiana, some back to Ontario or up to Alberta. The last I heard, Elias and Annie Reist had gone way out west to Sheridan, Oregon. The only thing that's left of the Iowa settlement now is the cemetery. Even the church was torn down."

"So why did you'ns move to Delaware?" another quilter asked.

"We were friends with the Kesselrings," Lydia said. "Jacob Kesselring was from a German family that immigrated to Ontario, and then wound up in Iowa. The Kesselrings weren't Mennonites, but Jacob met and married Mary Stauffer in May City. She joined the church there, but he never did. They moved to Dover in 1907, and when we left Iowa we decided to go to Dover too. The Kesselrings stayed there. Mary died a couple years back, but Jacob used to bring her to Lancaster County twice a year still, so she could take communion at the Pike church where she grew up. She'd always go around visiting her friends and Stauffer relatives then."

"How long did yous live in Delaware?" Aunt Mary asked.

"About six years," Lydia said. "We lived in Chester County a couple years after we left Delaware, but finally came back to good old Lancaster County where we belong."

As the women plied their needles and tongues, a small flame of affection for her stepmother flickered in Sarah's heart as she began to realize how unsettled Lydia's life had been. She could remember the train trip from Pennsylvania to Iowa when she was five years old. She had basically grown up in Iowa, but after that had moved from state to state and place to place every few years. *Maybe she does understand a little what it's like to move around all your life and not know where you belong,* Sarah thought. The next instant her warm feelings dissolved in a wave tinged with envy. *But at least she was always with her family. Even if they moved a lot, they were always together. She has no idea what it's like to be put out with strangers and have no home.*

Chapter 15

Winter howled into Lancaster County during the last days of 1939. On the final day of the year, the wind moaned and shrieked as if bewailing the loss of the familiar past and fear of the unknown future. At last, spent from the effort, the wind died away during the night. Soft flakes of white snow silently fell from the sky like a gentle benediction on the ending of a decade and blessing on the new one that was beginning.

On the morning of New Year's Day, Sarah scraped a hole in the frost on a window in the girls' bedroom and peered through the glass. The bare brown landscape was covered with a beautiful white carpet of snow that lay unmarked and undisturbed as far as she could see. Every branch of the peach and apple trees in Brossman's orchard wore a snowy white muffler. "Come, girls," she called to Mary and Anna. "Look what I see."

"It gave snow!" Mary and Anna chimed as they peered through the peephole Sarah had cleared on the glass. "Now we can go sledding!"

"Not until your morning work is done," Sarah reminded them. *So now it's 1940,* she thought as the three girls shivered into their clothes. *It'll seem strange to write 1940. Ever since I started writing dates on my school papers, the year has always been in the 30s. But all those years are over now, and in some ways I'm glad. I hope things go better in the 40s than they did in the 30s.*

The Great Depression that had strangled the economy of the entire nation slowly eased its grip as the decade of the "Dirty Thirties" faded into history. The reform measures Franklin Roosevelt had implemented during his six years as President had not provided the full economic recovery he had promised, but they brought enough improvement to give Americans hope that things would continue to improve during the 1940s. Sarah knew Daed's extreme poverty had begun to ease with his second marriage. He was not completely "out of the hole" yet, but he had high hopes of erasing his old debts within a few years. Although progress was slow, conditions were slightly improving for their family along with the gradual upturn in the national economy.

The first year of the new decade did not bring many great changes to Sarah's life. Month after month through the spring and summer, she continued to help John Good dress chickens and tend his market stand in Philadelphia. In the winter, cold air snaked into the market house even when the back door was closed. Sarah wore extra clothing to keep warm, but her feet were cold all day long. Spring turned into summer, making the cold of the past winter only a memory. Although the doors stood wide open during the long summer days, the market house grew stifling hot in humid weather.

Sarah dreaded market days more and more every week. She did not mind the work but grew increasingly wary of her employer. For weeks, she wrestled with the problem of how to tell Daed she did not want to go to market anymore. She was embarrassed to speak to her father about the delicate subject and afraid to tell Lydia of her brother's inappropriate actions.

"I had it!" Sarah declared fiercely to herself one day in the restroom of the market house. "I'm never coming back to market again. I just won't."

To Sarah's relief, Daed understood when she told him she could no longer go to market. "*Ya, wohl* (yes, well)," Daed consented. "If that's how it is, I'll tell John he has to find somebody else to go to market with him. I'll keep my ears open for another job for you."

Sarah knew she was old enough to be "working out" and earning something to contribute to the family finances. But, of course, it was not her responsibility to go job-hunting. Daed would find the job and tell her what she was to do.

"I found a job for you," Daed told Sarah a few weeks after she quit going to market. "Weaver Zimmermans are looking for a *maad* (maid). I told them you could come."

"Who are they?" Sarah asked.

"They're from the Wenger (Groffdale Conference) church," Daed began. "They had four youngsters, but one of the boys died in September. The oldest of the ones they have left is four and the youngest is no year yet."

"Where do they live?" Sarah wondered.

"Outside Akron, near Diamond Station. Weaver will fetch you right after breakfast Monday morning. You can come home again Saturday on the trolley."

"*Ya, wohl,*" Sarah consented, keeping her thoughts to herself. She did not object to doing housework. She knew how to wash and clean and look after babies. She had helped to care for babies all her life, beginning with her younger brothers and sisters. All four of the families who had given her a home had babies when she went to live with them and new ones had joined their families at regular intervals.

I was finally feeling at home here, Sarah thought. *I don't want to be sent out to live with somebody else again. But I guess I don't have much choice. If Daed told the people I'll come, I have to go.*

Sarah was coming down the stairs with a wicker basket of dirty laundry on Monday morning when she heard buggy wheels stop beside the house. She looked through the kitchen window and saw a man getting out of the buggy. By the way he was dressed and the fact that there were tiny windows in the side of the buggy, she knew he was from the Wenger church.

"Weaver's here," Daed announced unnecessarily. "Are you ready to go?"

"Yes," Sarah answered, knowing he was asking if she had packed her bag. But she was thinking, *No! I'm not ready. This is my home. I lived here for about two and a half years now and finally got used it. I don't want to be dragged off to live with strangers again.*

"We must not keep him waiting," Lydia said. "Go get your stuff. I'll take the wash out to the wash house."

Sarah ran up the stairs to the girls' bedroom and picked up the bag she had packed. For a one week stay, she needed only one or two dresses, several aprons, a flannel nightgown, and a few other basic necessities.

By the time Sarah came downstairs again, Weaver had come into the house and was talking to Daed. "This is Sarah," he told Weaver as she stepped into the kitchen.

"*Wie geht's* (How do you do)," Weaver said as he shook Sarah's hand.

"*Wie geht's*," Sarah politely returned the greeting.

"I guess we'll go then, if you're ready," Weaver said.

Sarah put on her coat and bonnet and found her black rubber boots on the back porch. She did not need to put them on but would take them along in case there was rain or snow before Saturday. Thanksgiving had already come and gone, so wintery weather could be expected to arrive any time.

The little girl who had been waiting in the buggy moved to the middle of the seat as Sarah climbed in and stashed her bag under the seat. "Are you Sarah?" the little girl asked boldly as the horse pulled the buggy onto the road.

"Yes," Sarah answered. "What's your name?"

"Ada. I'm this many," she informed Sarah as she held up four fingers.

Ada talked and asked questions all the way home. Sarah was glad for the presence of the little chatter-box, for the three-mile ride back to the Zimmerman home would have seemed long and awkward if she had been alone with Weaver.[14] By the time the buggy stopped at the barn, Ada had already introduced Sarah to the family. She had learned Ada had a two-year-old brother, Phares, and a baby brother, Adam. Her three-year-old brother, Ammon, was *dot ganga* (literal translation "went dead"), and her

---

[14] This farm is located on the corner of the present-day Pool and Tobacco Roads, Ephrata, Pa.

mother's name was *Memm*. Ada had a pet cat that was black with a white patch on its one eye and white feet.

Esther Zimmerman slowly rose from her seat in the rocking chair when Sarah followed Ada into the kitchen. "*Wie geht's*," Esther said as she shifted the baby to her hip and limply shook Sarah's hand. "You can take your bag up to the spare room. Ada, show her where it is."

Ada led the way to the stairs and the spare room on the second floor. Sarah could have found the spare room herself, for it was the only room in the house that did not have a lived-in look.

"I didn't get started today yet," Esther said from the rocking chair when Sarah returned to the kitchen. "It's Monday, so I guess you should do the wash first. The washboiler's out in the wash house. You can fill it and start heating water awhile. I'll gather up the dirty wash."

Esther helped Sarah sort the dirty laundry into piles. She poured the boiling water in the wash boiler into the wringer washing machine and added the white things. Esther coaxed the cantankerous gas engine to start running, threw a small piece of homemade soap into the washing machine, and went back in the kitchen. She took baby Adam with her but allowed Ada and Phares to stay in the wash house with Sarah. She did not object, for she knew how to work around youngsters.

While the white "go" (load) swished back and forth in the washing machine, Sarah refilled the wash boiler and set it on the stove to heat. She would add hot water every time one load was taken out and another put into the washing machine. She pumped more buckets of cold water and filled the metal rinse tub setting on a bench behind the washing machine.

While Sarah tracked back and forth carrying buckets of water from the pump to the wash house, the children played on the wash piles. She saw the dark and light colored piles would have to be sorted again before she could put the second load into the washing machine.

"I can do that," Ada eagerly offered when Sarah stopped the washing machine.

"You stay down," Sarah ordered as Ada started pushing an old, backless chair to the side of the washing machine. "Next you'll get your fingers pinched in the wringer."

Sarah lifted each piece of laundry from the hot water and fed it into the wringer. The dirty wash water ran back into the washing machine while the clothing squeezed through the twin rubber rollers and fell with a splash into the tub of rinse water. Ada dipped things up and down in the water as she "helped" to rinse them. Little Phares stirred in the water, succeeding only in wetting the clothing he was wearing and making puddles on the floor. When all the white things were in the rinse tub, Sarah put the second load into the water and re-started the washing machine.

"Now get back," Sarah ordered the children. "You're getting all wet." She swung the wringer back so it was positioned between the rinse tub on the bench and the wicker wash basket setting on the floor. After dipping each piece of laundry up and down several times to rinse it, she carefully pushed it through the winger again. The flattened pieces of clean laundry came through the rollers and fell into the wash basket below. She would hang the first load of laundry on the washline while the second load washed.

"You go in to your mom," Sarah said firmly, taking little Phares by the hand and leading him to the kitchen. For his own safety, a two-year-old could not be in the wash house with the washing machine in operation while she was outdoors.

"I can help you," Ada insisted as she trailed Sarah to the washline. She could have done the job faster herself, but she let the little girl hand the wooden clothespins to her. At last, the basket was empty and the laundry was flapping in the fresh, cool breeze.

Back and forth, in and out, around and around, Sarah went. There was never a moment without something to do. Loads of diapers, union suits and other underwear, towels, baby bibs, dresses, pants, shirts, and every sort of clothing a family wears went into the washing machine. By the time the last load was finally finished, the wash water was a muddy brown. Sarah's back ached and her stomach growled. Because she had gotten such a late start, she fully expected Esther to call her to come for dinner before the washing was finished.

"Are you done?" Esther asked when Sarah stepped into the kitchen.

"Yes," Sarah answered with a quizzical look at the clock in the corner. The hands showed it was past twelve o'clock.

"I put some sausage in the pan and fetched some potatoes," Esther said as she gestured toward the stove where meat was just beginning to fry in a black frying pan. "You can peel the potatoes and fry them."

Sarah peeled potatoes as fast as she could and sliced them rapidly into the melted lard in a second black frying pan. The lard sizzled and popped as the cold slices of raw potato dropped into the hot grease. Sarah's stomach twisted with hunger as the tantalizing smells of the cooking food teased her nostrils. She had not eaten anything since six o'clock that morning. She wondered what Esther had been doing all morning and what had kept her from starting to make dinner at the normal time.

When Weaver and the hired man came into the kitchen, Esther set plates and glasses on the table. Ada scattered some knives and forks among them while the men washed their hands and faces in an enamel basin. Sarah scraped the potatoes into a serving bowl and forked the sausage onto a plate. Esther sat Adam in the highchair while Weaver lifted Phares onto the Sears and Roebuck catalogs piled on the end of the bench where he always sat. Correctly concluding that the only empty seat at the table was hers, Sarah took her place and they all bowed their heads for silent prayer.

The tardy meal of homemade bread and butter, sausage, potatoes, and applesauce was quickly consumed. The thick slices of coarse brown bread were made from wheat which Weaver had grown and ground to feed the pigs. Esther had brought some of the ground wheat to the house and ground it a second time to make whole wheat flour. The applesauce was so tart Sarah knew very little sugar had been added.

Sarah avoided looking directly at the hired man who was seated across the table from her. His name, she learned, was Joel

Lindburg. He also lived with the Zimmermans during the week and went to his own home in the Ephrata area for the weekends. She did not know how old he was, but his car was parked outside so she guessed he must be about eighteen.

"These boys must go to bed," Esther said to Sarah over the noise of the whining and crying of the little boys after dinner. "I'll take them up and put them to sleep. I guess you know what to do."

Sarah nodded. She poured hot water from the teakettle into the dishpan and tackled the stacks of dirty dishes which appeared to have been accumulating for more than one meal. Ada stood at her elbow, chattering and asking questions non-stop.

"Here. Make yourself useful," Sarah said as she handed Ada a tea towel. "You're big enough to dry dishes."

"They can dry theirselves," Ada said in a matter-of-fact voice.

"But look!" Sarah exclaimed as she pointed to the wet plates. "See the tears on their faces. You feel better when your Memm dries your tears, don't you?"

Ada rose to the challenge, took the tea towel, and dried dishes in a four-year-old fashion. Sarah's homespun method of child psychology had accomplished her main objective of keeping the girl's hands out of the dishwater and usefully employed.

When the dishes were done, Sarah threw the dishwater out the back door and hung the dishpan on a nail. Then she "redd up" (tidied) the kitchen and swept the floor with the broom. The kitchen was in order, but Esther was still upstairs with the boys. Not a sound could be heard from the second floor. *She must've fell asleep with the youngsters*, Sarah thought wryly.

The breeze had increased to a stiff wind that lifted and filled the legs of the bib overalls. Round and full, they jerked and bounced a folksy farmer's ballet in tune with the tempo of the wind. On cold, damp days when there was no wind, wet clothing hung on the line all day and finally dried as stiff as a board. But today, the wind had dried all the clothing in one afternoon while also flapping it to a soft fluffy texture.

Sarah took the clean clothes off the line and piled them on the kitchen table. When she had lived with the Nolts, Lizzie had been very particular about how the wash was folded. Sarah was folding clothes and hoping she was doing it right, when Esther came downstairs with the children.

"How do you fold the diapers?" Sarah asked. She knew diapers must be folded to fit the child who wore them.

"Like this," Esther said, taking a diaper and folding it quickly. She sat down on the rocking chair with Adam lying on her lap to make immediate use of the clean diaper. He howled in protest until she finished changing his diaper. "It takes him awhile to wake up right," she said as she rocked the baby while Sarah went on folding diapers.

Because dinner had been so late, the afternoon was short. Esther cooked cornmeal for supper. They ate their main meal at dinner, so mush and milk was enough for supper.

"Where's the sugar bowl?" Sarah asked when she set the table for the evening meal.

"We don't use sugar," Esther replied. "It's not healthy."

Sarah had eaten many suppers of mush and milk, but she had always stirred at least one spoonful of sugar into the mixture. She ate the tasteless mush, trying in vain to ignore the absence of the sweetener to which she was accustomed.

"It's just for a week," Sarah consoled herself when she was alone in her room at the end of the day. "One day is over; five more to go. Then I can go home again."

For breakfast the next morning, Esther cooked a kettle of the wheat that had been coarsely ground. Sarah stirred a liberal amount of milk into the pasty cooked wheat and choked it down. She longed for just one spoonful of unhealthy sugar to make the healthy food more palatable.

Joel Lindburg spooned some applesauce into his bowl and stirred it into the cooked wheat. "Now that helps bring out the flavor," he said as he nodded his head in approval.

Following the hired man's example, Sarah stirred some applesauce into the mixture in her bowl. Applesauce was not equal with sugar, but it did help to improve the flavor of the cooked wheat. Weaver and Esther followed suit and agreed Joel's idea was a good one. A dish of applesauce was on the table for breakfast and dinner every day, so it was always available to be added to the cooked wheat they ate for breakfast every morning.

The days of the week passed in order and were filled with housekeeping tasks for Sarah to do. Every evening she said her prayers, crawled into bed, and mentally crossed out another day. On Saturday she cleaned the house and baked a cake. Then her work-week was finished and she was free to go home. She put on the good dress she had brought with her, for she had promised to meet Miriam Auker and go to town with her in the evening.

"You know where we live now, so Weaver won't be fetching you anymore," Esther said as Sarah put on her stiff black bonnet. "You can come on the trolley Monday morning."

"All right," Sarah agreed, knowing she had no choice in the matter. She drew the narrow black bonnet ribbon under her chin and fastened the hook and eye on the left corner to hold her bonnet in place. "I'll see you then," she promised as she stepped out onto the porch and closed the door.

She walked briskly to the trolley tracks on the southern side of the Akron hill, about one-half mile from the Zimmerman home. The weather was so mild it did not seem like early December. The yellow trolley rocked to a stop and stood still while Sarah climbed aboard. She paid her nickel fare and took a seat for the short ride to Ephrata. She wished now she could go straight home, but she must keep her promise to go to town with Miriam Auker. Sarah and Miriam were not related, but had become friends since they were the same age, went to the same church, and lived about a mile apart.

As the trolley rounded the curve that hugged the bottom of the wooded hill on the edge of Ephrata, Sarah walked forward to tell the motorman she wanted to get off at the corner of Fulton and Lake Streets. When the trolley stopped, she ran down the steps and walked in the lane of Ezra Auker's farm which bordered the railroad tracks on the outskirts of town.

"Come right in," Miriam invited when she answered Sarah's knock on the door. "Did you have supper yet?"

"No," Sarah admitted. "But that's okay."

"*Ach*, come on. Sit down and help yourself," Miriam urged.

"It's just mush and milk," Mrs. Auker apologized, "but there's plenty left. Want a bowl?"

"I don't care," Sarah accepted as she eagerly eyed the sugar bowl setting on the table.

Mrs. Auker filled a bowl with mush and set it in front of Sarah. The stream of rich milk she poured into the bowl formed a white ring around the yellow cornmeal mush. She scooped a heaping spoonful of sugar from the sugar bowl and sprinkled it liberally over the peak of the yellow island that stood up above the milk. She had taken sugar for granted and never noticed how tiny streams of sweetness ran down the island as the warmth in the mush melted the sugar. Taking up her spoon, she stirred the mixture and then tasted the first spoonful. It was delicious!

"I'll get ready 'til you're done," Miriam said as she turned and ran up the stairs.

The girls hopped a ride on the trolley to travel the two blocks from Miriam's home to the new Ephrata post office on the corner of Lake and Main Streets. The Main Street of Ephrata was brightly lighted with electric lights. Since Christmas was only weeks away, strings of bare red, green, blue, and yellow light bulbs were stretched from light post to light post on both sides of the street. A traffic light, mounted on a tall post with a concrete base, stood in the exact center of the town square.

On the four corners of the square stood the Mt. Vernon Hotel, the American Hotel, the Mentzer building which housed several businesses, and the new Royer's Drugstore. The stores and shops that lined both sides of the street offered a wide variety of merchandise to the crowds of shoppers who hurried from one store to another. Rural families came to town on Saturday evenings to do their shopping. For many of them, Saturday evening in Ephrata was the social event of the work week.

Sarah and Miriam walked slowly down the busy sidewalk, seeing who had come to town and meeting their friends and neighbors. As they neared the Peanut Man's stand on the east side of Sprecher's Hardware Store, the aroma of warm roasted peanuts teased their nostrils and made their mouths water.

"Want some peanuts?" Bud Sensenig asked as the girls approached the little group of Pike young people clustered around him. He was not from a Pike home but had made friends among their young people.

"Sure," Miriam said and reached into the bag.

"How did you get here?" Bud asked as he held the bag out to Sarah. "I didn't see you at Dan's shop."

"I came with Miriam this time," Sarah told him. "I need a way home though if you have room."

"Always room for one more," Bud said with a chuckle and nod of his head.

The small group of young people moved on down the street, enjoying the unusually warm weather and each other's company.

"What are yous doing tomorrow?" Miriam asked Sarah when the stores closed and it was time to go home.

"I wasn't home yet, so I don't know," Sarah replied. "What are yous doing?"

"The married ones are coming home for dinner," Miriam said. There was no need for her to mention names, for Sarah knew Miriam was referring to her sisters and brother, Mabel, Anna, and Irvin.

"It's 'Off Sunday,' so maybe we'll have company too. I guess I'll find out tomorrow," Sarah said as she waved good-by to her friend and headed toward Bud Sensenig's car. She crowded into the back seat with Kass Stauffer and the other girls while the young men filled the front seat. They had met at Dan Stauffer's Machine Shop which stood next to his house along the road to the Pleasant Valley School. Bud had stopped at Dan's shop on his way to town and taken the young people with him.

After they returned to their meeting place, the young people gradually drifted off toward their homes. Kass lived only a few steps from her older brother's shop; others rode bikes or had other ways to get home. Sarah's home was not within walking distance from the shop, so Bud dropped her off at her house.

How wonderful it was to walk into the familiar kitchen and back into the world that was normal and comfortable to her! Nothing had changed, but the deserted kitchen had never looked so beautiful to Sarah. The black stove generously shared its warmth, the oil cloth on the uncluttered table was shining clean, the clock in the corner ticked contentedly, and the red geraniums bloomed cheerfully in their tin can pots on the windowsills. Everything, from Daed and Arthur's barn coats on the wall hooks to the green shades drawn down to the exact center of the windows, was the way a home should look and smell.

Sarah tiptoed up the stairs to the girls' room where Mary and Anna were already asleep. She quietly put on her nightgown, crawled into her own comfortable bed, and fell asleep almost as soon as her head touched the pillow.

"Guess what!" Anna cried the next morning when she saw Sarah was awake. "Esther's coming home to stay."

"Is that right?" Sarah stretched and yawned. She did not doubt Anna's word, but she had not been expecting the news.

"When?"

"Today," Anna beamed. "Dan Goods are coming for dinner and bringing her home."

Sarah was suddenly, fully awake. "What brought that on?" she asked.

"Esther said Frank told Daed he didn't think it was fair that all the rest of us are home but him and Esther," Anna explained. "Daed said Esther can come home since you're working out now. She's so near fifteen she don't have to finish eighth grade. She can just stay home and take your place around here."

Because this was not a church Sunday, the girls put on their second-best rather than their Sunday dresses. They combed their hair neatly and washed their hands before sitting down at the breakfast table. There was no need for Sarah to wonder where she should sit, for no one had taken her place at the table. She knew where she belonged.

Breakfast was pleasant. Arthur did not have much to say during breakfast, but Mary and Anna must tell Sarah everything that had happened during the week while she had been gone. Sarah soaked up the familiar atmosphere like a thirsty sponge. She suddenly found herself looking at Lydia and seeing her in a new light. She was not Memm, but she was trying to be a good mother to her stepchildren. For the first time, Sarah realized she had been taking her stepmother's housekeeping skills for granted. She was a good cook, tidy housekeeper, and good manager. She worked as much as any of them and did not complain of the shortages they all endured.

Only the necessary barn chores and meal preparation were done on Sunday, so after the breakfast dishes were washed there was nothing to do until it was time to make dinner. Sarah read a chapter to herself in the little Testament she had been given when she lived with Norman Nolts. She played Tic-Tac-Toe with Mary and Anna and helped make dinner. The sisters glanced out the window every time a car passed, waiting and watching for Esther to come.

"They're here!" Mary cried when she finally saw Dan Good's car turn in the drive just before noon.

Esther wiggled from the car as soon as she could and jumped to the ground. She marched in the short walk to the house, leaving Dan and Mary Good to follow at their own pace with their two small daughters. Dan Good had been a widower with four grown sons when he married Mary nearly six years earlier. She was nineteen years younger than him and had given him a second family after he was fifty.

"Well, well! Here's Esther!" Daed chuckled as she let herself in the kitchen without bothering to knock on the door.

"Look what the wind blew in," Esther laughed. They were all happy because Esther had finally come home to stay. She had expected to go home when Mary and Anna did. Four years later, the day she had been waiting for had finally come.

After dinner, Dan got Esther's things from the car and brought them to the house. Sarah helped Esther carry everything upstairs to the girls' room.

"Now we're all home but Frank," Esther said as she started putting her clothes in the bureau. "He said John Weavers asked Daed to let them adopt him, but Daed won't do it. He said he could never give any of his children away like that."

"I think Frank likes it there," Sarah said. "He was there ever since Memm died and wasn't dragged around like some of us were. The Weavers have a real nice farm and everything."

"Yes," Esther agreed, "but he feels left out, in a way."

"You could come home now since I'm working out," Sarah said. "So maybe if Arthur gets a job Frank will be able to come home too."

"How do you like your job?" Esther asked.

"*Ach* well," Sarah shrugged. "Like Mammi Shaub says, 'It takes all kinds of people to make the world.'"

"What do you mean?" Esther frowned.

"They just do things kind of different from us, that's all," Sarah said. She had learned long ago there was no benefit in complaining about things that could not be changed. She had to work for the Zimmermans whether she liked their ways or not. "I dread going back tomorrow, but it would be a whole lot worse if I couldn't look forward to coming home weekends still."

"Well, I'm glad I could finally come home to stay," Esther said. "It's not that Mary wasn't nice to me. Her mom died when she was only three and she knows what it's like to live with strangers. But still and all, even if it isn't the same as before, I wanted to be home with the rest of yous."

"I know what you mean," Sarah acknowledged. "I was glad, too, when Daed said I could leave Weaver Aukers and come home. It's still our family, even if it's not the same as before. It took me awhile, but I'm getting used to—'her' now, too."

"But you still don't call her Memm?" Esther asked.

"No," Sarah admitted. "Nobody said I have to either. Mary and Anna do all the time, but I still can't yet."

"Neither can I," Esther confessed. "Mary and Anna don't remember Memm, but we do. I guess that's what makes the difference."

"I guess," Sarah agreed. "She's all right, but it seems like calling her Memm would make it sound like I forgot my own mother. I could never do that."

"I still can't figure out why God let our mom die," Esther sighed.

"Me neither," Sarah conceded. "I guess we never will. We just have to believe He knows what He's doing. But if Memm wouldn't have died, we would never have been separated and dragged around from one home to another like we were. I was home for awhile, but now I got sent off again to be a *maad* (maid). I know it costs too much to go back and forth on the trolley every day, but sometimes I wonder if I will ever have a home where I can settle down and stay forever."

"Maybe you'll get married someday," Esther speculated. "If you got married, you could settle down in a home of your own and stay there."

"*Ach*, don't talk so," Sarah laughed softly as her naturally pink cheeks grew more rosy. "I don't know anybody I'd ever want to marry; and nobody wants me either."

Chapter 16

As Sarah sat in the Pike Meetinghouse listening to the minister speak at Mammi Shaub's funeral service, her thoughts naturally returned to Memm's funeral. That had been in December 1933, and this was March 1941. Although less than eight years had passed, Memm's funeral seemed to have been eons ago. So much had happened and so many things had changed during those years. Sarah's own thoughts and memories spoke so loud they drowned out the words the minister was saying.

Daadi Shaubs had moved twice since Memm died. Daadi was now living a short distance west of the Pike Meetinghouse. The race between him and Jake Beicher to be the first person at church on Sunday mornings was over. After he had moved into his *daadi-haus* (grandpa house), Daadi Shaub had taken over the janitorial duties of the church and was always the first one there because he unlocked the building and started the fire in the coal stove.

Sarah could still hear Mammi fussing in a good-natured way during the years they had lived further away and driven the buggy to church. *Daadi's always in such a rush to be off for church. I have to fasten my cape and lace up my shoes on the way, and then we just sit there anyway and wait until it's time for church to start. He just wants to beat Jake Beicher to church, that's all.* After Daadi became the janitor, he could walk to the Meetinghouse whenever he wanted to and Mammi could follow whenever she was ready.

Mammi had suffered terribly during the last months of her life. One night she had reached for her cough syrup bottle without bothering to light a lamp. In the dark, she had accidentally grabbed the bottle of caustic soda she used when making homemade soap. The swallow she had taken from the bottle had burned her throat. Too embarrassed to tell anyone what she had done, she tried to purge her throat by drinking milk. Weeks later, when her sore throat did not heal, she finally went to see the doctor. But the damage had already been done and there was nothing the doctor could do for her. After weeks of suffering with a throat so raw she was not able to speak or swallow, she was finally out of her misery. Poor, dear Mammi Shaub!

Warm memories flooded Sarah's mind. Mammi had never been idle. She had given of herself in so many ways. She had helped her daughters with their housework, taken in her motherless grandchildren, bought things at the Bazaar for the express purpose of giving them away, invited friends and relatives to share delicious home-cooked meals, and fed tramps who came to her back door. She had always been there for anyone who needed her. Sarah knew she would miss Mammi. Without her, Sarah's closest link to Memm was now her mother's sisters.

When the funeral service ended, the Shaub family drifted back to Daadi's house. Aunt Ricky had come all the way from New York City for her cousin's funeral. She accepted the invitation to join the family for the customary meal that was served after every funeral. She was seventy-nine and so old she could remember not only all of Mammi's sixty-seven years, but Mammi's mother, Barbara, as well. Aunt Ricky stayed long after she had finished eating and could not seem to get done reminiscing.

"I can remember the house in Germany where Barbara was born," Aunt Ricky said with a faraway look in her eyes. "She was my father's sister. She often told me how she did washing and cleaning on a freighter to pay her way to America when she was eighteen. Her older sister, Anna, was living in Lancaster County, so Barbara came here too. Anna and Leonard Seibel were poorer than church mice when they came, but your church people helped them. So they joined the Pike church, and then Barbara did too. That's how Barbara Mink came to marry David Zimmerman.

"I remember how our grandma used to read us the letters she got from her relatives in Germany," Aunt Lizzie recalled.

"Oh, yes," Aunt Ricky's eyes twinkled. "My family came to America in 1872 when I was nine. They only stayed a few years and then went back to Germany when my father inherited the Münk family farm in Eich. But I married Fred and stayed in New York. Barbara kept in touch with my father and her other Münk relatives back in Eich. She never forgot her homeland or German ways."

"She said before she died that she wanted the pallbearers to carry her coffin on their shoulders the way they did in Germany," Great-aunt Maggie Reich remembered. "And they did too."

"I always liked to talk to Barbara," Aunt Ricky sighed. "I guess some of it was because we could both remember our Münk home in Eich. Of course, here in America the name got changed to Mink. The Minks and Reichs and Seibels and Foxes and Risslers all came over from Eich about the same time. The village was right along the Rhine River. Barbara used to tell how she would sit along the banks of the Rhine and watch the ships go by . . ."

"Let's go," Sarah said in an undertone to her cousin Edna. All this talk about faraway places and people from long ago did not interest her. The Barbara Mink of whom Aunt Ricky spoke so fondly was Sarah's great-grandmother, but she had died four years before Sarah was born. Sarah was more interested in the present and future than in what had happened in the past. A long stretch of time lay ahead of her, waiting to be lived. She never considered the possibility that someday she might be the old lady remembering people and places that seemed as foreign to her descendants as Aunt Ricky's beloved German homeland and aunt, Barbara Mink.

The fresh, brown mound over Mammi Shaub's grave was its own testimony of a life that had come and gone. In a few short weeks the earth settled and new grass grew over the scar in the cemetery. The give and take of the cycles of life continued, with both births and deaths being reported every week in the *Ephrata Review*.

There had been only one calendar year since 1936 when Weaver and Esther Zimmerman had not added a child to their family. The 1941 edition arrived on May 18 and was named

Weaver Jr. He did not replace the son who had been taken from them by death but did return to four the number of children in the house.

After little Weaver was born, Sarah's days were busier than ever. With three boys wearing diapers, the bucket of dirty diapers waiting to be washed was never empty. The floor always seemed to be dirty, even if she swept it with the broom every day. As soon as all the dishes were washed, another pile began to accumulate. She worked from morning until night to do the housework. She did not understand how Esther could always be so tired and get so little done, but she had not learned how much strength a woman needed to give birth to a child every year.

The small garden Esther had planted provided a welcome change to the starchy winter menu of mush and fried potatoes. Tending the garden was women's work, so Sarah hoed the rows and picked the vegetables as they matured. The first spring greens they ate were the saw-toothed dandelion leaves, cooked and garnished with crumbled bacon and slices of hard boiled eggs. The leaves turned bitter after the dandelion bloomed, but by then the lettuce in the garden was ready to be cut and eaten with a sweet/sour hot bacon dressing.

The long June days and short, warm nights pushed the peas to maturity. Sarah pulled one of the swelling pea pods from the vine and slit it with her thumbnail. She stripped the row of little green balls from the pod and ate them raw. She never would have believed she would get so hungry for vegetables. She had been used to canning enough vegetables and fruit during the growing season to last all winter, but Esther did not can many things. They would eat vegetables while they were fresh and in season, but when the garden was empty there would be no vegetables again until next summer. Even the applesauce that was on the table twice a day was not canned. Esther kept apples under a blanket in the cellar and made one dish of applesauce at a time as it was needed.

The weeks of the summer slipped by one by one. Every Monday Sarah walked nearly a mile to the trolley and paid a nickel for the three-mile ride to the Zimmerman home. Every

Saturday she walked back to the trolley tracks and paid another nickel to go home again for the weekend. Occasionally, if Esther needed extra help to have company for Sunday dinner or something special, Sarah did not go home for the weekend. She was always glad when those long two-week stretches were over. Then she could go home again and find out what had been happening at home while she was gone.

Every week Sarah counted the days until Saturday when she could go home again and dreaded Monday mornings when she would have to return to her job. *I wish so bad I could just stay at home,* she thought. *But I'm afraid to tell Daed. He needs the money I earn. I can't tell him again that I want to quit my job. I guess I'll just have to keep going and make the best of it somehow.*

The weekdays followed a pattern, but no two were exactly alike. Monday was always wash day and Saturday was always cleaning day. On the days in between there was ironing to do, butter to churn, garden to tend, meals to cook, and dishes to wash. The babies needed their diapers changed and noses wiped. Before it seemed possible, the first of September had once again come and brought with it Sarah's eighteenth birthday.

"Are you going to bake a cake?" Ada asked one Saturday when she saw Sarah was doing the weekly cleaning.

"After while," Sarah answered. She knew why the little girl was asking. The cake Sarah baked every Saturday before she went home was a treat the family enjoyed only on weekends.

"I get to lick the bowl," Ada informed Sarah.

Ada climbed up on a chair beside Sarah to watch as she stirred the cake batter. She usually made a white or yellow cake, but this week she had decided to make something different when she spied a tin of Hershey's cocoa that had been shoved to the back of the cupboard.

"What's that?" Ada asked when Sarah measured out the dark brown powder.

"Cocoa," Sarah told her as she dumped the cocoa into the batter and began to stir it again.

"It's all black," Ada frowned.

"It'll be good," Sarah laughed. "Wait and see." She knew that by Monday morning the cake would be gone. Neither she nor the hired man ever got to eat any of the cakes she baked on Saturdays.

When her work for the week was finished, Sarah walked from the farm to the trolley tracks to catch her ride home. The lights inside the trolley dimmed as the car strained to climb the steep Akron hill. Then it rushed down the other side of the hill and went on toward Ephrata. When the trolley stopped on Main Street, Sarah got off and joined the other young people who had come to town for the evening.

"Some of us are going to the hospital tomorrow to see Aunt Lena," Kass Stauffer told Sarah when the two young girls met on the sidewalk outside Sprecher's Hardware Store. "My brother Amos is driving, but his wife can't go. Do you want to go with?"

"Sure," Sarah accepted the invitation. Aunt Lena was Daed's sister. Her husband, Bishop Jacob Stauffer, was a brother of Kass's father.

"Good," Kass smiled. "I didn't want to be the only girl. We'll pick you up right after dinner."

Sarah was ready when Amos Stauffer drove his 1936 Chevy in the lane. She put on her coat and bonnet and hurried out to the car. The front seat was filled with Amos's younger brother, Phares, and Aunt Lena's son, Ivan. In one way or another, Ivan was a cousin to everyone who was making the trip to visit his mother.

Phares got out of the car and pushed the back of the passenger seat forward so Sarah could climb in the back seat beside Kass. As she brushed past him, he suddenly noticed her naturally wavy hair, the sparkle in her eyes, and the natural pink blush of her cheeks. She did not notice the questioning look he gave her before he resumed his seat in the car and closed the door. Could it be possible that this charming, slender young lady was the same girl he had thought was so homely and ignorant when they both went to the Pleasant Valley School? They attended the same church and were with the same young people. Why had he never taken notice of her before?

Unaware of the effect her presence had made on the young man in the front seat, Sarah turned to Kass and asked, "What's Florence doing today?"

"She's helping her mom have company for dinner," Kass said as Amos turned the car around and drove out onto the road. Both of them knew the real reason Amos' wife had not wanted to make the trip was because Amos and Florence were expecting their first child soon. Women did not go out in public the last month before a child was born.

"Is your mom getting better?" Kass asked Ivan as Amos drove east toward Valley Forge.

"No," Ivan shook his head. "It looks like her cancer was too far gone already."

The Fort Washington Hospital at Valley Forge was a larger, more modern hospital than any in Lancaster County. Uncle Check (Jake) had taken Aunt Lena to this big hospital as a last resort when he saw cancer was winning the battle for her life. Even in Amos' comfortable closed car, the trip to Valley Forge would take them more than an hour. Sarah felt fortunate to be able to go on such a long trip.

"Anybody want some Hershey Kisses?" Phares asked as he opened a bag and passed it around.

As the bag of chocolate candy was passed from hand to hand inside the car, the conversation of the young men in the front seat turned to the war threat that loomed on the horizon. Sarah did not understand politics, so she listened without adding anything to the discussion.

"It wonders me how much longer the United States will stay out of it," Amos said. "President Roosevelt calls it a Limited National Emergency and more boys are being drafted all the time."

"Japan is getting more unhandy too," Ivan added. "They're making trouble in the Pacific while the Germans are sinking ships in the Atlantic. The President said he just don't have enough Navy to keep things under control on both coasts."

"Some people think the new Japanese premier might be able to work things out," Phares said, trying to be hopeful. He threw a Hershey Kiss over the seat, aiming perfectly so it landed in Sarah's lap.

"I wouldn't count on it," Amos shook his head.

The men went on discussing the sinking of ships, German U-boats, embargoes, and other complicated things Sarah did not try to understand. But she did understand the undercurrent of fear in their voices. People everywhere where afraid the country would become involved in the war that had begun in 1939 and continued to spread through Europe. Now the trouble with Japan was worsening and complicating matters. No one knew what might happen if the United States entered the war.

"Amos is probably safe because he's married and farming, but you and me are bound to be drafted if it gives a war," Phares said to Ivan as he threw two Hershey Kisses over the seat into Sarah's lap.

"If that does happen, do you think we'll be able to get farm deferments?" Ivan asked.

"Maybe. If we work it right," Phares answered as he fired a volley of Hershey Kisses into Sarah's lap.

Why do all the Hershey Kisses he throws land in my lap? Sarah wondered. Is he doing it on purpose, or does it just happen that way? She could not tell.

The countryside they were passing through showed definite signs of fall. Leaves were starting to color and flocks of honking wild geese hurried south ahead of the approaching winter. The open country grew less and less as they neared Valley Forge. The subject of possible war was dropped in favor of the more immediate need to find the right road to the hospital.

After the car was parked outside the hospital, the little group found their way down the long corridor to Aunt Lena's room. Sarah was shocked when she saw Aunt Lena's wasted body. She lay on her bed looking like only a shadow of her former self. She was in too much pain to enjoy visiting.

"I'm glad you came," Uncle Check (Jake) told the young people as they prepared to leave. Having visitors helped to fill the long hours he spent sitting at his wife's bedside.

"Take care," Ivan said as he pressed his mother's hand. Every one of them knew Aunt Lena's time on earth could not be long, but they avoided mentioning the fact. To them, opening the subject of approaching death was like courting disaster.

Darkness fell as Amos drove west toward home. Although Sarah could not watch the passing countryside, the return trip seemed short. The Chevy bumped across the rut at the end of the lane and then stopped at her yard gate. Phares got out and pushed the back of the front seat forward so Sarah could climb out of the two-door car.

"Thanks for taking me along," Sarah said to Amos as she slipped out of the back seat.

"Sure thing," Amos acknowledged her gratitude.

"I'll see you around," Phares said to Sarah before he got back in the car. She nodded in reply and turned to open the gate. She did not know his eyes followed her as she tripped lightly toward the house. He had known her since school days, but either she had changed or he had terribly misjudged her. He wondered if she might have changed her opinion of him, too, in the years that had passed since they had been in school. He did not know but determined to find out one way or another.

"Nice evening, isn't it?" Phares said when he met Sarah the next weekend.

"Yes, it is," she answered politely. She expected him to move on, but he did not.

"I hear you're working for Weaver Zimmermans now," he said in an obvious deliberate effort to make conversation.

"Yes," she repeated.

"Been there long?"

"Not quite a year."

"Do you like it?"

"It's okay."

What's he talking to me for? she wondered. *Why should he care where I work or anything?*

As the weeks passed and October gave way to November, Sarah realized Phares was paying special attention to her. She knew now the Hershey Kisses he had thrown on the trip to Valley Forge had not landed in her lap by accident. She remembered their school days and was not excited about this turn of events.

In spite of his efforts, Phares could not tell where he stood with Sarah. She did not give him a cold shoulder, but neither did she encourage his attention. For weeks, he alternated between hope and despair as he tried to find the courage to ask her for a date.

"Are you going to the crowd tonight?" Esther asked Sarah one Sunday afternoon.

"Oh, I don't know," Sarah sighed. "Ivan said he'll take me along if I want to go, but I don't care if I do or not."

"Why?" Esther probed. She could not understand why anyone who was old enough for *rumschpringe* would not want to go to the deacon's house where the young people were gathering for the evening.

"I just don't, that's all," Sarah said flatly. She pinched her lips, refusing to tell Esther she was afraid Phares might ask to bring her home. The things she had seen in the past few weeks told her he was no longer a school boy, but she was not convinced she wanted to "go with" him.

"*Ach*, I guess I'll go along," Sarah decided when her cousin Ivan stopped in to see if she was going to the crowd. She did not bother to put on a good dress but went in the old one she had worn for the afternoon.

"How's your mom?" Sarah asked Ivan as she rode with her cousin to the deacon's house.

"Getting worse," Ivan told her. "I don't think she'll make it much longer."

"It must be hard to see her suffer like that," Sarah remarked.

"Yes," Ivan nodded. "She says she wishes she could go once."

Thoughts of aging, pain, and death were pushed out of the minds of the crowd of young people who had been invited to the supper at Ivan and Mary Martin's home along Snapper Creek Road. Their conversation and laughter filled the house with happy sounds. After supper, Bud Sensenig and other young people who had not been raised in the Stauffer (Pike) church joined their friends at the crowd. The young people sang English songs from the *Church and Sunday School Hymnal* and played games until it was time to go home.

Phares watched Sarah all evening, debating with himself whether he should ask to take her home or not. Her shy, quiet ways were more outstanding and attractive to him than the fluttering wings of the social butterflies who vainly attempted to draw attention to themselves.

She can't do more than say no, he decided at last. *Then at least I'll know how I'm at it.* He went out early to get his horse and four-wheeled open buggy ready to go.

When Sarah stepped off the porch, Phares emerged from the darkness and fell into step beside her. "May I take you home tonight?" he asked. His heart was hammering so loudly he wasn't sure he had spoken loud enough for her to hear his question.

"I guess," Sarah heard herself give permission. She could not stand there a long time trying to decide what to say after the question had been asked.

She touched Phares' extended hand lightly for the sake of courtesy and sprang into his buggy without further assistance. His heart sang in triumph as he took his seat beside her and spread the buggy blanket over their laps. There was no protection from inclement weather in an open buggy, but young people would not think of driving enclosed family buggies.

Cap trotted briskly through the cool November air toward Fairmount, needing only a gentle tug on the reins to tell him which way Phares wanted him to go. Phares got out and walked beside the buggy until they reached the top of the steep *Katze Boucle* (Cat's Back) Hill at Fairmount. Then he jumped back in the buggy for the fast ride down the long western slope of the hill. Sarah was glad it was dark and everyone was sleeping when they passed Weaver Auker's place and went through the covered bridge that spanned the Conestoga Creek at Eberly's cider mill. She knew exactly what her uncle would have said if he had seen Phares taking her home: *The thing you throw the furtherest away is what you go fetch again.*

"This is pretty far out of your way," Sarah said as Phares guided Cap around the short jog of the road that went to Diamond Station and onto the road that bordered Brossman's Orchard.

"Not too far," he assured her. "And besides, Cap is young. He likes to go the long way around."

Pretending she did not get the hint, Sarah made no answer. He was only bringing her home, so this was not a full-fledged date. Just because she had agreed to let him bring her home this time did not mean she had totally changed her opinion of him. Yet, she could think of no valid reason to refuse if he should ask her for a date for the next weekend.

Phares gave her a hand to get down from the buggy at her yard gate. He walked her to the door, but she did not ask him to come inside. "Will I see you in town next Saturday?" he asked.

"Probably," she replied.

"I'll meet you at the trolley stop then," he planned, "and bring you home again if that's all right with you."

"Y-Yes," she stammered.

"Until then," he smiled as he tipped his hat. "Good night."

"Good night," she answered politely. She stepped in the kitchen, closed the door, and leaned weakly against it. *Now you did it!* she chided herself.

Phares walked to his buggy with a spring in his step while Sarah quietly crept up the stairs to the girls' room. She put on her nightgown and slipped into bed beside Esther. She did not have to wonder what Esther would say when she found out who had brought her sister home and that she had accepted a date with Phares the next weekend.

I know I'll have to eat crow, Sarah thought. *Maybe I shouldn't of talked so loud when Weaver Auker said, "The thing you throw the furthest away is what you go fetch again." But I never, ever thought . . . I guess I should forget the things that happened in school and not hold them against him. People do grow up and change over the years. The least I can do is give him a chance to prove himself. Ya, wohl (yes, well) . . . maybe if crow is fried just right, in lots of butter, it don't taste too bad.*

Chapter 17

Aunt Lena was mercifully released from her suffering on December 5, 1941. By the time her funeral was held at the Pike church, the United States had plunged into war.

The December 7 sneak attack by the Japanese on the United States Naval Base at Pearl Harbor, and the 3,700 deaths that resulted, shocked the nation. The following day President Roosevelt signed a declaration of war against Japan. On December 11, Germany and Italy declared war on the United States and Congress retaliated by declaring war on both of those countries. Twenty years after the Great War, which had been promoted as "the war to end all wars," the United States was embroiled in another, more deadly war that reached around the globe. From this time on, the Great War was known as World War I and this new war was World War II. The hope for continuing economic improvement in the 1940s was put on hold for the duration of the war. No one knew when or how the war would end.

While many young men were saying good-by to their families at the Ephrata depot and beginning their journey to the war front, the Wenger family was finally reunited.

"Daed's going to fetch Frank tomorrow," Esther told Sarah when she came home for the weekend on the last Saturday in December. "It's five years since Daed got married again, and we're finally all going to be at home once."

"That's good news," Sarah joined in the rejoicing. "But what do John Weavers think?"

"They're not happy at all," Esther confided. "They wanted to keep Frank until he's of age and help him start farming."

"What does Frank want to do?" Sarah asked. She knew the question was immaterial, for her brother had no choice. Underage children had to do whatever their parents decided.

"He likes it at Weavers' place," Esther admitted, "but he'd like to be home like the rest of us."

"I can understand that," Sarah said with empathy. "It makes you feel like there's something wrong with you if the rest go home and you don't."

"I know," Esther nodded, understanding perfectly. "It sure took long enough, but tomorrow we'll finally all be back together at home again."

"Well, almost," Sarah said. "I'm only home weekends right now. But Daed said in the spring I can come home to stay."

When the family gathered around the supper table on Sunday evening, December 28, Frank took a seat beside Arthur. Daed's eyes smiled at his children. Sarah, Arthur, Esther, Frank, Mary, and Anna—every one of them was seated around the table.

"Let us give thanks," Daed said quietly. Those were the same words he always said before they bowed their heads to pray, but this time Sarah thought the words conveyed an unspoken message. Daed had waited a long time to bring the last of his six children home.

The Wenger family had little time to savor the pleasure of being reunited. After supper Phares came to take Sarah away for the evening, and the next morning she went back to her live-in job at the Zimmermans' home. A month later, at the end of January 1942, Esther went to be David Stauffer's live-in hired girl until spring.

As much as Frank had wished to be with his family, he was soon homesick for his foster family. Since he had been six years old when his mother died, he had only a few memories of life with his natural family. After being part of the John Weaver family for eight years, he found he missed them much more than he had expected.

John Weaver was a prosperous farmer with the kind of farm which had helped to make the Weaverland Valley of Lancaster County become known as The Garden Spot. There was no comparison between the flourishing Weaver farm and Daed's poor little farm with its inferior horses and worn equipment. While John seemed to have a "Midas touch," things had usually gone backwards for Daed. Since the Wengers lived in a different school district than the Weavers, Frank was forced to change schools in the middle of eighth grade. He did not like riding the school bus or the big four-room Bergstrasse School. In reality, being at home with his family was not what he had imagined it would be. The adjustments to living at home were much greater than he had anticipated.

Despite the changes the years had brought to her family, Sarah had lived at home long enough to be comfortable there. Although she would have preferred to stay at home all the time, her job forced her to move back and forth between her weekday and weekend homes. Yet, some of the bond that had formed between the Nolts and herself still remained. They kept in contact and shared occasional visits.

"Norman Nolts invited us for dinner in two weeks," Sarah told Phares at the end of February. "They heard we're going together and want to meet you."

"Tell them we'll come," Phares said. "I wouldn't mind seeing where you used to live before I knew you."

Sarah could not begin to tell Phares the feelings and memories that flashed through her mind as she walked toward the door of the Nolt home. She could see a skinny, terrified eleven-year-old girl following Norman and Lizzie to that same door seven years earlier. The two and a half years she had lived with them had seemed much longer at the time than it did now when she was looking back. Never in her wildest dreams had she foreseen the day when she would be escorted to the door of her old home by a boyfriend. She felt flustered and nervous, wondering what the Nolts would think of Phares.

"Come right in," Norman said as he opened the door. "*Wie geht's?* (How do you do?)" he said warmly as he shook hands with both Phares and Sarah.

Lizzie bustled in from the kitchen to welcome her guests. "I'll take your wraps," she said after she shook hands with the young couple.

While Lizzie hung the visitors' coats on the clothes tree, the children stared bashfully at the stranger who had brought Sarah to visit. She was no stranger to them, but seeing her with a boyfriend was something new.

"My, but you're getting big," Sarah said to Mary. "How old are you now?"

"Nine," Mary said. "I'll be ten in May."

"Then Melvin must be seven," Sarah said as she turned to the little boy. "Is that right?"

"Yes," Melvin nodded.

"You were the baby when I came here," Sarah remembered. "Alta was born while I lived here and Anna Mae after I left."

"Clarence is the baby now," Melvin reported.

"Yes, I heard you have a new baby. I should've got here before to see him," Sarah apologized.

"He's sleeping now," Mary informed her.

"I'll see him later then," Sarah said as she turned to follow Lizzie to the kitchen. "Maybe I can do something now to help your mom."

While they ate dinner, Sarah saw she need not have worried how Phares would get along with Norman. Since they were both farmers, they had much in common.

"I'm hired out to my brother Amos," Phares said in answer to Norman's question. "Since he's married, he took over my Daed's farm. In the summer I work on Harvey Burkholder's threshing crew. Right now, though, I'm helping my brother, Aaron, do some logging in Bill Bauman's woods. Amos rigged a saw on the front of one of his tractors to saw cord-wood."

"What kind of tractors does Aaron have?" Norman asked.

"John Deere," Phares answered in a tone that implied the green and yellow tractors were the only brand anyone would want to have. "He got a B model brand new in 1937. Last year he got a 1934 A model he found in pieces, stuck under the stairway in A. B. C. Groff's store. Charlie Groff didn't want to sell it to him because he thought it could never be fixed. But Aaron convinced him to sell it and soon had it back together and running."

"You don't say," Norman marveled.

"Leave it to Aaron," Phares grinned. "He does plowing and disking for farmers but was losing too much time on the road driving between farms. He and my brother, Dan, put their heads together and figured out how to add some gears to the B so it would have six speeds instead of four. They just used junkyard parts, but it worked. So Dan drew the plans on tablet paper and sent it to the John Deere Company. They sent him a $100 check for the idea in 1940 and the next year they started making six-speed A and B models."

Well, that part hasn't changed since we were in school, Sarah thought as she listened to Phares talking about tractors. *He still likes John Deere tractors as much as ever.*

As the weeks of dating lengthened into months, Sarah had gradually changed her opinion of Phares. She found herself looking forward to meeting him at the trolley stop in Ephrata on Saturday evenings. He would not have missed meeting that trolley for anything, and she would have been disappointed if he had not been there. They spent the evening walking up and down the sidewalks together, meeting and talking with friends and neighbors. When the stores closed, he took her home in his buggy.

Late one Saturday afternoon, Joel Lindburg stuck his head in the door and announced with a broad grin, "Your beau is here."

Sarah closed the oven door on the weekly cake and looked out the kitchen window. Sure enough! Bud Sensenig's car was parked beside the stone wall that enclosed the barnyard. She could see Phares sitting in the passenger's seat. Her work for the week was finished, but she was still wearing her everyday dress and shoes.

"Tell him I'll be out soon," Sarah told the hired man, throwing the words over her shoulder as she raced up the stairs to change clothes. She had not been expecting Phares to come for her instead of meeting her at the trolley stop as usual.

Joel went out, with Ada following in his trail. The hired man passed on Sarah's message and chatted briefly with the waiting young men before going to finish his work for the week.

"Do you like your maid?" Phares asked the little girl when the hired man had gone away.

"*Ya,*" Ada answered with a nod of her head.

Phares liked children, so he went on talking to Ada and asking her questions about the maid. Ada was not bashful. She told him all sorts of things about Sarah.

"Can she cook?" Phares asked.

"Yes," Ada answered, and then added, "but she burns the cake."

"Is that so?" Phares laughed as he saw Sarah coming toward the car. He opened the door and slid to the middle of the front seat to make room for her.

"What's so funny?" Sarah asked as she got in and closed the door. She was sure the reason both Phares and Bud were laughing had something to do with her.

"Ada said you burn the cake," Phares chuckled as Bud turned the car toward Diamond Station.

"What?" Sarah gasped.

"I asked her if you can cook and she said you can, but you burn the cake," he repeated.

"I do not!" Sarah cried indignantly. "What all else did she say?"

"Oh, she told me all about you," Phares grinned. "It was all good, except that you burn the cake."

Phares did not take Ada's word seriously or doubt Sarah's ability to cook. Although he was not "scared off," Sarah did not see the humor in the incident. The weekend at home was not long enough for her to forget the embarrassing episode.

"Why did you tell Phares I burn the cake?" Sarah asked Ada on Monday morning.

"It was all *schwatz* (black)," Ada defended herself.

"*Ach!*" Sarah exclaimed, suddenly understanding. "That was a chocolate cake. It was *supposed* to be black. It wasn't burned."

"I thought . . ." Ada began, but Sarah did not let her finish.

"After this, you stay in the house where you belong when Phares comes," Sarah scolded Ada. "You don't go out there and be such a little tattle-tale, especially if you're going to say things that aren't even true." By the time Sarah finished, Ada had been thoroughly *ver-deutsched* (instructed in Pennsylvania Deutsch) to mind her own business in the future.

As things turned out, Ada did not have many more opportunities to be a little tale-bearer. Daed sent Arthur to bring Sarah home because Lydia was sick. Sarah took over at home until her stepmother could be out of bed again. Then she went back to the Zimmermans' for a short time and came home to stay on March 21. Daed had promised she could quit her job in the spring, so she went home the day the calender said spring had arrived.

All six Wenger siblings lived under one roof for two days. Then Arthur went to be John Zimmerman's live-in hired man. John Zimmerman's farm was less than two miles away. The buildings stood at the end of a long lane between fields that reached down to the Conestoga Creek. In addition to his room and board, Arthur would earn $30 per month.

"I guess that's just how it'll be," Sarah told herself. "We'll probably never all be at home at once anymore. Even if Frank is home to stay, one or two of us older ones will always be working out somewhere from now on. *Ya, wohl. So geht's* (Yes, well. That's how it goes.) I guess there's nothing I can do about it."

Although Sarah uttered no complaint about the instability in her family's life, she wondered if she would ever have a stable, secure home life. Was she destined to spend her life being a live-in maid, shuffled from home to home and place to place? Why could her family not remain intact? Why did Daed keep finding jobs for his children that required them to live away from home? Why had it taken five years for Frank to come home after Daed remarried?

Frank hated going to the Bergstrasse School more and more each week. "Can't I quit school now?" he asked Daed. *"Must* I finish eighth grade? Esther didn't."

"Well," Daed considered, "there's only a couple more weeks left this term. But if you hate it so bad, I guess you can stay home."

Frank's relief was short-lived. A few days later, Constable Royer paid Daed a visit and informed him that Frank must finish the school year.

"Your son has had the three unexcused absences he is allowed in one year," Constable Royer firmly told Daed. "If he is not back in school tomorrow, I will have to arrest you and lock you up for non-compliance with the law. Parents don't decide anymore when their children can quit school. Those days are over. The law says children must go to school until they are fifteen and it is my job to see the law is enforced."

Seeing the constable meant what he said, Daed sent Frank back to school. A few days later, Daed went all the way to Lancaster to see School Superintendent Mylin. Daed asked the superintendent to issue a permit for Frank to stay out of school, but the superintendent was as adamant as the constable had been that the law must be upheld. Frank must go to school until he was fifteen.

"I guess there's nothing I can do," Daed told Frank when he got home. "You'll have to finish school. I feel bad that things went like they did and want to make it up to you somehow. I'm going to buy you a real nice horse."

Daed kept his promise. He went to William Martin at New Holland and bought two horses. One was a strawberry roan and the other a spirited sorrel.

"The sorrel is yours," Daed told Frank when he came home with the horses.

The pleased smile on Frank's face as he stroked the nose of the sorrel was the only reward Daed desired in return. "I'll name him Sammy," Frank decided

Arthur knew Sammy was a better horse than the white one Daed had bought for him, but he was not jealous. The whole family hoped that having the nice horse would help to make up a little for the hard time Frank was having in adjusting to his change of homes.

Frank had worked with quality horses on the Weaver farm and knew a good horse when he saw one. He truly appreciated Daed's effort to please him and took good care of Sammy. The spirited sorrel was exactly the kind of horse a young man liked to hitch to his buggy. Frank did not have a buggy yet, of course, but he could expect Daed to buy one for him in another year or two. Daed had learned to shoe his own horses, but his attempt to shoe the strawberry roan he had bought for a work horse was unsuccessful. Dick would not stand still when Daed tried to lift the horse's foot. He lunged and kicked until Daed finally gave up. Three days later he started out early in the morning and walked Dick to a blacksmith seven miles away in Mt. Airy.

"They got him shod," Daed reported when he returned late in the afternoon from the fourteen-mile round trip. "But they had to put him in stocks to get the job done. He's a mean one."

"We just have to tame him down a little," Frank said, trying to keep a positive attitude. "He'll make a good work horse yet."

"Maybe," Daed allowed. "But it isn't easy to work the mean streak out of a horse."

The first days of April were warm enough to reassure mankind the growing season had begun. The puff and whistle of Milt Wanner's steam engine going around the neighborhood to steam tobacco beds was as much a sign of spring as the first robin of the season.

When Daed's turn came, Mr. Wanner steamed two long tobacco beds along the chicken yard and smokehouse. A hose directed the steam from a valve in the engine to seven-feet-long metal pans that were laid on the ground. The steam killed all the weed seeds and bacteria in the soil under the pans. Mr. Wanner moved the pans about every twenty minutes to steam a new section.

The engine was still running and the men were still working when Sarah went to bed. She fell asleep to the sound of the chugging of the steam engine and did not hear when it finally lumbered away at 11:30 that night. The thirty-four pans Mr. Wanner had steamed were sterilized and ready for planting. The tobacco seeds would be sowed and covered with a long strip of white muslin. The muslin would keep the seeds warm so they would sprout quickly. In May, when the danger of frost was past, the seedlings would be pulled up and transplanted to the fields.

A few days of warmth and gentle rain in April turned the world from drab brown to brilliant green. There was never enough time in a day to accomplish everything that should be done when planting season was in full swing. In addition to the fields and family garden, Daed planted 1500 strawberry plants in a big patch behind the barn. There would be no crop to pick the first year, of course, because strawberries need a year to establish themselves in their new home. But Daed hoped to have a good crop to sell on market the second year. The little plants put down eager roots and grew by leaps and bounds. The weeks of spring marched by with the rush of work that stretched from dawn until dark, pausing only on Sunday for a well-earned day of rest.

"I met Paul Sensenig today at Burky's auction," Daed told Sarah one Friday evening. "He said they need a maid and wondered if you could come. Esther's home from David Stauffers now, so I said you can come."

"All right," Sarah agreed. She knew Paul and Elizabeth Sensenig. They were members of the Pike church who lived double with Paul's maternal Wanner grandparents. Paul raised produce which he peddled from his wagon in Ephrata. Elizabeth was Phares' older sister.

Once more, Sarah packed her bags and went to live in another home. As she had done when she worked for the Zimmermans, she lived with the Sensenigs during the week and went home for the weekend. The work she did for Elizabeth was the same housework she was accustomed to doing at home. The Sensenigs' four small children, Phares, Esther, Florence, and Anna, were all under school age. The fifth child would arrive in September. Caring for the children, doing the normal housework, tending the garden, and canning food for the winter was enough work to keep two women busy.

The townspeople, who had no gardens of their own, savored the farm-fresh fruits and vegetables they bought from Paul. The convenience of having fresh produce brought to their doors by the barefooted farmer helped them stretch their ration stamps and the eight gallons of gas they were allowed to buy each week. The gas rationing which had begun in May had little effect on Paul, for his horse and wagon needed no gas to make the trip to town.

The armed forces had priority access to the things that were available. As supplies became scarce, only a limited amount was available for the general public. In June, the Rationing Board began issuing sugar cards. As with gas, each family was allotted a specified amount of sugar for a certain length of time. No amount of money could buy sugar unless the buyer also had a sufficient number of tokens in his ration card to authorize the purchase. Coffee, pineapples, coconut, and other imported foods were practically unobtainable. People learned to stretch, substitute, or do without things which they had formerly taken for granted.

Farmers who produced foodstuffs played an important part in the nation's war-time economy. They were allotted an extra portion of gas to run their tractors. Each farmer was evaluated and issued points according to the edible products his farm produced. If he was awarded twenty points, he or his draft-age son could obtain a farm deferment and be excused from military duty. As a result, many nonresistant Mennonite farmers began milking cows and growing edible cash crops such as tomatoes and potatoes instead of raising tobacco.

When Phares was ordered to report for an army physical, he saw he needed to adjust his plans for the future. He intended to make farming his career, beginning as soon as he turned twenty-one. But with the threat of the draft dangling over his head, he knew he could not wait two more years. The custom farm work he was doing with his brother, Aaron, would not provide enough points to earn a farm deferment. Even working on the farm for his brother, Amos, was taking a risk. A deferment must be renewed every six months. If he failed to qualify, he would be drafted. Somehow, he had to start farming on his own as soon as possible.

Phares slapped the reins on Cap's back to start him trotting toward Sarah's home. The warm June air was sweet with the fragrance of mown hay and honeysuckle vines. The war that was being fought on the other side of the world lurked in the shadows but was too far away to spoil the beauty of the summer night. The dark canopy of the summer sky above the young couple was brilliantly lighted by a full moon and generously sprinkled with the glitter of millions of stars. The night air around the buggy flickered like an old fashioned tin-punch lantern as the blinking yellow lights on the back ends of the fireflies punched tiny holes in the darkness. There was no way to force these natural lights to comply with the 9:45 p.m. wartime curfew and blackout the government had imposed on the country.

They had dated so long there was no need for Sarah to invite Phares into the house when they reached her home. He knew she expected him to follow her into the parlor where they had their dates. She lighted the oil lamp and pulled the window shades all the way down to the windowsills. The soft light of the oil lamp would not break the blackout rules if the shades were tightly drawn.

Although Sarah had never been talkative, she had found it both easy and pleasant to talk with Phares. But this night he seemed preoccupied and was unusually quiet. When he did not keep up his half of the conversation, there was a long, awkward pause.

"I was wondering," he said at last. "Would you be agreed to get married this fall?"

The question hung in the air between them for a moment. She had known, of course, that dating could be expected to lead to marriage, but she had not expected him to "pop the question" so soon.

"We're pretty young," Sarah replied, without directly answering the question.

"I know our parents want us to wait to get married until we are of age," Phares began pleading his case. "But the way things are, with the draft and all, I think they'll understand if we say we want to get married this fall. What do you think?"

"I guess you're right," Sarah agreed. "But you still have to ask Daed first. If he don't object, then I am agreed."

As Phares had hoped, Daed understood the situation. Although he would have preferred for Sarah to wait, he did not forbid her to marry before she was twenty-one. Seeing the way was clear, Phares made a special trip to town to buy an engagement gift for Sarah.

"Ah-hah!" Esther exclaimed knowingly when she saw the new mantle chime clock. "Now we know! When's the wedding?"

Sarah blushed and lightly caressed the polished wood of the clock case with two fingers. She had known the appearance of the traditional engagement gift would give away the secret she and Phares had been keeping to themselves. "Not for a long time yet," she hedged.

"It can't be too long if you got a clock already," Esther declared. "Sometime this fall, or I miss my guess."

Typical of prospective brides, Sarah lived in the rosy glow of anticipation. Her nineteenth birthday was bright with hopes and dreams for the future. She did not worry about how she and Phares would manage to begin farming in a wartime economy with a purse that contained only petty cash. She knew they would begin marriage on a very short shoestring, but was sure they could "make things hold out" somehow as they went along. Growing up during the Depression had taught her to live by the "use it up, wear it out, make it do, or do without" policy. She had never known any other way of life.

Chapter 18

The heat of summer paid little attention to the passing of Labor Day, which marked the traditional end of the season. Because comfort eclipsed vanity, Mary and Anna joined the parade of country scholars who went back to school barefooted and let their shoes at home to wait for cooler days. Frank watched his two younger sisters walk up the road on the first day of the 1942-43 school term and was thankful he could stay at home this year.

On the tenth day of September, Sarah's second-floor bedroom in Paul Sensenig's house was uncomfortably warm from the unrelenting heat. But the nocturnal serenade of the crickets drifted through the open bedroom window and lulled her to sleep. She did not hear the clock downstairs solemnly striking twelve times to announce the arrival of September 11.

Honk! Honk! Sarah jerked awake at the sound of a car horn outside. *Honk! Honk!* The horn blew again. *Honk! Honk!*

Somebody wants something, Sarah thought. *Why don't Paul get up and see who it is?* she wondered. But Paul and Elizabeth were both fast asleep. Neither of them heard the horn blowing. *Honk! Honk!*

Sarah took the screen out of the bottom half of the window and stuck her head through the opening. "Who's there? What do you want?" she called down to the dark outline of the man she saw below.

"I'm Ez Burkholder," the man called back. "I must talk to Sarah."

"I am Sarah," she answered as an unexplainable foreboding settled in the pit of her stomach. There must be some kind of trouble. She knew her neighbor man would come for her in the middle of the night only for a life or death matter.

"Your Daed sent me to fetch you," Ez called up. "Get dressed and come down. You must go home right away. Your brother Frank died."

The wooden window frame fell with a bang as Sarah's arms suddenly turned limp. The room spun crazily as the words she had heard echoed in her mind. *Frank died! Died?* It couldn't be true! *I must be dreaming*, she thought. Her empty, rumpled bed clearly testified she was not asleep. She turned and looked out the window again. Yes, Ez Burkholder was still standing there beside his machine.

"What's going on?" Elizabeth asked as she waddled into Sarah's bedroom. "Who's out there?"

"It's Ez Burkholder," Sarah choked. "Daed sent him to fetch me. He said my brother died."

"No!" Elizabeth exclaimed. "Which one?"

"Frank."

"When?"

"I don't know. He didn't say," Sarah spoke in short, chopped sentences. "But I must go home. Right now."

"What am I going to do?" Elizabeth cried. "My baby is coming any day. I need you."

"I know," Sarah admitted as tears spilled from her eyes. "But it can't be helped. I must go home."

"*Ya, wohl* (Yes, well)," Elizabeth granted permission with a sigh. "I don't know what we'll do, but we'll just have to make out somehow."

Sarah dressed rapidly in the dark, stuffed a few things in her bag, and ran down the stairs. Ez had already started his machine and turned it around. As soon as Sarah hopped into the car, he tramped on the gas pedal and tore out the driveway to the road. She slammed the door of the moving car and set her bag at her feet. "What happened?" she asked as she turned her white face toward Ez.

"Frank was kicked by a horse," Ez told her. "They took him to the hospital, but it was too late. He died a little after midnight.

That's all I know. Your Daed stopped at our place on the way home from the hospital and asked me to come fetch you right away."

Ez drove through Hinkletown and Murrell in silence. No words could convey the pity he felt for the stunned young girl who had already endured so much suffering in her nineteen years. Sarah's mind whirled with questions Ez could not answer. Which horse had kicked Frank? When? Where? How long ago? Had her brother suffered long from his injuries or been instantly killed?

When Ez braked to a stop at her yard gate, Sarah stumbled from the car without remembering to thank her neighbor for bringing her home. Still unable to believe what he had told her was true, she walked numbly to the kitchen door. The moment she stepped inside, all doubts vanished. The room was filled with ministers and relatives. Every one was dressed in black and had obviously been crying.

When Daed looked up and saw Sarah standing in the doorway, he broke into fresh sobs. She stood there awkwardly, not knowing what to do or say.

"It's my fault," Daed cried brokenly. "It's my fault. I never should've bought that horse."

"It wasn't your fault," Uncle Jacob said gently. "Dick didn't know Frank was there."

While the bishop went on trying to comfort Daed, Sarah slipped into a seat on the settee between Esther and Arthur. "What happened?" she asked in an undertone.

Arthur lifted his eyes and looked at her, but only shook his head. His only brother had been home just eight months. He could not get the words past the lump in his throat to tell her what had happened.

"Dick kicked him," Esther said. She blew her nose and then went on. "You know how mean Dick could be. He was stabled beside Frank's horse. Whenever they were too close together they would fight. Frank came in the barn and saw Sammy's legs were bloody because Dick was kicking him. Frank was on Dick's blind side. He should have yelled or something first, or gone around to the other side, but he didn't take time to think. He just went in and kicked Dick. Of course, Dick thought Sammy had kicked him, so he kicked back. He got Frank right in the gut."

"When was this?" Sarah wondered.

"On Wednesday," Esther answered. "When I came in from the tomato field for dinner, I found Frank laying on the ground beside the water trough. I asked him what's wrong and he told me Dick kicked him. I went in and told Daed. They carried Frank into the house and called the Dr. Wissler. He came and looked Frank over, but said nothing was broken and he'll be all right. But he wasn't.

"The next day Frank helped pick the grapes. By the time they were done he was in so much pain he couldn't stand up straight. He walked in to the house, all bent over, and went upstairs to bed. After awhile he said he feels like he should use the night bucket, but he couldn't. So Daed called the doctor again. He said to give Frank a laxative. They gave me a pill and a glass with just a little water in it, and told me to take it up to Frank. When I went in his room I found him on his hands and knees vomiting black stuff on the floor. I knew then something was terrible wrong."

Sarah and Arthur wept with Esther as her memory replayed the awful scene. *If only I could have been at home*, Sarah thought. She knew there was nothing she could have done to help Frank, but she felt as if she had been cheated again. Frank had been fine on Sunday when she had last seen him. She had not known he had been hurt. Now he was gone. She had missed the last days of his life, just as she had missed the last months of Memm's life. *Why do I always get sent away?* Sarah's heart wept. *Why must I always miss it when these things happen in our family?*

"Daed called Dr. Wissler again and he finally came out," Esther said when she could speak again. "He decided Frank should go to the Ephrata Hospital and called an ambulance to take him. It seemed like it took them forever to get him on that stretcher and out of the house. I thought they'd never get him out of the house alive, but around eleven o'clock they finally did."

"Why didn't they take him to Lancaster?" Sarah wondered. She questioned the value of taking her brother to the small hospital at Ephrata which had been operating for only five years in a portion of the old Mountain Springs Hotel on top of the Ephrata hill.

"I guess the doctor sent him to Ephrata because it was the closest hospital," Esther said. "Daed rode in the back of the ambulance with Frank. When they got to the crossroad, Frank asked if they were there yet. Daed told him, 'No. We're just at Milt Wanners.' That was the last Frank said anything. When they got to the hospital Daed told him, 'We're there now,' but he didn't answer."

"The doctors at the hospital saw Frank was too far gone and there was nothing they could do for him. His intestines tore when Dick kicked him and gangrene had set in. The doctors asked Daed if they could operate anyway, because they thought maybe they can learn something to help somebody else. Daed said they can, so they rushed him into the operating room. But before long the doctor came out and told Daed he can go in and talk to Frank. They knew he was in his last minutes. He died a little after midnight."

When daylight came, the undertaker brought Frank's body home and took it into the parlor to prepare it for burial. He turned the room into a temporary morgue by pulling the green window shades down to the windowsills. Then he washed Frank's body, dressed it in the traditional plain white shroud, and placed it in the narrow, unlined wooden coffin he had brought with him. He opened a pair of collapsible turned wooden legs and set the coffin on top of them. The coffin would stay in the parlor until it was time to go to the church for the funeral on Sunday afternoon.

No one was hungry for breakfast, but the family sat down and tried to eat some of the food that had been prepared for them. Sarah had forced down only a few bites when she saw Phares coming. Glad for an excuse to leave the table, she left her uneaten food in her bowl.

"Uncle Check (Jake) came first thing this morning and told us," Phares said gently when Sarah met him at the door. "I couldn't believe it."

"Neither could I," Sarah choked as she wiped her eyes with her hankie. "But it's true."

"I came as soon as I heard," he told her. " I thought maybe you needed a way home."

"Ez Burkholder fetched me during the night," she said and went on to tell him how she had received the shocking news. At length, she took him into the parlor to see Frank's body.

Dropping his own plans for the day, Phares spent the day with Sarah's family. He knew the work that needs to be done on a farm does not stop when there is a death in the family. Other men came throughout the day to do Daed's work for him. Women volunteers brought food, canned the grapes, and cleaned the house, leaving Daed and Lydia free to receive the visitors that dropped in to offer their sympathy.

Daed could hardly bear to face John Weaver and his family when they came to pay their respects. Daed knew they had loved Frank as their own and felt responsible for the grief they suffered. He wished now he had let Frank stay with them, but it was too late to go back and do things differently.

Daed sat next to Frank's coffin while the long line of friends and relatives filed by on Saturday evening. Lydia sat next to Daed, with the children seated next to her in order by age. Sarah shook hands woodenly with the callers and anxiously twisted the sodden hankie in her lap. She had never really learned to know her brother. While the family was separated, he had lived so far away they had seldom seen him. She had been away, working as a live-in maid, most of the eight months since Frank had come home. No one had guessed he would die in his teen years. *Why did God allow this to happen?* Sarah wondered. *Didn't our family suffer enough already? Why do things always go backwards for Daed?*

By one o'clock on Sunday afternoon, the first floor of the house was filled with friends and relatives who had joined the Wenger family for the beginning of the funeral. After a short time of Scripture reading and prayer, Frank's coffin was carried outside to the waiting horse-drawn hearse. A long line of buggies followed the hearse to the Pike church where a final viewing was conducted before the burial. Then they all went into the meeting-house for the funeral service.

Sarah went through the motions, doing what was expected of her at the moment and trying not to think of the future. She took her seat on the front bench beside Lydia, with Esther, Mary and Anna in line after her. Daed and Arthur sat facing them on the men's side of the building.

When everyone was seated, the bishop stood up and began to speak in his sing-song preacher's voice. While Sarah's ears heard the words the minister said, she found her mind wandering out to the cemetery and the growing row of graves the Wenger family had filled. First there had been the stillborn Margaret they had never known. Then another tiny baby girl had been buried with Memm. And now Frank lay beside them. *How many more times must we gather here to bury one of our family?* Sarah wondered. *Who will be next?*

Frank had been snatched away so suddenly at such a young age. Any one of them could follow him at any time and be the next to be lowered into place beside him. In spite of the warmth of the afternoon, shivers ran up and down Sarah's back. She had been looking forward to being married soon and living a long, happy life with Phares. Would her married life be filled with the same kind of reverses and sorrows that had marked the trail of Daed's life? The rosy future she had assumed lay before her could change without a moment's notice. Where could she find the courage to face the unknowns in the future?

The sound of the minister clearing his throat came through Sarah's mental fog. She heard him begin reading in German the first six verses of John 14. "Let not your heart be troubled: ye believe in God, believe also in me. In my Father's house are many mansions: if it were not so, I would have told you. I go to prepare a place for you. And if I go and prepare a place for you, I will come again, and receive you unto myself; that where I am, there ye may be also. And whither I go ye know, and the way ye know. Thomas saith unto him, Lord, we know not whither thou goest; and how can we know the way? Jesus saith unto him, I am the way, the truth, and the life: no man cometh unto the Father, but by me."

The words were simple, yet profound and enormously comforting. Combined with what she already knew from reading her English translation of the Bible, Sarah understood the passage. Jesus was the Son of God. He had come from heaven to earth to die on a cross and make it possible for every person on earth to have eternal life. Believing in Jesus was the way to reach God and heaven. Jesus is in heaven now, preparing places for all those who believe in Him. Christians do not cease to exist when they die, but go to live forever in the place Jesus has prepared for them. Memm had been there for nine years. She would never leave that wonderful Place.

"Peace I leave with you, my peace I give unto you: not as the world giveth, give I unto you. Let not your heart be troubled, neither let it be afraid," the minister read again from John 14.

As Sarah pondered the peace Jesus gives, a ray of light shone through the darkness of her troubled spirit. She could not have put her thoughts into words, yet she began to realize that true peace is not the absence of trouble, but the presence of Jesus. Fear and anxiety are not eliminated by knowing the future, but by having faith in the all-wise God who is in control of the present and the future. He can be trusted to keep His promises to carry His children through life and take them to be with Him forever when this life is over. Encouraged by the words of Jesus which had been read, Sarah knew she could put her hand in the Hand of God and step out in faith trusting Him to carry her safely through this life and into eternity.

After the funeral ended and the traditional post-funeral meal was over, the Wenger family set about the task of trying to go on with life. Sarah had learned from experience that a family cannot pick up where they left off and go on as before after death has claimed one of their members. But neither is it possible to stop living. Life goes on and one must go with it, accepting and making the best of the changes it brings.

After spending about a week at home with her family, Sarah returned to her job as Paul and Elizabeth Sensenig's maid. Their new baby, Sam, had been born the day of Frank's funeral. Paul's sister, Mary, had filled in for Sarah during the emergency. She would keep the job until she was married. By then Sam would be two months old and Elizabeth would manage without her.

At times, it seemed to Sarah as if Frank's death and funeral had been a bad dream. But any loud noise in the night wakened her and set her heart pounding until she was sure no one was outside blowing a car horn. When she was at home on Sundays, Frank's empty place at the table verified his permanent absence. The family had been scattered and incomplete ever since Memm died. All possibilities of being fully reunited had been terminated by Frank's death. Sarah would soon be married and leave to establish a home of her own.

"I've got to get something to make a wedding dress," Sarah told Phares when the days turned cool in October. "I need time to make it yet. Our day is only a little over a month away anymore."

"We'll go to Lancaster next Saturday," Phares promised.

"We wouldn't have to go that far," Sarah protested. "I could probably find something in Ephrata."

"You'd have better picking choice in Lancaster," he insisted. "We'll go in on the trolley next week."

The eager couple made the trip as planned, but it was a failure. Empty-handed, they boarded the trolley for the return trip to Ephrata.

"Well! That was a wild goose chase," Phares exclaimed. "We went all that way for nothing."

"I'll see once what I can find in Ephrata," Sarah said sensibly. "I know the stores don't have much because of the war, but maybe I can find something somewhere that'll do."

The second shopping trip the next week was almost as discouraging as the first one had been. The store shelves which had once been filled with bolts of dress goods were nearly empty.

"Next I'll have to make my dress out of feed bag material," Sarah groaned as they trudged from one store to another in their fruitless search. "Let's try Seldomridges."

The shelves of Seldomridges store were just as empty as the shelves in the other stores. Then Sarah spied a bolt of light blue crepe. It was the right color and type of fabric for a wedding dress.

"I'd like to see that blue crepe," Sarah told the clerk.

He took the bolt from the shelf and lay it on the counter. Sarah fingered the fabric. She could tell it was not a good quality fabric, but it was the best thing she had seen in town. She asked the price and knew she could do no better elsewhere. "I'll take four yards," she decided.

The clerk silently measured and cut the fabric from the bolt. Then he folded the fabric, wrapped it in brown paper, and tied the bundle with string. He handed them the bill and their change without speaking a word. From previous experience, they knew he did not want to wait on them because they were Mennonites. He probably had a son fighting in the war and thought it was not fair that the Mennonites were excused from military duty.

Phares and Sarah left the store and moved down the sidewalk. A man walking behind them shouted, "Yellow bellies! Cowards!"

Since the war had begun, the town was no longer a pleasant gathering place for the young people on a Saturday night. Some people deliberately tried to pick a fight with Mennonites in order to test their nonresistance. Girls whose sweethearts had been drafted were jealous of the Mennonite girls who had not been separated from their boyfriends. Easily identified by their clothing, the plain people had learned it was wise to control their words and actions in town. The best way to avoid conflict was to do their business quietly, ignore the antagonists, and leave town as soon as possible.

The young couple ignored the heckler and walked swiftly toward Phares' car. His horse, Cap, had died from foot disease about the same time his brother, Amos, decided to sell his car. Following the old tradition that had been practiced for generations, Amos and Florence had waited until after they were married to join the church.[15] Phares was quite willing to take the 1936 Chevy off his brother's hands so he could join the church. Amos had traded his car for Phares' bicycle and buggy.

The next week, Sarah made her wedding dress from the same pattern she always used to make her dresses. By the middle of November, the dress was ready and waiting for the big day. She had never expected to have an actual wedding. She and Phares would be married in a private ceremony in the home of a minister and have a wedding dinner at a later date. Their parents knew of their plans and did not forbid them to marry before they were twenty-one, but neither set of parents would make an exception to their family rules and provide the signatures required to grant them permission to obtain a marriage license in Pennsylvania. This was not an unusual situation, and the solution to the problem was equally common.

"Listen to that knocking," Phares told Sarah when he brought her home on Sunday night. "I have to replace the valves and rings on this thing so it'll take us to Maryland."

"I hope you can get the parts," Sarah fretted. "We have to go no later than Thursday."

"Don't worry. I'll get it fixed," he assured her. "We're going to Maryland, come hail or high water."

True to his word, the Chevy was repaired by Thursday and carried Phares and Sarah sixty miles to Elkton, Maryland, without breaking down. In Maryland, they could obtain a marriage license at the age of eighteen without a parental signature, and without the expensive blood tests required by the state of Pennsylvania. With the precious paper in hand, they went to find the minister their friends had told them to see. They made arrangements with the minister to be married at his house on Saturday, November 21, and then went home until the required two-day waiting period ended.

Sarah was ready when Phares came for her on Saturday morning. Her light blue dress was becoming in its simplicity. She

---

[15] Since the 1970s, a large percentage of young people raised in Stauffer Mennonite homes have joined the church in their teens and before marriage.

Phares and Sarah, photographed in September 1942.

needed no bridal veil, for her head was always veiled with a square, white covering. She had the roses on her cheeks for flowers and a white hankie with delicate lace edging to carry in her hand. She was the most beautiful bride Phares had ever seen.

Phares' sister, Kass, and Sarah's brother, Arthur, had agreed to accompany the bridal pair and witnesses their marriage. Kass and Arthur sat on the back seat of the Chevy with the box of lunch Kass had packed for the four of them setting on the seat between them.

"I could hardly get away," Phares told Sarah as he drove east. "Amos knew I was going to get married and what time I wanted to leave. But, once again, he left too much work for Saturday. Finally, I just told him I had to quit and left."

Phares drove east into Chester County and then south into Maryland. "Here we are," he announced as he backed into a parking space in front of the parsonage.

Now that the long trip was over and the moment had come, Sarah's hands were cold and clammy. She could tell Phares was nervous too. Were they doing the right thing? Should they have waited until they were twenty-one to be married? Yet, they had come too far to turn back now.

The minister welcomed the young people on his doorstep into the parsonage. He took them into the parlor, which was the most finely furnished room of the house and a fitting place to conduct a ceremony of holy matrimony. They hung their coats, hats, and bonnets on the clothes tree and then turned to face the minister. The ceremony was performed quickly. Within minutes, Phares and Sarah were married for better or worse, for richer or poorer, as long as they both should live.

Hand in hand, the newlyweds left the house and flew on light feet to the car. Sarah giggled nervously as Phares started the car to begin the return trip home.

"What tickles you, Mrs. Stauffer?" Phares asked in a buoyant tone. She could hear the delight in his voice as he tested the words on his tongue for the first time.

"Oh," she laughed, "I just remembered what Uncle Weaver Auker used to say. 'The thing you throw the furtherest away is what you go fetch again.' I guess I did it now!"

Phares chuckled. She had told him the story months earlier, so no further explanations were needed now. "Maryland isn't so far away you can't go there to fetch something," he teased.

"Remember what you said in school?" Kass chimed in from her place on the back seat. "You said if he ever gets married someday, you pity his wife. *Dauererst dich nau?* (Do you pity yourself now?)"

They all laughed, and it helped relieve the tension. Phares and Sarah were man and wife, bound together as one for life, yet still the same two people as before the ceremony. The countryside under the gray November skies was the same as it had been when they had been going the other direction. People were going about their normal Saturday lives, unaware that a life-changing event had just occurred in the lives of the two people who were passing through on their way home.

"Where's that lunch you packed?" Phares asked his sister. "I'm as hollow as a rotten log."

Kass opened the lunch box and passed out the food she had packed for their dinner. She had splurged on Velveeta cheese and

Ritz crackers. The special store-bought foods added a festive touch to the ordinary lunch of bologna sandwiches and other homemade fare.

Phares and Sarah did not feel deprived because the first meal of their married life was only a packed lunch, for the love they shared was rich and sweet. More delectable than any wedding cake could ever be, their love would last a lifetime and grow with the passing years.

Chapter 19

"That should do it," Phares declared as he settled a can of gas in the trunk of his Chevy and closed the lid. "The tank's full to the top and we got another five gallons in the trunk. Fifteen gallons ought to take us into Ohio."

"And from there on we'll be all right, because gas rationing isn't so strict once we get out of the state," Phares' brother, Aaron, repeated what they already knew. "I'll drive first if you want me to."

"Fine with me," Phares agreed as he handed Aaron the keys. "Just say whenever you want to trade off."

Phares and Sarah climbed into the back seat of the Chevy with his sister, Kass, leaving the front seat to Aaron and his wife, Stella. The newlyweds had brought Arthur home after they were married, eaten supper, and picked up Aaron and Stella. Now, the wedding trip to Indiana which Phares had planned was beginning at six o'clock in the evening. He had arranged for his married brother and single sister to accompany them, for driving so far with a half-empty car would have been a foolish waste of space and gas. Aaron would help with the driving on the long non-stop trip, and Kass would enjoy visiting with their Indiana cousins.

Aaron drove through all the little towns that bordered Route 322 and threaded through the city of Harrisburg. Near Carlisle, he got on the Pennsylvania Turnpike. The new superhighway, which had opened in 1940, was the first of its kind in the nation.

"Now this is traveling!" Phares exclaimed in approval as the Chevy rolled rapidly west on the smooth concrete highway. "No stop signs or traffic lights anywhere."

"I'll say," Aaron agreed. "Too bad it only goes to Irwin."

"It's supposed to go all the way across the state someday," Phares remarked. "But this war is holding things up. I'm afraid it's going to take a long time to get it done."

"I'm anxious to see those tunnels they made under the mountains," Aaron said. "Somebody must've laid awake nights figuring out how to do that. Who would've thought the day would ever come when we'd drive *under* the mountains instead of over them!"

"It seems strange to pass the towns without going through them," Kass observed. "There's no gas stations or anything along this road. What if people need gas or something?"

"There's a Howard Johnson every so often," Aaron told his sister. "They have service stations and restaurants."

"Yes, but they're way too expensive for us," Stella protested.

"I know," Aaron agreed. "You don't want to pay twenty-five cents for a gallon of gas unless you absolutely must."

Sarah listened to the conversation without adding anything to the discussion. She knew they were well prepared for the trip. They would not have to buy expensive gas along the turnpike, because they had an extra five gallons in the trunk. They had packed their own food so they would not have to eat in restaurants, and they were driving overnight so they would not have to spend money to sleep in cabins. By morning they would be in Indiana where they would stay with Phares' relatives for the next five days. The price of the gas was the biggest expense of their wedding trip, but Aaron would pay his share of the cost.

The long wedding night passed as Aaron and Phares took turns driving and napping. By morning, they had crossed both Pennsylvania and Ohio to enter Indiana just east of Fort Wayne. From there, Route 30 angled northwest to take them within a few miles of the Goshen area where their Bauman, Martin, and Zimmerman cousins lived.

Sarah had complied with Phares' plans for a wedding trip, but she did not enjoy the week. Phares and his siblings had a great time with their western relatives, but they were all strangers to Sarah. Ezra, Lowell, Amos, Lorene, Lydia, Noah. These and more names and faces tangled themselves in Sarah's memory. Although the Indiana cousins spoke Pennsylvania Deutsch, they had a western accent that sounded strange to her ears. She had always hated meeting strangers and never knew what to say to them, so she simply listened to the others talk and endured the daily round of visits. She had never been so far from home and desperately wished to be back in her own familiar territory, but she had learned to endure difficulties without whining and complaining. The homesick bride bravely stuffed her misery inside to keep from spoiling her groom's outing.

The ground was covered with a thick layer of snow on Thanksgiving Day. The last thing Sarah wanted was to be snowed

This picture of the wedding trip was taken in Indiana. The three children standing in front of Phares' 1936 Chevy are some of the children of the Stauffers' cousins. Behind the children are Aaron and Stella Stauffer, Phares and Sarah Stauffer. Kass Stauffer is standing to the side of the group.

in and unable to go home. But the sky cleared and the wind was still, so the roads did not drift shut. Cousin Amos Martin invited all of the relatives to his house for a big reunion the night before the carload of Stauffers headed home. The Martin house was full of the noise of the people who had come for this grand finale reunion. It was over at last, and only the long return trip lay between Sarah and home. The miles fell away as the Chevy rolled east on Route 30. Once again, the men would take turns driving for eighteen hours until they were home.

"We better stop for gas in East Liverpool," Phares said as he studied the unfolded map that lay on his lap. "That's the last town in Ohio before we cross the river."

"Right," Aaron agreed. "We want the tank and the can both full before we hit the Pennsylvania line."

The attendant at the service station filled the Chevy's gas tank to the top and put five gallons in the can in the trunk. Then he cleaned the windshield and checked the oil. "You're all set," he said after he closed the hood with a slam.

As they drove steadily east, the needle of the gas gauge moved steadily toward the empty mark. When the needle touched the big E, they stopped at the side of the road. The men poured the gas from the can into the car. The extra five gallons took them back into Lancaster County and all the way home. The wedding trip was over. Sarah knew they had been fortunate to be able to travel, for many newlyweds were not able to go on a wedding trip during these war years, but she had not seen any place that looked better than her own familiar home.

They had come home late on Saturday evening and had one more day together to rest from the trip and be refreshed. Phares went home early on Monday morning. He would return on Saturday to spend the weekend with his wife. Following the tradition of the generations before them, the bride and groom would continue to live with their respective parents until spring when farms changed hands. Then they hoped to find a place to rent and establish their first home. Since she was married, Daed would not send Sarah out again to be someone's maid.

I'm glad I can stay at home until we set up housekeeping, Sarah thought with relief. *I'm done living in other people's homes. Come spring, we'll have a home of our own and I'll finally have a place where I can always stay.*

A week after the newlyweds returned from their wedding trip, Daed and Lydia hosted a wedding dinner for Phares and Sarah. Although they were already married, everyone considered this dinner to be the wedding. Sarah wore her wedding dress and, as guest of honor, was totally excused from helping with the meal.

The house was crammed with Sarah's Wenger and Shaub relatives, as well as some of Lydia's Good relatives. The long table was set and reset to serve all the guests the delicious meal Lydia had prepared. The gifts the guests brought were displayed in the spare bedroom and duly admired after the meal was over. The assortment of practical housewares were the first installment in the collection of necessities the bridal pair would gather during the winter months. The handsome wooden chest filled with shiny new flatware which Phares had given Sarah was the center of attraction. He had paid several weeks' wages for a gift he felt was deserving of his cherished bride.

Everyone understood why the Stauffer relatives were not invited to the wedding dinner at Sarah's home. Just before Christmas, Phares' parents hosted the traditional second wedding dinner, called *die infahr* (the infare), for the young couple. This time the groom's Stauffer and Brubaker relatives were invited to the wedding dinner in his home and brought more gifts to add to the couple's small hoard.

During the first weeks of 1943, friends and relatives who had not attended either of the wedding dinners honored the newlyweds with an invitation to dinner at their homes. The gifts they received at these dinners were added to those they had already received. By spring, they had accumulated most of the essentials needed to "set up housekeeping."

"I found us a farm!" Phares jubilantly announced one weekend in the middle of January. "It's at Sandy Beach."

"Sandy Beach!" Sarah cried. "So far away?"

"It's just a little south of Akron," he countered. "That's not far to drive in a car."

"I guess," she conceded.

"The man that owns the place is a Thirty-Fiver and got himself in trouble with the draft board," Phares explained. "One day the authorities came and hauled him off to jail. His wife can't farm the place alone, so she's going home to her parents and put the place up for rent. We can move in next month already."[16]

Winter had softened but not lost its grip on the county the Saturday Phares and Sarah moved into their first home. The snow that had covered the ground for weeks had been reduced to a few patches lying in hollows and sheltered places. The bare, frozen ground was brown and the trees stretched naked black limbs into the sky. Soon the brown earth would become a sea of mud and the tiny buds on the tree branches would swell to the bursting point.

Arthur was at the farm where he was working as a hired man, but Daed hitched his horses to his wagon and helped Phares load the used furniture he and Sarah had bought. The men tied old quilts over the load to keep the furniture dry on the trip. Lydia wrapped newspaper around glass jars of home canned foods and packed the green Mason jars in boxes. She filled a bag with potatoes, scooped some corn meal into an empty Quaker Oats box, and added a can of lard to round out the small hoard of starter supplies. Sarah's sisters helped her carry the wed-

---

[16] A group of thirty-five people separated from the Groffdale Conference in 1942 over issues which included participating in the draft and war-time food ration stamp program. This Reidenbach group, commonly referred to as "The Thirty-Fivers," was a more conservative wing of the Old Order Mennonites. The government provided a program for conscientious objectors in World War II called Civilian Public Service (CPS) in which men could serve their country doing public service projects such as forestry and road building. Some Old Order Mennonites, such as the Reidenbach group, believed participating in the CPS program represented compromise with society. They supported their young man's refusal to participate in the draft, which resulted in jail sentences for several of them.

ding gifts from the spare room to Phares' car. Kettles, dishpans, pot holders, drinking glasses, tablecloths, and much more was loaded into the trunk of the Chevy. Lydia brought the quilt she had made for Sarah and piled it on the back seat with her clothes.

"I guess that's it," Sarah said as she stuffed the last items in the back of the Chevy. The prospect of setting up her own house was exciting, but now the time had come to leave her old home. For a moment, she felt torn in two, half of her wanting to go and the other half wanting to stay.

"Here," Anna cried as she came running from the back porch holding high Sarah's old black boots. "Don't forget these."

They all laughed as Sarah took the worn out boots and threw them onto the floor in the back of the car.

"You might be glad for them yet," Anna defended her reasoning. "You can't get new ones 'til this war's over, you know."

"She'll wear 'em in the barn," Mary reassured her younger sister as Sarah got in the front seat. "Can us girls ride with yous?"

"I don't care," Sarah gave permission. The two younger girls made room for themselves on the back seat and Esther sat in the front with Sarah. She was glad her sisters were in the car with her when Phares drove away. Somehow, that made her feel as if she was not really leaving home.

Phares drove to Diamond Station and passed Weaver Zimmerman's farm where Sarah had once lived. They went a short distance south on the old Akron Road to the place where it met the new Route 222 (now 272). By taking this route he had skirted the town of Akron and come out at a point on the south side of the steep hill on which the town was built.

They waited at the junction of the roads for a long convoy of soldiers in olive green army vehicles to drive past on their way toward Lancaster. Sarah knew this road could be seen from the place they were going to live. She quaked inwardly at the thought of living where so many soldiers passed through.

"One Sunday us boys rode out here on our bicycles to see where they were cutting that hill away to make this here road,"

Phares told Sarah. "It was really something to see all those big machines they used. It makes sense now, but at the time we couldn't figure out why they went to all the trouble of cutting the rocks away instead of just going up over the hill. They started out at Shaum's Corner and took the road in to Akron. Now it goes right through Akron, past Ephrata, and all the way to Adamstown without going through the towns. The only thing that's not done yet is the bridge over 322 at the cloverleaf."

"Daed said they can't get the steel to finish it," Sarah said.

"*Ya*," he nodded. "All the metal is going to make planes and tanks for the war. Everything else has to wait."

When the way was finally clear, Phares pulled out onto the new concrete road and drove south about a mile. Then he turned sharply to the right and followed the road which wound up a hill toward the Cocalico Creek. None of them knew how the area had gotten the exotic name of Sandy Beach. The Cocalico Creek flowed under a bridge to join the Conestoga Creek in a meadow on the other side of the new road, but the creek banks contained muskrat holes rather than sandy beaches.

"Here we are!" Phares announced as he turned into a farm lane that took them to the back of a bank barn and then curved around to end between the house and barn. This was the place where they would begin farming and trying to make a living for themselves.[17]

Sarah looked at the house which was to be their first home. It was a typical square two-and-a-half-story farmhouse set a respectable distance from the barn. The buildings had once been painted white and had faded green trim on the corners and around the windows. A wide porch stretched all the way across the front of the house. The meadow dipped down in front of the buildings and then rolled up a long slope to the edge of the new road.

"Let's go in and see the house 'til Daed gets here," Mary urged.

---

[17] The current address of this property is 161 Rose Hill Road, Ephrata, Pa.

They walked slowly through the three rooms on each floor, but there was not much to see in the cold, empty house.

"Oh!" Anna squealed when she opened a fourth upstairs door. "A bathroom!"

"Yes, but it don't work," Phares apologized. "The man that owns this place disconnected the electric when he lived here, and then the pipes froze up and busted in here. So we have a bathroom, but we can't use it."

"That's a shame," Esther lamented.

"It don't matter," Sarah declared. "We never had such a luxury before. We can do without."

The little troop strolled through the barn and investigated every outbuilding on the place while they waited for Daed and Lydia to come with the wagon. When they arrived, the few pieces of used furniture they had brought were soon carried into the house and put in place. Upstairs, there was one bed and a bureau for the main bedroom, and another bed for the spare room. The kitchen was furnished with a cookstove, table, a few chairs, and a red and white Hoosier kitchen cupboard. Appliances were "as scarce as hen's teeth" in these war years, but they were spared the problem of finding a refrigerator for it would have been useless without electric in the house. An old-fashioned wooden ice box would probably have been available, but they could make do without one.

"Where shall I put this?" Esther asked when she brought Sarah's ironing board into the kitchen.

"Oh, I guess back there," Sarah said as she waved a hand toward the back corner of the room. The wooden ironing board was the only new thing they had bought. She did not want to iron on the table as they had done at home, so she had splurged and bought a real ironing board.

The wedding gifts and their personal things were brought into the house and put in place. With so much help and so few things, the new home was soon in order. Then the girls climbed into the wagon to go home with Daed and Lydia, leaving Sarah behind to begin life with Phares.

Sarah looked dreamily around the sparsely furnished kitchen. The coal fire in the cookstove spread a cozy warmth through the room. She had lived in many houses and various homes of other people, but this was different. For the first time, she had a home of her own. Everything in this house belonged to them. Every dishpan, tea towel, dish, spoon, kettle, frying pan, paring knife—everything was hers. She had worked in other women's kitchens all her life; now she would do her own work in her own kitchen with her own things.

"What's for supper?" Phares asked, interrupting her reverie.

"Oh!" Sarah came back to reality with a jolt. She had not made any plans for the evening meal. "I don't know. What do you want?"

"Food." His vague answer did not help.

"Lydia sent some jars along," Sarah remembered. "I'll see what I can find."

"I'll be out in the barn. Call me when it's ready," Phares said as he clapped his hat on his head and went out.

Sarah opened a jar of canned sausage and dumped it in a frying pan. The meat had been cooked in the canning process, so it would only need to be heated now. *I guess I can fry some potatoes to go with it,* she decided. She had helped to make many meals, but planning menus had not been her responsibility. As she peeled the potatoes, she suddenly realized that from now on she would have to cook three meals every day. Not only would she have to cook the food, but she would also have to decide what to make and have everything ready to eat at the proper time. She would have to bake the bread and churn the butter by herself. No one was there to answer her questions if she was not sure how to do something. Having her own kitchen was going to be more work and responsibility than she had realized.

Out in the barn, Phares was having similar thoughts about his new responsibilities. The owner of the farm had not finished stripping his tobacco, so Phares would finish the job for him. By the time the tobacco was shipped, it would be time to begin plowing and preparing to plant the crops. He had been forced to borrow money to buy what he needed to begin farming. He was not only making a living for himself, but he had promised to provide for Sarah as well. He would have to manage things so he had the money to pay the bills and provide the things the two of them needed to survive.

Every morning, Phares milked the six cows by hand while Sarah made breakfast, but she helped with the evening milking. Without refrigeration, they had no way to cool the milk. Sarah ran the milk through a hand-cranked separator to separate the cream from the milk. The butter she made from the cream was sold or exchanged at the grocery store for sugar, flour, or other staples. Phares took the skimmed milk back to the barn and fed it to the pigs they were raising for meat to eat in the winter.

"You won't have to make butter to sell anymore," Phares told Sarah a few weeks after they started farming. "I found out there's a place at New Holland that takes cream to make cheese. I made arrangements for them to pick up our cream from now on. It'll be less work and pay better than making butter."

Twice each week, a truck came to the farm to pick up the cream and take it to New Holland. The cheese plant would mail a check to pay for the cream which had been shipped.

"Look at this!" Phares crowed as he held up the first cream check.

"Twelve dollars!" Sarah cried. She could not believe her eyes. Twelve dollars was a lot of money.

As large as the check had looked when it arrived, they could not believe how fast the money disappeared. The expenses of starting to farm were more than they had imagined. There was rent to pay, seed to buy for spring planting, interest on the money Phares had loaned to get started, and many more expenses. Sarah had never liked book work and gladly let the bookkeeping to Phares. But she did her best to make things "hold out" by stretching every dime and pinching every penny.

Whenever he could, Phares worked in his brother Dan's machine shop to earn a little extra money and Sarah dressed chickens for a neighbor to earn something to help pay for the groceries. They never had enough money for everything, but Sarah was no stranger to poverty. She bought at the store only the necessities which she could pay for with the cash in her pocketbook.

"I guess I'll try to plow again today," Phares told Sarah after breakfast one Monday morning.

"I hope the horses cooperate this time," she tried to encourage him.

"They better," he growled. "I'm getting fed up with them."

Sarah heated water in the washboiler and poured it into her wash tub. They did not have the money to buy a washing machine, even if they would have been able to find a used one for sale. So she washed their clothes by hand on a wooden washboard. As she hung the clean clothes on the washline, she could see Phares struggling to plow with the horses. He was not lacking in experience, for he had grown up working with horses on his father's farm. But the horses his father had given him to start farming were young and inexperienced. They did not know how to work together.

Suddenly, the horses broke loose and ran away. "Whoa! Whoa!" Phares yelled as he ran behind them, trying to grab the reins that trailed on the ground. But the horses were tired of working and raced away toward the barn. The plow bounced on the ground behind them like a toy on a string. Sarah watched Phares running after the horses, but he could not catch them. They did not stop until they were at the barn.

"That does it!" Phares declared in disgust as he unhitched the runaway horses. "I'm going to make myself a tractor."

"How are you going to do that?" Sarah asked skeptically.

"I don't know yet, but I'll figure something out," he assured her. "I used Aaron's John Deere tractors long enough to know there's other ways to plow if the horses don't want to work. Tractors are scarce these days, and I couldn't afford to buy one anyway, but I'm going over to Dan's shop tomorrow and see what I can put together."

"Can I go along?" Sarah asked eagerly. "I wasn't home for awhile. You could drop me off there on your way to Dan's shop."

"Sure," Phares agreed. He knew his wife missed her sisters and spending a day at home would be good medicine for her spirits.

Phares spent more than one day in his brother's machine shop before he finished making his tractor. Sarah almost laughed when he brought the contraption home. It certainly was not a John Deere! This "tractor" was made of parts he had salvaged from junked cars and trucks. His tractor was basically a short frame, two axles, a rear, an engine, two transmissions, a steering wheel, and a seat.

"You can plow with this thing?" Sarah asked incredulously.

"Just watch!" he challenged. He attached a plow to his tractor and drove it out to the field. The plow scratched a shallow furrow in the thin, stony soil. The tractor obediently dragged the plow to the other end of the field, turned around when Phares turned the steering wheel, and plowed another shallow furrow on the way back. He drove slowly so the engine would not overheat and carefully so the tires would not spin uselessly. The homemade tractor went back and forth across the field without getting notions of its own to run away to the barn.

The young couple did not know their neighbors had been watching to see how this nineteen-year-old pair would manage to farm, nor did they care what the neighbors thought of the home-made tractor. In these war years, almost everyone had to make do with what they could scrape together from the limited resources that were available. The tractor worked, after a fashion, and would have to do until they could get something better.

Sarah liked working outdoors more than working in the house. Keeping house for two was not a full-time job, so she helped Phares in the barn and fields as much as she could. Although she was terrified of his homemade tractor, she summoned all her courage and learned to drive it. They planted a large pea patch with hopes of selling peas on market. The stony soil did not hold moisture very long and the tiny green shoots that had started out so bravely in the spring dried up and died before they produced a crop. Sarah canned the small yield for their own use in the coming winter, and Phares was left scratching his head to figure out another way to make up for the loss of the expected income.

The hot, dry days that killed the peas were just right for ripening the wheat. Phares cut the wheat and stored the bundles of sheaves on the big barn floor until the threshing crew could come.

Early in August, Phares told Sarah, "The threshers will be here next week."

"I'll get Esther to come help me with the cooking," Sarah told him. She had been dreading cooking for the threshers and decided to recruit her sister to help with the momentous task of feeding the crew of hungry men.

Esther spent the night in the spare room and was on hand to help first thing in the morning. The sound of the threshing machine running at the barn came through the wood-framed screen door of the kitchen as the sisters cooked and baked all morning in a race with the clock. Esther was younger than Sarah but more confident of herself. Although they were working in Sarah's kitchen, Esther was not afraid to give orders and make suggestions. Rather than being offended, Sarah was glad to have someone to consult with and help her get everything done on time.

The table was set and the food was ready when the men came in to eat dinner. Sarah knew the meal she had prepared could not compete with the spread some farm wives set out on threshing day, but she had done her best.

"Well, that's done," Sarah said with a long sigh of relief when the men went back to the barn. She lifted the hem of her apron and wiped the sweat from her face.

"All but the cleaning up," Esther remarked, as she cleared one end of the table to make room for the dishpan.

"How did we make such a mess just to cook one meal?" Sarah groaned as she surveyed the stacks of dirty dishes. "I don't believe there's a clean dish on the place anymore."

The job of restoring order to the kitchen was made more pleasant by having a sister to visit with while they worked. Soon after they finished, the noise at the barn stopped. The men had threshed Phares' small crop and were finished early.

"Let's go see how big the straw pile is," Sarah suggested.

A fan had blown the straw through a long stacker pipe at the back of the threshing machine. The pipe stuck out the open doors in the top of the barn, making the straw fall in a golden heap on the ground in front of the barn. The straw would be used for bedding the animals on the ground floor of the barn, so this was the most convenient place to keep a straw stack.

Sarah and Esther saw Phares climbing the straw stack with a pitch fork in his hand. The straw slid down as he climbed, but he climbed faster than the straw could slide. He leaped on top of the stack and stood up.

"The straw covered up these wires," he called down to the women looking up at him. "I have to dig them out."

Sarah saw that the old, frayed electric wires which sagged down from the pole to the barn had been buried in the top of the straw stack. Phares tramped down the straw as he dug around trying to free the buried wires. Suddenly, the wires sprang up into the air, touched each other, crackled and sparked.

"*Geb acht!* (Watch out!)" Sarah cried as the wires swayed in the air.

"I thought those wires were dead!" Phares bellowed in astonishment. He scrambled down the straw stack even faster than he had climbed up.

"You could've been killed," Esther stated the obvious in a stunned voice.

"That, or the straw could've caught fire," Phares agreed. "The electric was disconnected before we moved in here, so I thought there's no hot wires on the place."

The wires were safely out of the straw and no damage had been done. There was nothing more to do, but the sisters stood there looking up at the wires after Phares had walked away.

"That was close enough!" Esther exclaimed. *Aie yi yi!* All the things that happened to you already—. You could write a book."

"I guess I could," Sarah admitted ruefully. "But if I'd put *everything* in, it would be so awful I wouldn't want to read it. All I know is, Somebody was looking out for us this time," Sarah gave credit to the Lord for sparing her young husband from harm.

Chills went up Sarah's back at the thought of what might have happened. When she and Phares had set up housekeeping, she thought she finally had a home of her own and a place she belonged forever. Now she realized there was no guarantee on the future. Everything she thought was her own could be snatched away without a moment's notice. Her home and marriage could be broken by the long, bony fingers of an early death, just as Daed and Memm's had been. Marriage was no guarantee of security. Nothing on earth was totally secure. Was she destined to live in fear, always waiting for the next disaster to strike? How could a person even hope for security in an unstable world?

Chapter 20

Sarah sat on a stump, keeping Phares company as he worked on their car. The 1936 Chevy had been nearly worn out when he bought it from his brother. The rusty door hinges were coming out of the wooden frame. The doors sagged so badly they had to be lifted up to be closed, but that was one of the car's lesser problems.

"Come hold this for me now," Phares grunted as he struggled to put the clutch back together.

Sarah knew what to do. She had helped her young husband tear the Chevy apart and put it back together so many times she thought she could almost do it herself. They often worked on the car all week in order to be able to drive it on Sundays. It was the only car they had and there was no use thinking of getting another one.

Car and truck production had virtually stopped in this year of 1943 as manufacturing plants turned out military trucks, tanks, and jeeps. New cars were simply not available to the public anywhere in the United States and used cars sold for high prices. The metal shortage was so severe the 1943 pennies were being made of zinc rather than copper.

"Do you think you'll get it together tonight yet?" Sarah asked anxiously. They were planning to go to church in the morning and then to her family for dinner.

"I hope so," he answered. "But it gets dark earlier than it used to."

Sarah knew what he meant. If the repair was not completed before the sun went down and the light was gone, he could not see to finish the job. The hours of daylight and dark were almost equal now that they were in the last half of September. The days would continue to get shorter as winter approached.

Sarah dreaded the short winter days and the long nights that were made even longer by the blackout laws. The government had decreed that the nation should be cloaked in darkness at night to prevent German war planes from identifying targets in potential air raids. Before bedtime, all lights must be turned off and window shades pulled down to the windowsills so the light of oil lamps or flashlights could not escape from the room.

A hard freeze in October ended the growing season. As the weather grew colder with the passing weeks, Sarah was confined to the house more of the time. When Phares went to work at his brother Dan's machine shop for a day, she went with him and spent the day with her family. She had no sewing machine of her own, so she used her stepmother's treadle machine to make a little stack of tiny garments from soft flannel. She did not know if she should make pink or blue sacques and kimonos, so she made a few of each color. She hemmed squares of bird's-eye cloth for diapers and larger squares of flannel for receiving blankets. One white dress completed the simple layette, for all babies, whether they were boys or girls, wore dresses. Crocheted booties, bibs, caps, and other necessities could be expected to be given as baby gifts. The things that were not given could be added as they were needed.

Esther had agreed to be Sarah's nurse when her first child was born. When the November page of the calender was torn off to make way for December, Esther knew she could expect to be called any time. One after another, the days passed by without a call. Then on the morning of December 17, Phares came to fetch Esther. He was so excited he could hardly wait for her to get her things together and be on the way. Then he drove faster than Esther thought was safe to get back home.

Dr. Ralph Goldin came from his office in Brownstown to deliver the baby. They waited for hours and hours. The long ordeal finally ended after dark.

"Congratulations!" the doctor said as he stuck out his hand to shake the hand of the new father. "You have a fine, healthy son. You may come in to see your wife and the little fellow now."

Sarah could manage only a tired smile when Phares bent over the bed to look at the tiny bundle nestled at her side. Esther held a lamp so he could see the baby's face. For a moment, he was too overcome with emotion to speak. This was his son! He was a father!

"Don't you want to hold him?" Esther asked.

"Why, sure," Phares said grandly. He bent down and carefully picked up the baby. He liked children, but he had never held one so newly born.

"He's awful tiny," Phares observed as he touched the tiny hand swathed in blankets. "Are you sure he's okay?" he asked the doctor.

"Yes," Dr. Goldin assured the anxious father. "He's tiny, but he's fine. Don't worry. He'll grow. Do you have a name for him?"

"Yes," Phares nodded. "We had decided if it's a boy we'll name him Leroy. His name is Leroy Wenger Stauffer."

Doctor Goldin sat at the kitchen table and filled out the forms for the birth certificate. "Call me if you have any problems," he said as he closed his bags.

"I'll do that," Phares promised, although he knew he would have to walk to the neighbors to use their telephone if he needed to call the doctor. "What do I owe you?"

"Don't worry about that now," Dr. Goldin said as he shrugged into his overcoat. "I'll send the bill later."

The doctor did not get his billing done until New Year's Day, 1944. Then he made out a bill for $34.50 for his home delivery services and sent it to Phares. The bill looked huge to the young couple, for it was the equivalent of several weeks' wages. But somehow, someway, they would scrape together the money to pay the bill.

At their first opportunity, Daed and Lydia went to see their first grandchild. Mary and Anna, savoring their new role as aunts, could hardly wait to hold their only nephew.

"I'm the oldest, so I get to hold him first," Mary declared as she rushed to the small crib where Leroy lay.

"Whoa! You're not the oldest. I am," Lydia corrected as she scooped up the baby. "But *Daadi* (Grandpa) gets the first turn."

Sarah almost laughed. How strange it sounded to hear Daed being called *Daadi* as if he was an old man! And yet it was true. When she became a mother, he had become a grandfather.

"*Ach!* I don't know if I still know how to do this," Daed chuckled as he took the baby in his arms. "I got out of practice."

"I'll take him if you don't want him," Anna offered eagerly.

"You'll get your turn after while," Daed promised. "You heard what Mammi (Grandma) Wenger said. *Daadi* gets him first."

Mammi Wenger! Sarah thought as she turned the sound of the name over in her mind. *Mammi Wenger. I never could bring myself to call her Memm, but I think I could call her Mammi. Mammi Wenger. That's the name for her,* Sarah decided. *I'll call her Mammi Wenger.*

Although Sarah's problem of what to call her stepmother had finally been resolved, a new problem soon took its place. Phares was informed that the farm where they were living was going to be sold. He would have to find another place to live and move his little family in the spring. Of course, he would not consider living in town. He was a farmer at heart and needed to stay on a farm in order to be able to renew his farm deferment. Buying a farm of his own was not an option he could even consider since he was scraping the bottom of the barrel to pay the rent on the one where they lived. Sarah tried not to worry about where they would go while Phares looked for another place to live.

"I found a farm!" Phares told Sarah one day as winter moved on toward spring.

"Oh?" Sarah questioned anxiously. "Where is it?"

"Outside Ephrata; right at the cloverleaf on the new 222," he told her. "It's Martin Zimmerman's place. He's a deacon in the Horning (Weaverland Conference) church. He's getting too old to farm anymore himself, so he's looking for younger people to move in the tenant house and help. We can move out there in March."

"That'll be closer to both of our families," Sarah smiled in relief and approval.

The spring of the year is the farmer's New Year, for it is the time of new life and new beginnings. Farms generally changed hands in March, just before the new crops were planted. Phares borrowed a truck to move their things from one farm to the other. Moving the remains of the previous years feed crops, farm equipment, and cows, required many eight-mile round trips between farms.

When the household goods were piled on the truck, Sarah looked around the empty kitchen. She had always known this was only a rented farm, yet she felt a tug on her heart to be leaving the place which had been their first home. Somehow, she had supposed they would live here longer than one year. That year had been a struggle to survive. Yet, now that it was over, how quickly that year had flown! With three-month-old Leroy in one arm and the diaper bag over the other, Sarah closed the door on the first year of her life as a farmer's wife and moved on to begin the second year.

Martin and Mary Zimmerman were in their sixties. They had two single daughters who still lived at home. The electric was connected to their farm, so it was a slight improvement over the farm where Phares and Sarah had first lived.[18] There was a good spring under the house which they could use for a refrigerator, so they did not bother putting their name on the list of those waiting to purchase an electric refrigerator. But Phares did manage to find a used wringer washing machine for Sarah. The only receptacle into which she could plug the washing machine was dangerous because it often shorted and sparked. She had to be very careful not to be shocked while working with the metal machine

---

[18] This property is now the location of the Cloister Shopping Center. The stone house at the back corner of the parking lot was the main farmhouse. It is the only building which was on the farm that is still standing. A commercial bank now occupies the spot where the barn was located. The tenant house stood about where Issac's Restaurant is now located in the shopping center. The site of the chicken house is marked today by the golden arches of McDonalds, and the meadow is covered with an asphalt parking lot.

and water. Still, wash days were easier after the old-fashioned washboard was hung on the wall of the wash house and the washing machine did the work of scrubbing the clothes clean.

Phares shared the barn with Martin Zimmerman. The cows of the two farmers were stabled on opposite sides of the alley in the barn. In the spring and summer, the cows grazed together in the meadow which stretched all the way to the cloverleaf. They lay down in the lush, green grass and contentedly chewed their cuds, blissfully unaware that the empty road which bordered their pasture would suddenly be filled with traffic whenever the bridge over Route 322 was completed.

"I'm going to get some peeps to put in the chicken house," Phares told Sarah. "We can raise chickens and sell them to people that dress chickens for market."

"I'd like that," Sarah endorsed the idea. She had always liked birds and the prospect of caring for chicks appealed to her.

Phares went to Moore's Hatchery at Lancaster to buy chicks. When he came home, the trunk and back seat of the car were loaded with big brown cardboard boxes filled with chicks. Sarah helped him set up the brooder stove in the chicken house and place the little chicks under the stove's round metal hood where they would stay warm.

"See the *gackie* (pet name for chick)," Sarah said to little Leroy as she picked up a chick and held it in front of him. Both he and the chick were too young to understand, but she went on talking to both of them. If they did not understand her words, they did understand the loving, motherly tone of her voice.

The little chicks clustered under the warm stove, pecking and scratching at the sawdust bedding with the curiosity of youth. They ate finely ground corn from the feeders and drank water from the glass waterers. Sarah filled the water bottles at least twice a day, for it is important for chicks to have plenty of water to drink. She filled an ordinary glass canning jar with water, placed a special round watering dish over the mouth of the jar, and turned the whole thing over. The water bubbled down from the jar by gravity flow and filled the watering dish. The little legs of the chicks were so short they hopped up on the rim of the round base, dipped their beaks in the water, and lifted their little yellow heads to let the water run down their throats.

As the chicks grew, little white feathers began to appear in the downy yellow baby fuzz that covered their bodies. They began to explore the world beyond the brooder stove, going further and further as they grew bigger and bigger. Then the brooder stove was no longer needed, so Phares took it apart and put it away until it would be needed for a new batch of chicks.

When the chickens were big enough to be dressed for market, Phares sold them. "We did pretty good on them chickens," he announced with pleasure after he finished adding the columns in his record book.

"I'd much rather raise chickens than dress them," Sarah endorsed the little business venture. "I'd say I had my turn doing the dirty work."

The empty chicken house must be cleaned and disinfected before a new batch of chicks could be moved into it. When the building was ready, Phares went to Lancaster and brought home another batch of chicks to put under the brooder stove. Then they started a new cycle of raising broilers for market. They could raise several batches in a year and make a nice profit to add to their income.

During the summer, the long-awaited steel beams finally arrived to finish the bridge over Route 322 at the cloverleaf. Phares finished what he was doing and walked down to the cloverleaf to watch the exciting action. The huge steel beams lying on the ground were made from one long piece of solid steel and stood about four-feet high.

"The man that was running the crane saw me standing there watching," Phares told Sarah later. "He told me to come up in the cab with him, so I did. I had a ring-side seat to watch him swing a couple of those beams in place!"

Sarah listened to his glowing account with interest. "It sure took a long time to get that bridge finished," she commented. "One time when Noah Aukers were at our place for dinner, Daed and

Noah walked out here to see the cloverleaf. They were just putting it in then. It was the winter before we started going together."

"It must have been early in 1941 then," Phares guessed.

"That would sound about right," she nodded.

"So it took over three years for them beams to come," he said after some quick mental calculations. "Of course, the bridge isn't finished yet. They still have to put the road down over the beams and make concrete walls on the sides. But that shouldn't take long now that the beams are in. Getting the steel for the beams was the hold-up."

Just as Phares had predicted, the bridge was soon finished and open to traffic. The completed Route 222 (now 272) replaced the old, narrow winding road that had gone through the center of all the little towns from Adamstown to Lancaster. At last, it was possible to bypass all the towns and travel rapidly all the way to Lancaster on the wide two-lane concrete road.

As the year wore on, Phares saw that farming with Martin Zimmerman was not working to the satisfaction of either of them. Phares wanted to be able to farm independently but was in no position to buy a farm, so he started looking for a farm he could afford to rent.

Both Leroy's first birthday and the first day of 1945 had passed when Phares came home with good news. "I found us a farm to rent," he announced cheerfully.

"Where?" Sarah asked.

"Below New Holland," he told her. "It's Frank Hurst's farm near the Greenbank School. We'll finish out our year here and then move in March."

"Oh, it *ferlates* me," she groaned.

"Why?" he asked. "You don't want to stay here, do you?"

"Not really," she admitted.

"We'll do better if we can farm someplace we don't have to share the barn and be under the landlord's thumb all the time," he persisted.

"I know," she agreed. "But I am so tired of moving all the time."

"We only moved once," he protested "From Sandy Beach to this place."

"*You* only moved once," she countered. "*I* moved more times than I care to count. You grew up in the house where you were born. You always lived at the same place, went to the same school, and the same church all your life. You have no idea what my life has been like. My parents moved around all the time when I was growing up. After Memm died, I lived with strangers and went to different churches. I went to five different schools and sometimes changed schools in the middle of the year. Even after Daed got married again and I went home, I worked out and lived with other people. You have no idea how it feels to always be moving around and never know where you will have to live next. I'm *so* tired of moving. I want a home where I can put down roots and STAY."

Phares had listened to her long speech without interrupting. He knew the basic outlines of her childhood, but she had not colored in all the details. He knew she had quietly endured more than he could begin to understand.

"I know you had a hard life," he acknowledged. "I don't like moving every year either. I hope things go better at this place so we can get on our feet once and stay put."

Sarah had learned long ago that complaining or pitying herself did not help or change the difficult circumstances in her life. As much as she dreaded being uprooted again, she knew Phares was right. Moving to a place where he could farm on his own would be an improvement over the current situation. He was not afraid to work and knew how to manage money. If only the war would end, then perhaps things would improve for them and everyone else.

Once again, Phares borrowed a truck and enlisted the help of his brothers to move from Ephrata to New Holland. This move took more time, because the farms were eleven miles apart. Moving in March would give them just enough time to get settled in the new place before their second child would be born early in May.

When the Ephrata tenant house was emptied, Sarah closed the door on their second year of farming and walked away to begin the third year. She had not become attached to this place and did not regret leaving, but she wished Phares would have been able to find a farm that was not so far away from their homes and families. The farm he had rented lay at the foot of the Welsh Mountain, which was populated by poor white and black people. The Buzzard gang of white outlaws that had once swept down from the mountain to terrorize the people in the valley was gone now, but the reputation they had given the mountain remained. Sarah was afraid to live so close to the Welsh Mountain.

The fifty-acre farm was south of the town of New Holland and a little beyond Ranck's Church. Nestled between the hills, the fertile fields would produce good crops for a farmer who was willing to work. The farm buildings were set close to the road that hugged the bottom of a steep hill and then split off to go up over the Welsh Mountain. They reached the barn first and

The New Holland farm photographed in 1950. The barn is nearly hidden behind the trees on the right side of the picture. The current address of this farm is 816 Ranck's Church Road, New Holland, Pa.

approached the house from the back. The kitchen was in a two-story wing that had been added to the back of the main house. The roof on the addition sloped only one way, making it look as if the wing had been cut in half. In addition to the usual assortment of out buildings normally found on a farm, a wooden silo stood on guard at the front of the barn.

With the help of their families, the meager household furnishings were soon put in place. The addition of a child to the family had added only a wooden play pen, crib, and high chair to their short list of furniture. A cooling trough in a cement block milk house set a little distance from the kitchen would provide the only refrigeration on the place.

"Well, it's starting to look like home already," Phares smiled in approval as he pushed his chair back from the supper table at the end of the busy moving day. The familiar red-trimmed white kitchen cupboard, table, chairs, stove, and rocker were like old friends in the unfamiliar room.

"We had good help," Sarah said gratefully, giving credit where it was due. "We never would've got so much done in one day by ourselves."

"Well, I still have work to finish at the barn," he said as he clapped his hat on his head.

After Phares had gone out, Sarah lifted Leroy from the high chair and sat down in the rocking chair to rest while water heated in the teakettle on the stove. He would have been content without being held, but rocking him was a comfort to her in this strange place.

Sarah thought back as far as she could remember and began counting the places she had lived. She did not remember living at the place where she had been born. She had only faint memories of the Horst farm, which was the second place Daed and Memm had lived. She clearly remembered the Miley place, then the Burkholder farm at Springville, the Morrow place, and Red Run where they had lived when her mother died. From there she had gone to be "at home" with other people—John Aukers, Ammon Aukers, Norman Nolts, and Weaver Aukers.

Then she had finally gone back to her own family after Daed married Mammi Wenger. Even while she considered that place to be her home, she had lived with Weaver Zimmermans and Paul Sensenigs. Then she and Phares had been married and established a home of their own. She had expected to settle down and finally have a permanent home when she got married. But, so far, not much had changed. She was still packing up and moving on, just as she had done all of her life.

Sarah knew they could not afford to buy a farm, but renting was too uncertain. How long would they be able to live here before something happened to make it necessary for them to move on? Would they continue to move from one rental place to another every year? Sarah drew a deep breath and let out a long, quivering sigh. Was there no place of peace and security; no home for her troubled heart?

As if in answer to her unspoken questions, the words of Jesus that had been read at Frank's funeral floated through the gathering darkness and spoke gently to the deep inner longings of her heart. "Peace I leave with you, my peace I give unto you: not as the world giveth, give I unto you. Let not your heart be troubled, neither let it be afraid."

Peace. . .My peace . . . not as the world giveth . . . She had lost sight of the truth that had dawned on her at Frank's funeral and allowed fear to rob her of the peace Jesus gives. Now she remembered. *Peace is not the absence of trouble, but the presence of Jesus. Fear and anxiety are not eliminated by knowing the future, but by having faith in the all-wise God who is in control of the present and the future. He can be trusted to keep His promises to carry His children through life and take them to be with Him forever when this life is over.*

Suddenly, Sarah understood. She had been looking for security in the wrong place. Nothing on this earth is totally secure. All things change with the passage of time. Kingdoms rise and fall. Generations come and go. Seasons change. Plans change. Only God and His Word are unchanging. Jesus gives His peace to those who put their trust in Him and follow Him wherever He leads.

Softly, Sarah began humming a song she had learned when she went to singings with the young people. The words poured down like healing oil into her anxious, fearful heart.

Anywhere with Jesus I can safely go,
Anywhere He leads me in this world below,
Anywhere without Him dearest joys would fade,
Anywhere with Jesus I am not afraid.

Anywhere with Jesus I can go to sleep,
When the darkening shadows round about me creep;
Knowing I shall waken never more to roam,
Anywhere with Jesus will be Home Sweet Home.

A great peace settled like a benediction over Sarah's troubled spirit as the Savior wrapped her securely in the mantle of His grace. His love covered the scars of the pain in her past. Where she lived on earth was of no consequence. Jesus had promised to be with His children even to the end of the world. No matter where she went, or how many times she had to move to another house, He was with her. She was secure in Him. Her heart and soul had found a home that would endure through all time and eternity.

Epilogue

Phares and Sarah Stauffer lived on the New Holland farm for eight years. During that time, they joined the (Lancaster Conference) Weaverland Mennonite Church and added four children to their family. When the farm was sold in 1953, they moved to a farm they purchased at Bernville, Route 2, in Berks County, Pennsylvania. Five more children were added to their family in the following years. They transferred their church membership to the Texter Mountain Mennonite Church, which was a little mission outreach that had begun in 1952.

In 1977, Phares sold his farm and retired from farming. He and Sarah built a house near Myerstown, Pennsylvania. They transferred their church membership to the Fairhaven Mennonite Church in Myerstown and were active in the church for the rest of their lives.

Phares spent his retirement years as a chauffeur for the local Amish people, restoring nearly a score of John Deere tractors, and doing milling work in his garage. He was a loyal member of the Rough & Tumble Engineers Association at Kinzers, Pennsylvania, (also known as the Old Thresherman's Reunion), and spent many days there giving live threshing demonstrations. Sarah was a homemaker all of her life. She made many quilts and comforters which she donated to relief work.

Phares and Sarah were married for sixty-one years. On July 12, 2004, Phares was suddenly called to his eternal home. In addition to his wife, he was survived by 27 grandchildren and 21 great-grandchildren. At the time of this writing, Sarah is 82 years old and continues to live in their house near Myerstown, Pa. Her quiet, steady faith and uncomplaining acceptance of the many hardships which have been a part of her life, including her recent adjustment to widowhood, has been an inspiration to all who know and love her.

Children of Phares and Sarah Stauffer:

1. Leroy W. Stauffer, born December 17, 1943, married July 15, 1967, to H. Romaine Burkholder.
2. Kathryn W. Stauffer, born May 11, 1944.
3. Edwin W. Stauffer, born December 29, 1946, married May 20, 1967, to Carol Ann Sensenig.
4. Sallie Ann Stauffer, born December 13, 1948, married September 25, 1971, to Luke A. Martin.
5. Irene W. Stauffer, born May 13, 1951.
6. Marian Jane Stauffer, born August 3, 1954, married October 5, 1974, to Clifford G. Martin.
7. Rose Marie Stauffer, born January 28, 1958, married October 1, 1977, to Randy Boll.
8. Bonita Jean Stauffer, born June 2, 1960, married July 21, 1979, to John H. Hurst Jr.
9. Nelson Jay Stauffer, born September 12, 1961, married August 17, 1996, to Teresa Kay Zimmerman.
10. Gloria Kay Stauffer, born September 8, 1963, married October 30, 1982, to Paul H. Hurst.

Sarah learned to appreciate her stepmother and call her "my mother." Lydia (Good) Wenger died on January 10, 1967, at the age of 74. Sarah's father, Amos Wenger, died December 19, 1976, at the age of 82. They are buried in the Pike Mennonite Cemetery.

Neither Arthur nor Esther were ever married. Arthur moved to Kentucky and later to an Old Order colony in Belize. Esther continues to live in Lancaster County and is a member of the Pike Mennonite Church near Hinkletown. Mary married H. John Martin. They raised a family of ten children and live in Lebanon County, Pennsylvania. They are members of a Weaverland Conference church. Anna married Paul Z. Martin. They raised their seven children on his father's farm in the Hinkletown area. Anna died of cancer on March 14, 1984, at the age of 53. She is buried in the cemetery of the Pike Mennonite Church, of which she was and Paul continues to be a member. Their youngest son has taken over the family farm. Paul continues to live alone in one side of the house.

Other Books by Romaine Stauffer

Published by
Christian Light Publications

Hidden Riches, 1983
Circle of Love, 1988
Sandi's Anchor of Hope, 1997
Crayonbox Collection, 2005

To order these books contact:
Christian Light Publications
P.O. Box 1212
Harrisonburg, VA 22801

———

Printed by Masthof Press

Annie's Day of Light, 2003
A Home for Sarah, 2006

To order these books contact:
Romaine Stauffer
15 Harry Stoudt Dr.
Bernville, PA 19506

or

Masthof Press
219 Mill Road
Morgantown, PA 19543-9516